THEORY OF
MECHANICAL REFRIGERATION

THEORY OF
MECHANICAL
REFRIGERATION

BY

N. R. SPARKS

Associate Professor of Mechanical Engineering
The Pennsylvania State College

FIRST EDITION
THIRD IMPRESSION

McGRAW-HILL BOOK COMPANY, INC.

NEW YORK AND LONDON

1938

PREFACE

The field of refrigeration is so broad and involves the application of so many basic studies that any attempt to incorporate the subject matter in one comprehensive volume will, even though successful, result in a book not well adapted to general classroom use in the majority of engineering colleges. It is the author's belief that most of the purely descriptive matter and empirical data related to a subject is best and most quickly learned during active practice in the field, not in engineering curricula already hard pressed to instill fundamentals and their applications within the allotted time.

This book has therefore been prepared with the object of confining the content solely to that necessary for a thorough presentation of the fundamental thermodynamic approach to the subject of refrigeration, excluding such material as may appear elsewhere in works of the handbook type. To this ideal the author has rigorously adhered. In the exposition he has attempted to provoke clear and logical thinking, occasionally dwelling at some length upon details which might appear to be of little immediate importance in order that no part of the foundation matter may be misunderstood.

The study of refrigeration cycles and systems, providing as it does such excellent examples of applied thermodynamics, is peculiarly favorable for driving home principles commonly applicable in other fields. For this reason, this book has been designed, not specifically for students specializing in refrigeration, but for general use as a text demonstrating the application of fundamentals.

The presentation of the subject throughout the book assumes, on the part of the reader, a reasonably thorough knowledge of engineering thermodynamics, such as seniors and, in some instances, juniors in engineering colleges may be expected to possess. However, in order to allow for the natural lapse usually suffered by those who have been out of contact with the subject for some time, there have been included a chapter devoted to the brief review of thermodynamics and a chapter dealing with the air refrigerating cycle, which, though obsolete, is nevertheless valuable for restoring dexterity in the application of principles.

For the cooperation of the Department of Mechanical Engineering of the Pennsylvania State College, as well as for personal assistance and advice, the author is indebted to its head, Professor H. A. Everett. Grateful acknowledgment is also rendered the author's associates, Professors F. C. Stewart and J. S. Doolittle, for many helpful suggestions and, in the case of the latter, for a critical reading of the manuscript.

N. R. SPARKS.

STATE COLLEGE, PA.,
  August, 1938.

CONTENTS

vii

viii

CONTENTS

CHAPTER VII

CHAPTER VIII

CHAPTER IX

CHAPTER X

CHAPTER XI

CHAPTER XII

TABLE OF SYMBOLS

For quantitative values, capital letters in general represent total quantities and small letters specific quantities.

A—heat equivalent of work, Btu per ft.-lb. $= 1/J$.

c—specific heat, Btu per lb. per deg. F.

c_p—specific heat at constant pressure, Btu per lb. per deg. F.

c_v—specific heat at constant volume, Btu per lb. per deg. F.

d—density, specific weight, lb. per cu. ft.

e—efficiency.

e_d—diffuser efficiency.

e_e—entrainment efficiency.

e_m—mechanical efficiency.

e_n—nozzle efficiency.

e_t—thermal efficiency.

e_v—volumetric efficiency.

h—enthalpy, heat content, total heat, Btu per lb.; also head, feet.

J—work equivalent of heat, ft.-lb. per Btu $= 778.3$.

k—exponent in $PV^k = $ const. for isentropic change.

M—weight, lb.

n—exponent for general polytropic change, as $PV^n = $ const.

p—pressure, lb. per sq. in.

P—pressure, lb. per sq. ft.

q—heat of absorption or adsorption in Btu as designated.

Q—any quantity of heat exchanged, Btu.

R—gas constant $= Pv/T$.

s—entropy, Btu per lb. deg. F.

t—temperature, deg. F.

T—temperature, deg. F. abs.

u—internal energy, Btu per lb.

v—specific volume, cu. ft. per lb.

V—total volume, cu. ft.; or velocity, ft. per sec.

W—mechanical, or shaft, work, ft.-lb.

x—quality of a vapor; concentration of a solution.

Subscripts

f—denotes saturated liquid or solid property, as h_f, s_f, v_f.

x—denotes wet vapor property, as h_x, s_x, v_x.

g—denotes dry saturated vapor property, as h_g, s_g, v_g.

fg—denotes property change during transition from liquid or solid to vapor, as h_{fg}, s_{fg}, v_{fg}.

THEORY OF MECHANICAL REFRIGERATION

CHAPTER I

INTRODUCTORY

In the engineering sense, **refrigeration** means the artificial withdrawal of heat, producing in a substance or within a space a temperature lower than that which would exist under the natural influence of the surroundings. **Mechanical** refrigeration further classifies the cooling effect as one created by machine or other mechanical device.

Perhaps no other single factor has played a more vital part in the growth and attainment of our present day standard of living than has the art of refrigeration, either directly or by incidental contribution to the store of scientific knowledge. From the earliest times artificial cooling was recognized as desirable but was utilized, by primitive methods, strictly as a luxury rather than as a necessity. On the small scales employed, snow, ice, and cold water were used when available, and the atmospheric evaporation of water was to some extent crudely applied to cooling without much understanding of the principles involved.

Later, in favorable climatic locations, the use of naturally frozen ice increased, but it was not until 1755 that an attempt was made to cool mechanically. Although the initial experiment was followed from time to time by others, several using water as the refrigerant, the problem was so difficult in view of the limited scientific knowledge existing at the time that a century elapsed before successful refrigerating machines were built. Of the early machines, the air system was probably the most successful until the development about 1870 of both the absorption and the vapor compression systems using ammonia as the refrigerant. By 1891 the refrigerating industry was fairly launched, and within the space of a few years machines using ammonia, carbon dioxide, and sulfur dioxide were developed to the point where their inherent superiority over air machines forced the latter into obsolescence. More recently, new refrigerants have been introduced, new fields have been invaded, and development work has been carried out to an advanced degree with the result that the industry must now be rated among the foremost.

Modern refrigeration is mostly applied in four general fields: ice making, preservation of perishables, air conditioning, and special industrial purposes. Under preservation of perishables come cold storage warehouse and commercial installations, refrigerated transportation, and domestic refrigeration. Air conditioning, according to the purpose for which it is intended, may be classed under two headings: that for manufacturing and that for human comfort. The field of air conditioning as a whole has within recent years given a tremendous impetus to the refrigeration industry and is potentially so enormous in its extent that the present magnitude may well mark only the beginning. In the comparatively short span of fifty years, mechanical refrigeration has advanced from relative insignificance to the dominant and indispensable position it now holds, with the health, provisioning, and general welfare of whole communities dependent upon it and a considerable portion of the economic activity of the nation supported by its means.

The science of engineering thermodynamics in refrigeration, to which this work is mainly devoted, deals primarily with the conduct of the working fluid, or refrigerant, and with the energy involved in the operation of refrigerating devices; it provides the basic theory upon which all mechanical refrigeration is founded. But the actual *design* of modern refrigerating equipment demands a knowledge of other subjects equally fundamental in nature. The scope of these may be briefly outlined to advantage.

Heat transfer normally falls into two categories: that in which the object is to *promote* the exchange of heat, usually between two substances; and that which seeks to *prevent* heat flow. The former is applied in the design of **heat exchangers,** while the latter is associated with **thermal insulation.** Because refrigerating machines are fundamentally concerned with the transfer of heat, the heat exchanger is a vital part of any system. While heat exchangers may be haphazardly built without any great application of the principles of heat transfer, such equipment would be bulky, expensive, and inefficient in comparison to that of proper scientific design. The common problem is the reduction of size and cost without sacrifice of effectiveness. In the other field of heat transfer, the insulation of piping and other mechanical parts may be considered as one division, while the insulation of cold storage spaces—rooms, buildings, railway cars, trucks, and the holds or other compartments of ships—comprises another that is intimately associated with building materials, structures, and specialized applications requiring, in many cases, considerable ingenuity and technical skill. Most heat transfer problems in either class are necessarily economic in nature, involving a balance between the cost of purely technical efficiency and the savings to be derived therefrom.

Fluid mechanics is a subject of which the designer is becoming increasingly conscious. In refrigeration, the particular application is to the flow of fluids—refrigerant, water, brine, and air— in ducts, pipes, valves, heat exchangers, and pumps. It is also necessary in the design and use of metering devices. The properties of fluids and their velocities and resistance to flow over surfaces have such a profound bearing upon the characteristics of both flow and heat transfer that the two subjects are interdependent to a considerable degree, and the one will frequently impose limitations which will affect the other. For this reason, they must, in some phases of design, receive simultaneous consideration.

The principles of **mechanical design** will finally dictate the form in which a piece of equipment is to appear in the finished state, including the materials to be used, dimensions, and all details of construction. The theories of heat transfer and of fluid flow will contribute an essential part to the complete design of such items as piping and heat exchangers; the laws of **machine design** will do the same for pumps, compressors, compressor drives, and control apparatus; and the whole will be made to conform to the stipulations of **shop practice.** The final product will thus be a compromise between that which is theoretically desirable and that which is practically possible or feasible. It is also the function of mechanical design to select this compromise and to correlate the various favorable features to the best advantage.

Among the sciences which contribute in a lesser degree directly to the design and development of refrigerating equipment are **chemistry** for application to such problems as refrigerants, the study of corrosion, lubricating oil reactions, and the properties and behavior of solutions; **metallurgy** for questions dealing with material; and **electrical** and **heat power engineering** for the power supply. Biology, architecture and architectural engineering, bacteriology, and other apparently remote subjects may also in some circumstances be of value to the builders and operators of refrigerating machinery.

Aside from theoretical and practical aspects of the design itself, the purpose to which a refrigerating load is to be applied has such an important bearing upon the type and characteristics of equipment that the designer must have information concerning the particular field in which a given machine is to operate. Such a knowledge not only would include the usual applications previously mentioned but would also have to extend, upon occasion, to special cases. The kind of service may thus govern the type of system, the selection of the refrigerant, compressor, compressor drive and auxiliaries, the design of condenser and evaporator, and the layout of the system in general. An air cooler in air conditioning and a brine cooler in an ice plant would, for instance, introduce certain problems of an entirely dissimilar nature; hence consideration must necessarily be given to specific requirements before the formal design is undertaken.

It may thus be readily appreciated that although the thermodynamic theory of refrigerating cycles is properly the starting point in any comprehensive study of the art, it by no means completes such an undertaking which requires also a practical understanding of the principal subjects mentioned in the preceding paragraphs as well as the judgment which may only be acquired by practical experience in the field.

CHAPTER II

BASIC THERMODYNAMICS

A thorough knowledge of the governing principles is required for an understanding of the refrigerating cycles which will be studied. Because the theory of all forms of mechanical refrigeration is based upon thermodynamics, the subject matter presented in this chapter consists principally of a review of the fundamentals of that subject, with particular emphasis upon those elements which have direct application to refrigeration.

1. Perfect Gases, Permanent Gases, and Vapors.—The three expressions **perfect gases**, **permanent gases**, and **vapors** are used rather freely and, in order to avoid confusion, the terms should be perfectly clear from the beginning.

According to the kinetic theory of heat, the only characteristic wherein a so-called perfect gas differs fundamentally from ordinary gases or any actual substance is that its particles are assumed to move in purely rectilinear paths between contacts. Since a rectilinear path is possible only in the absence of inter-molecular attractive forces, the particles of a perfect gas may possess no potential energy of position relative to each other, and the gas does not have that portion of the internal energy known as heat of disgregation or internal latent heat. It follows from this that a perfect gas may not achieve liquefaction. Furthermore, the specific heats of a perfect gas are constant regardless of the pressure or temperature to which the gas may be subjected, and the laws of Boyle, Charles, and Joule are exactly followed at all times. This purely hypothetical substance is useful in the elementary study of thermodynamics because the laws governing the action and properties, or change in properties, of a *perfect* gas are relatively simple and form a substantial foundation upon which to build a knowledge of the behavior of actual substances.

The term "permanent gas" dates from a time when certain gases such as air (a mixture), oxygen, nitrogen, hydrogen, etc., were thought to be incapable of a change in phase while, at the same time, it was recognized that these actual gases did not possess the exact qualifications of a perfect gas. Since that time, most of the so-called permanent gases have been liquefied and even solidified so that the term now is a misnomer but usually applies to those substances which appear normally, *i.e.*, within the ordinary ranges of pressure and temperature, in the gaseous state and well above their boiling points. As will be noted later, these substances, under certain conditions, may approximate the perfect gas very closely in their behavior.

When a substance, which normally exists as a solid, liquid, or gas, is in the gaseous phase and relatively near its saturation temperature or boiling point, it is known as a vapor. Thus we speak of water *vapor* or steam, ammonia *vapor*, sulfur dioxide *vapor*, mercury *vapor*, etc. Vapors, owing to their proximity to the liquid state, deviate from perfect gas behavior to such an extent that it becomes impossible to apply gas laws to them with any degree of accuracy except in special cases.

2. Properties of Substances.—In dealing with a substance, irrespective of its phase, it is ordinarily desirable, from the thermodynamic standpoint, to be familiar with at least the following properties together with the units in which they are customarily expressed and the units in which they are used. The six properties most essential for ordinary usage are:

a. Pressure; expressed in pounds per square inch gage or absolute and used in pounds per square foot absolute. (The use here referred to is in fundamental equations.)

b. Volume; expressed and used in cubic feet.

c. Temperature; expressed in degrees Fahrenheit, used in degrees Fahrenheit absolute.

d. Internal energy; expressed as Btu per pound.

e. Enthalpy, heat content, or total heat; expressed as Btu per pound.

f. Entropy; expressed in units of entropy per pound.

Of these, the first three may be called the *observable* properties and are not difficult to comprehend. The last three may not be determined directly by observation but should not for that reason be more difficult to understand than the first three since they are just as truly properties of the substance. In the use of these properties there is a difference between the two groups in that pressure, volume, and temperature are used both in their

absolute values and in differential, whereas internal energy,
enthalpy, and entropy are all more useful as differences than in
the absolute values. For this reason, a zero may be chosen for
the last three quite arbitrarily without affecting the results.
This is done in tables of the properties of vapors and occasionally
in compiling data on gases.

The internal energy of a substance is the mechanical energy
possessed by the particles of which it is composed.   This mechanical energy is of two forms: kinetic, due to velocity of the particles;
and potential, due to the position that they assume against
mutual attractive forces. The former is represented by the
absolute temperature, is sensible to the touch, and is, therefore,
called **sensible heat,** while the latter, being related to the phase
of the substance, is called **heat of disgregation** or **internal latent
heat.**   Internal energy, then, is equal to the sum of the sensible
heat and the internal latent heat for all actual substances, and
to the sensible heat alone, since there is no heat of disgregation,
for the perfect gas.   The use of the word "heat" in designating
the two components of internal energy is unfortunate because
it tends to confuse our conception of heat as a term restricted to
the description of energy *transferred* to or from a substance and
not inherent in it.   The terminology is based upon customary
and established usage but must be excepted as not applying
in the transitional sense.

If heat be added to or rejected from a substance during a
reversible process, the ratio of the quantity of heat so transferred
to the absolute temperature at which the transfer takes place is
the change in entropy.   That is,

$$ds = \frac{dQ}{T}$$

Note that there may be an increase or a decrease of entropy
depending upon whether heat is added or rejected.   When the
process is accompanied by a change in temperature, the entropy
change may be determined by integration as follows:

$$s_2 - s_1 = \int_{T_1}^{T_2} \frac{dQ}{T} = \int_{T_1}^{T_2} \frac{cdT}{T} = c\int_{T_1}^{T_2} \frac{dT}{T} = c\log_e \frac{T_2}{T_1}$$

in which c is the specific heat considered as a constant for the
gases to which this equation will be applied.

In the case of an irreversible process, the above expression represents only a portion of the entropy change, the remainder being the ratio of the energy which has been degraded during the process, owing to internal losses, to the absolute temperature. Thus

$$ds = \frac{dQ}{T} + \frac{dQ_l}{T}$$

where Q_l is the loss of available energy which accompanies an irreversible change. The last term in the above equation is always positive indicating that an irreversible process results inevitably in an entropy increase except when sufficient heat is at the same time withdrawn from the substance to counterbalance this effect.

Enthalpy (variously termed heat content, total heat, thermal potential) is an arbitrary and exceedingly useful compound property devised for the purpose of facilitating the solution of certain types of thermodynamic problems. Its numerical value is obtained by adding to the internal energy the product, divided by the mechanical equivalent of heat, of the absolute pressure in pounds per square foot and the volume in cubic feet. Expressed mathematically in Btu per pound of substance,

$$h = u + APv$$

Of the commonly used functions, enthalpy is perhaps the least generally understood while, at the same time, having very wide practical applications. The internal energy portion is clearly inherent in the substance both as a property and as energy, but the APv product, while inherently a property, is not, as an energy quantity, possessed by, or "contained in," the substance in the usual sense, nor is it necessarily energy at all. The energy concept of the APv term in enthalpy is analogous to that of a spearhead steadily penetrating a plastic material. The spearhead utilizes the necessary energy to do work in piercing the material which opposes it, but this energy is merely transmitted through the shaft from the person manipulating the spear and is not in any sense inherent in the head. If the communication with the operator, $i.e.$, the shaft, be severed, the head must come to rest since it no longer has the ability, in the form of energy, to advance, irrespective of whatever internal or inherent energy it may possess. In the case of a flowing fluid, the portion under consideration may be compared to the spearhead constantly doing work upon the material ahead of it by virtue of the energy received from the source through the material behind it. That this flow work is equal to Pv/J for 1 lb. of substance may be readily seen by considering 1 lb. of material of volume v and pressure P flowing through a pipe as in Fig. 1. The pipe may be considered as having a cross-sectional area A. Now, the work done in delivering each pound of material from any part of the pipe or of causing it to flow past any section such as X-X is the force acting times the distance through which it acts, or $F \times l$. But $F = PA$, and $Al = v$. Therefore the flow work is $PAl = Pv$ in foot-pounds per pound, or Pv/J in Btu per pound. Obviously this energy is neither transmitted to nor expended

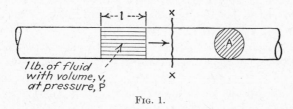

Fig. 1.

by the substance at rest, and accordingly, the APv term is not an energy quantity under static conditions. A proper conception must thus fully appreciate the fact that enthalpy, although *always a property*, is *energy only during flow*.

3. Energy Equations.—Most of the energy transformations in which we are interested may be classified as occurring under either nonflow or steady-flow conditions, with reference to the energy passage and to the working substance. The single process, such as compression or expansion of a gas which remains within a cylinder, in which no transfer of matter is involved is a **nonflow** process. The term **steady flow** may be applied where there is a continuous and unvarying flow of energy or material, over a period of time, into and out of the apparatus as in the cases of internal combustion engines, boilers, turbines, condensers, pumps, compressors, etc. There may also be instances utilizing intermittent flow to which the proper combination of nonflow and steady-flow principles may be applied. All cycles conform as a whole to the steady-flow principle and may be analyzed on this basis, but cycles are usually made up of individual processes each of which may be treated separately, when desired, according to the principle applicable in the particular instance.

For nonflow, a mathematical statement of the fact that a given quantity of heat supplied to or taken from a substance during a single process must be represented by a change in internal energy of the substance or in external work done, or in both, is called the "nonflow energy equation." Its expression is

$$dQ = dU + AdW \tag{1}$$

This equation may take several forms. One term may drop out for certain processes; or the signs may be changed according to whether heat is added or rejected, the internal energy increases or decreases, or work is done on or by the substance during the process in question.

For steady flow, an expression representing an energy balance, conforming to the principle of conservation, constitutes the energy equation. This is further predicated upon the fact that most engineering devices, while in steady operation, have no capacity for storing varying energy quantities within themselves and, therefore, that the input of energy in its various forms must equal the total energy output. Energy may thus be supplied to and taken from a unit as follows: kinetic energy of flow of the working substance $(V^2/2gJ)$; internal energy of the working substance (u); potential energy of the working substance as a whole above a certain datum plane (E_p); energy introduced by the working substance by virtue of the work transmitted through it to produce flow against a head (APv); chemical energy as in a fuel (E_c); work (AW); and heat (Q). It should be noted that the first five items mentioned are forms of energy *associated with the working fluid*, while the last two, work and heat, are forms supplied to or withdrawn from the system *quite apart from the working substance*. The sum of all these forms constitutes the total quantity of energy to be dealt with. Although energy transformations take place within the unit—diminishing certain forms, increasing others—this total quantity must be the same leaving as entering and the steady-flow energy equation, expressed in heat units per pound of working fluid passing, is

$$\frac{V_1^2}{2gJ} + u_1 + E_{p1} + AP_1v_1 + E_{c1} + AW_{in} + Q_{in} =$$

$$\frac{V_2^2}{2gJ} + u_2 + E_{p2} + AP_2v_2 + E_{c2} + AW_{out} + Q_{out}$$

where subscript 1 denotes the initial and 2 the final state. Enthalpy, h, may be substituted for $u + APv$, and by a rearrangement, the equation may be written

$$\left(\frac{V_1^2 - V_2^2}{2gJ}\right) + (h_1 - h_2) + (E_{p1} - E_{p2}) + (E_{c1} - E_{c2})$$

$$+ A(W_{in} - W_{out}) + (Q_{in} - Q_{out}) = 0$$

This clearly demonstrates that we are dealing with differences between, or changes in, similar forms of energy entering and leaving the unit, such differences being zero or negligible in many applied cases. By the omission of such terms as have no significance, the equation may be modified to suit the individual case.[1] For use in this work, a simplified form which will generally be found to be sufficiently complete is

$$h_1 + AW_{in} + Q_{in} = h_2 + AW_{out} + Q_{out} \tag{2}$$

[1] The following examples will serve to illustrate the manner in which the steady-flow energy equation may be simplified for specific cases:

For the compressor, eliminating unnecessary terms:

$$Mh_1 + AW_{in} = Mh_2 + Q_{out}$$

For the internal combustion engine:

$$Mh_1 + ME_{c1} = Mh_2 + ME_{c2} + AW_{out} + Q_{out}$$

in which ME_{c2} represents the chemical energy of the unburned fuel in the exhaust.

For the steam engine or turbine:

$$Mh_1 = Mh_2 + AW_{out} + Q_{out}$$

For the condenser or gas cooler:

$$Mh_1 = Mh_2 + Q_{out}$$

For the boiler, evaporator, or heater:

$$Mh_1 + Q_{in} = Mh_2$$

For cases in which the action approximates the adiabatic, or when adiabatic action is assumed, Q also may be dropped from these special forms of the equation.

Probably no other single item is so essential for the solution of the various problems which will arise as is a complete understanding of the principles upon which the steady-flow energy equation is based.

4. Diagrams.—Any two properties of a substance may be used as coordinates for a curve which will show the relation of one to the other during a particular change of state. Other properties may be shown on any of these charts as noncoordinate lines. Of the 15 combinations of coordinate axes possible with the six commonly used properties, the *P-V* and the *T-s* are preferable for the study and analysis of cycles because areas on

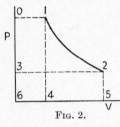

Fig. 2.

those diagrams represent energy quantities in transition. Other diagrams, such as *h-s* and *P-h*, are more useful in actual problem solutions but rather as a substitute for, or accessory to, tables of properties, since the areas of these diagrams have no significance insofar as energy quantities are concerned.

The *P-V* diagram presents a picture of pressure and volume changes during a single process or during a succession of processes forming, together, a cycle. The area beneath a curve on this plane represents the work done in foot-pounds while the substance is progressing from one state point to another *if the process is reversible.* An irreversible process may be shown insofar as the pressure-volume relations are concerned, but the area bounded by such a curve has no significance. Irreversible actions are therefore customarily represented by dotted paths. Figure 2 represents a reversible expansion during which the pressure and volume undergo changes from those represented at point 1 to those at point 2 according to a definite law whose equation governs the form of the curve. The work done during the expansion is the quantity of energy equal to the area under the curve (area 12541), or $W = \int P dv$. While this is the total work accomplished by the fluid under nonflow conditions, it represents only a part of that done by the working substance under circumstances of steady flow since the *Pv* energy utilized by the gas initially is expended in doing the work of entrance, $P_1 v_1$ (area 01460), and the final flow work is imparted to the gas at exit by having done upon it the work required for its discharge,

P_2v_2 (area 32563).   Hence, the net area representing the work done by the fluid expanding under flow is that to the left of the curve (area 01230) or $W = \int v\,dP$.   The final form of the work equation after integration depends, for both nonflow and steady flow, upon the equation for expansion.

This illustration has been considered as an expansion with work done *by* the substance.   A compression might operate along the same curve in the reverse direction, the respective areas then showing work done *on* the substance.

As the *P-V* diagram presents a picture of work quantities, so the *T-s* plane shows the quantities of the other form of transitional energy in which we are primarily interested, *i.e.*, heat supplied and rejected, by representing the variations of temperature and entropy during a state change.   The heat added to or withdrawn from the working substance along a curve on these coordinates is the area beneath the curve, or

$$Q = \int T\,ds$$

The same limitations regarding the representation of irreversible processes apply to the *T-s* as to the *P-V* diagram.

It is frequently convenient and desirable to use the two diagrams in conjunction, employing the same notation in each so that processes representing identical changes are denoted in both cases by the same letters or numbers.

5. P-V Curve; Work.—The types of expansion and compression most used in this study will range from the adiabatic to the isothermal and will follow in general the polytropic form $PV^n = $ const. for both gases and vapors.   The exponent n, however, while having a definite value for each type of change for perfect gases, is variable for vapors depending not only upon the type of change but also upon the state of the vapor while undergoing such change.   The laws governing the compression or expansion of a vapor over an appreciable range are thus complicated by the variation in the exponent as the process progresses.   So long as the state during such a change does not pass from the superheated to the saturated condition, or vice versa, the average value of the exponent, determined from terminal properties, may be used with sufficient accuracy. When, however, during a change, the state point crosses the saturation line, the exponent at that point undergoes a sudden numerical change, being, in general, considerably less in the saturated than in the superheated region for the same type of process. In such cases, where the action takes the substance over the saturation line, it is preferable to integrate the P-V curve in two parts for each of which a reasonably representative exponent may be determined.[1]

The work involved in any particular expansion or compression is evaluated by integration, between the desired limits, of the representative curve on the P-V plane. As previously mentioned, the choice of the independent variable will depend upon whether the action represented by the curve is under conditions of nonflow or of steady flow. The form of integration is determined by the value of the exponent in the equation $PV^n = $ const., as shown by the following expressions for work.

For $n = 0$:

Equation, $P_1 = P_2$

$$\text{Nonflow: } {}_1W_2 = \int_{V_1}^{V_2} PdV = P(V_2 - V_1) \tag{3}$$

$$\text{Steady flow: } {}_1W_2 = \int_{P_1}^{P_2} VdP = 0 \tag{4}$$

[1] In this connection, consider the isentropic expansion of steam from 400 lb. per sq. in. abs., 640°F., to 5 lb. per sq. in. abs. The saturation line is crossed in this instance at 90 lb. per sq. in. abs. The average exponent for that portion of the expansion in the superheated state is 1.296. The average exponent for the expansion after crossing the saturation line, i.e., in the saturated region, is 1.132. The average for the entire range based only upon the terminal pressures and volumes is 1.183.

The steady-flow work done by 1 lb. of steam in this expansion is here determined by three methods for comparison. Method a gives the correct value.

(a) $A_1W_2 = h_1 - h_2 = 344$ Btu

(b) $AW = \int_{400}^{90} vdP$ (with $k = 1.296$) $+ \int_{90}^{5} vdP$ (with $k = 1.132$) $= 344.7$ Btu

(c) $AW = \int_{400}^{5} vdP$ (with $k = 1.183$) $= 366$ Btu

It will be noted that method c is most in error due to the use of a single exponent, determined from terminal conditions, for the entire range during which the steam is first superheated and then saturated. On the other hand, method b is relatively accurate.

For $n = 1$:

Equation, $PV = $ const.

Nonflow: $_1W_2 = \int_{V_1}^{V_2} PdV = PV \int_{V_1}^{V_2} \frac{dV}{V} = PV \log_e \frac{V_2}{V_1}$ (5)

Steady flow: $_1W_2 = \int_{P_1}^{P_2} VdP = PV \int_{P_1}^{P_2} \frac{dP}{P} = PV \log_e \frac{P_2}{P_1}$ (6)

(Note that these expressions are numerically equal.)

For $n = \infty$:

Equation, $V_1 = V_2$

Nonflow: $_1W_2 = \int_{V_1}^{V_2} PdV = 0$ (7)

Steady flow: $_1W_2 = \int_{P_1}^{P_2} VdP = V(P_2 - P_1)$ (8)

For any other value of n, including $n = k$:

Equation, $PV^n = $ const.

Nonflow: $_1W_2 = \int_{V_1}^{V_2} PdV = PV^n \int_{V_1}^{V_2} V^{-n}dV = \frac{P_2V_2 - P_1V_1}{1 - n}$

$$\text{or } \frac{P_1V_1 - P_2V_2}{n - 1} \quad (9)$$

Steady flow: $_1W_2 = \int_{P_1}^{P_2} VdP = P^{\frac{1}{n}}V \int_{P_1}^{P_2} P^{-\frac{1}{n}}dP$

$$= \frac{n}{n - 1}(P_1V_1 - P_2V_2) \quad (10)$$

6. The Adiabatic Change of State.—Any thermal action taking place without reception or rejection of heat by the working substance is characterized as adiabatic. There are, however, an infinite number of adiabatics—one thermally reversible, the others irreversible in varying degrees.

The completely reversible adiabatic takes place without change in entropy of the working substance (isentropic). For this, the exponent in the *P-V* equation is denoted by k. If an isentropic compression or expansion occurs under nonflow conditions, the work done is

$$_1W_2 = \frac{P_1V_1 - P_2V_2}{k - 1} \qquad \text{[See Eq. (9)]}$$

Reference to the nonflow energy equation shows that the work done is also equal to the change in internal energy, $A_1W_2 = U_2 - U_1$. For the steady-flow isentropic change,

$$_1W_2 = \frac{k}{k-1}(P_1V_1 - P_2V_2) \qquad \text{[See Eq. (10)]}$$

When other forms of energy in the flow equation are negligible, it may be seen that the work done in this case is equal to the change in enthalpy, $A_1W_2 = H_2 - H_1$.

The strictly irreversible adiabatic most frequently occurs as an expansion and under flow conditions. In this process there is no over-all transformation of energy, *i.e.*, the forms of energy possessed by the working substance at the beginning of the change are individually unchanged in quantity in the outgoing fluid, though the properties of the substance will be changed. The best example of such an adiabatic change is the throttling process for which the energy equation is

$$\frac{V_1^2}{2gJ} + h_1 = \frac{V_2^2}{2gJ} + h_2$$

for the usual case in which $V_1 = V_2$ and therefore $h_1 = h_2$.

Essentially adiabatic changes are common occurrences in practice, although the isentropic form is rarely approached closely. Actual adiabatics range from throttling action to processes in which there is relatively little thermal irreversibility.

7. Thermodynamic Treatment of Gases and Vapors.—It has been previously mentioned that the perfect gas conforms to relatively simple laws which are readily applicable to each case under consideration. Thus the thermodynamic properties and the relation existing between properties of this imaginary fluid are determined from straightforward expressions so easily applied to a particular state that any tabulation of properties is unnecessary.

Vapor properties, however, are governed by laws sufficiently complex to render their fundamental application to each particular case laborious and undesirable. The treatment of vapors is therefore facilitated by the use of tables of thermodynamic properties for various states, these tables having been prepared by special investigational work. In this connection, it should be borne in mind that, although the methods for treatment of gases and vapors are somewhat different for the reasons just mentioned, the same basic scientific principles are applicable in the broad sense to both.

Actual gases, sometimes classified as "permanent," approximate perfect gas behavior only within moderate ranges of pressure and temperature, and problems which involve a wide scope of these properties must consequently consider deviations from perfect gas laws. For refrigeration, where gases are rarely used other than through moderate ranges of pressure and temperature, it is unnecessary to complicate the theory by an exact analysis of the gas laws, and air will be treated as a perfect gas except in the consideration of throttling.

PERFECT GASES

8. Properties and Property Relationships.—Any gas, or mixture of gases, considered as perfect, follows precisely the laws of Boyle and Charles. From these may be deduced a characteristic equation[1] expressing the pressure-volume-temperature relationship $Pv = RT$, in which R is constant for any particular gas. Since $v = V/M$, this equation may also be written,

$$PV = MRT \tag{11}$$

Using this and the equation of the P-V curve, the following useful relationship may be derived:

$$\frac{T_1}{T_2} = \left(\frac{V_2}{V_1}\right)^{n-1} = \left(\frac{P_1}{P_2}\right)^{\frac{n-1}{n}} \tag{12}$$

Expressions for the other three properties in which we are ordinarily interested involve specific heat c, a characteristic which expresses the thermal capacity of a substance. Specifically, it is the heat required to be supplied to, or rejected from, a unit weight of material in order to produce a unit change in temperature. The English unit is Btu per pound per degree Fahrenheit. The specific heat of a gas may have any value, positive or negative, from zero to infinity depending upon the type of state change which the gas is undergoing while heat is being supplied or rejected. If, however, the specific heats at constant pressure c_p and at constant volume c_v are experimentally determined,

[1] It is noteworthy that this characteristic equation may also be derived mathematically from the kinetic theory of heat.

these are sufficient to permit the evaluation of the specific heat c for any other process by use of the relationships

$$\frac{c_p}{c_v} = k \quad \text{and} \quad c_p - c_v = AR$$

and the development of the nonflow energy equation for a process which has any value of n other than $n = 1$ or $n = k$, as follows:

$$_1Q_2 = (U_2 - U_1) + A_1W_2$$

or for unit weight of material,

$$c(T_2 - T_1) = c_v(T_2 - T_1) + \frac{AR(T_2 - T_1)}{1 - n}$$

from which

$$c = c_v + \frac{AR}{1 - n} = c_v + \frac{c_p - c_v}{1 - n}$$

Thus

$$c = c_v\left(1 + \frac{k - 1}{1 - n}\right) = c_v\left(\frac{k - n}{1 - n}\right) \tag{13}$$

Joule's law states that the internal energy of a perfect gas is dependent upon the temperature alone. Now if heat be added to a perfect gas under nonflow conditions while the volume is held constant, inspection of the energy equation will show that the heat thus supplied is exactly represented by an increase in the store of internal energy possessed by the gas. Therefore any expression for the quantity of energy involved must be the same for both, i.e.,

$$dQ = c_v dT = du \quad \text{or} \quad _1Q_2 = c_v(T_2 - T_1) = u_2 - u_1$$

Since this expresses the change in internal energy between the random temperatures T_1 and T_2, it must also show the internal energy change between *any* temperatures and, in accordance with Joule's law, *for any mode of state change.*

Changes in enthalpy for perfect gases may be expressed in terms of comparable simplicity as follows:

Fundamentally,

$$h = u + APv$$

Differentiating,

$$dh = du + APdv + AvdP$$

Now, differentiation of the characteristic equation shows that

$$Pdv + vdP = RdT$$

from which by substitution,

$$dh = c_v dT + ARdT$$

But $AR = c_p - c_v$
therefore,

$$dh = c_v dT + (c_p - c_v)dT = c_p dT \qquad \text{and} \qquad h_2 - h_1 = c_p(T_2 - T_1) \quad (14)$$

Inasmuch as this expression was derived for no specific case, it holds for any state change of a perfect gas.

Entropy change in general was expressed in Sec. 2 as

$$s_2 - s_1 = c \log_e \frac{T_2}{T_1}$$

where c is the specific heat applying to the particular process in question. Thus, for the constant pressure process,

$$s_2 - s_1 = c_p \log_e \frac{T_2}{T_1} \qquad (15)$$

for the constant volume process,

$$s_2 - s_1 = c_v \log_e \frac{T_2}{T_1} \qquad (16)$$

and, for any reversible process with a particular value of n (except 1 and k),

$$s_2 - s_1 = c_v \left(\frac{k-n}{1-n} \right) \log_e \frac{T_2}{T_1} \qquad (17)$$

VAPORS

9. Characteristics.—The treatment of vapors differs from that of perfect gases because the vapor is not amenable to perfect gas laws and because the substance must be considered in the forms of solid, liquid, saturated vapor, and superheated vapor and in the transition from one phase to another.

Vapor characteristics under various conditions may perhaps most readily be seen by reference to Fig. 3, which is a typical temperature-entropy diagram for substances extensively used as working fluids and refrigerants.   The so-called "boundary curves" are shown—the **saturated liquid line** 3-8, and the **saturation line** 8-9.   The latter might more properly be called the dry saturated vapor line since it represents the condition, upon this plane, of dry and saturated vapor at various temperatures. The **saturated solid line** 1-2 may also be classed as a boundary curve with the same significance for the solid as the saturated liquid line has for the liquid phase.

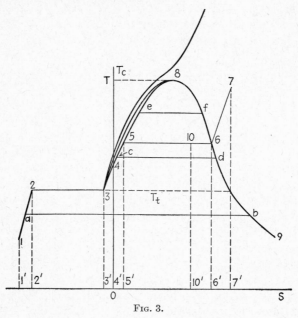

Fig. 3.

There are indicated upon the diagram two temperatures which are particularly worthy of note.   The temperature at the point 8, T_c, is called the **critical temperature** above which the substance cannot be liquefied.   At this point the latent heat of vaporization is zero and the transition from the liquid to the gaseous phase involves but little apparent physical or thermal change.   The temperature along the line 2-3, T_t, is the **triple point**,[1] so called because at that temperature the substance may exist as solid, liquid, or gas.   Below the triple point,

[1] Since the melting point is slightly affected by pressure, the triple point, strictly, is the temperature at which melting occurs when the substance is acted upon only by its own vapor pressure corresponding to the temperature.

the two possible phases are solid and gaseous for a saturated state in thermal equilibrium.   Above the triple point but below the critical temperature, the substance may exist as liquid or gas.   Above the critical temperature the phase must be gaseous.

The *T-s* diagram may be divided into several zones which are significant in representing the state of the substance.   Thus the area between the solid and saturation lines is the zone wherein a gas-solid mixture exists and where sublimation takes place.   Between the liquid and saturation lines, the saturated condition exists with part gas and part liquid, *i.e.*, "wet vapor" of some quality ranging from all liquid on the one side to a dry vapor on the other.   The area to the left of the saturated solid and liquid lines, with the critical temperature forming the upper boundary, is that of the solid and liquid, respectively, existing at high pressures—the higher pressures being farthest from the boundary curve.   Two typical high pressure liquid lines, one representing the critical pressure and one exceeding it, are shown on the diagram (Fig. 3).   Moderate pressure liquid lines, well below the critical, usually lie so close to the saturated liquid line as to be indistinguishable from it on diagrams to ordinary scale.   The remaining area on the diagram, *i.e.*, above the high pressure liquid zone and above and to the right of the saturation line, is the superheated vapor region.

Within the saturated vapor zone (both vapor-liquid and vapor-solid), equilibrium temperatures are related to absolute pressures and are known as **saturation temperatures** or **boiling points.**   Thus within this region, constant pressure lines are also isothermal, as *a-b*, *c-d*, 5-6, and *e-f* on the diagram.   It may be seen, therefore, that the state of a saturated vapor is not definable by pressure and temperature alone.   This renders desirable the use, for saturated vapors, of a physical property, **quality,** which is the proportion by weight of the material that exists in the vapor phase for any particular state.   The term **moisture content,** the converse of quality, is widely used but, strictly, is not applicable to a vapor below the triple point where no moisture exists.

For the purpose of illustrating the behavior of solid, liquid, and vapor under the influence of heat reception, consider a unit weight of solid at point 1, Fig. 3, to be heated at a constant pressure sufficiently moderate so that the state path will closely

follow the saturated solid and liquid lines.   At first the temperature will rise until the melting point is reached and will then
remain constant during the transition from solid to liquid while
the state point is traversing the diagram to the liquid line near 3.
Entirely liquid, the substance resumes its temperature rise, and
3-5 represents the heating of the liquid.   At 5 the boiling point
is reached for the particular pressure represented, and the temperature ceases to rise while a change of phase from liquid to
vapor is in progress, 5-6.   During this process the quality
progressively changes from zero on the liquid line to unity on the
saturation line.   At 6 the change is complete and, though still
saturated, the vapor is dry.   From 6 upward through 7 the
substance is a superheated vapor and, in character, approaches
more nearly the perfect gas as the temperature is increased above
that of saturation.   The permanent gases that may ordinarily
be treated as perfect are, at ordinary temperatures, simply
highly superheated vapors which would show characteristics
at low temperatures somewhat similar to the vapor in Fig. 3.

The position of the T-axis, *i.e.*, the zero of entropy, is arbitrarily
chosen so as to be most convenient since the chief interest is in
property differences and not in absolute values.   That this
depends somewhat upon the range in which the substance is
most used is shown by the fact that for H_2O the zero of entropy
and sensible heat is taken at 32°F., while for NH_3 and most
refrigerants it is −40°F.   It so happens that the zero point for
water was chosen at the solidification temperature for atmospheric
pressure, while for ammonia and many other vapors it is at a
higher temperature than that at which the substance fuses.

The area beneath the constant pressure curve in Fig. 3 is
divisible into several well-defined sections.   Knowing this
area to represent the heat supplied to the substance during the
change from 1 to 7, the subdivisions picture the heat added
during the individual processes.   Thus the area 1′122′ represents the heat supplied in heating the substance in the solid
phase from T_1 to T_2, and the area 2′233′ is the heat supplied
to change the state of the material from solid to liquid without
temperature change.   This is the latent heat of fusion.   Area
3′355′ is heat absorbed in raising the temperature of the liquid
to T_5; area 5′566′ represents latent heat of vaporization; and
6′677′ is heat required to superheat the vapor.

10. Properties.—If the fundamental expression for enthalpy be differentiated,

$$dh = du + APdv + AvdP$$

or, for nonflow, since $dQ = du + APdv$,

$$dh = dQ + AvdP$$

from which, for a constant pressure process, $dh = dQ$. That is, the change in enthalpy for this type of process is the heat supplied or rejected. The sum of the individual areas mentioned in the preceding article is thus the change in enthalpy between points 1 and 7, and the individual areas show the change in enthalpy between their respective points. Considering only the positive areas, *i.e.*, to the right of the T-axis, a vapor in the state 7 would have an enthalpy composed of the three areas shown which are: area 4'455' called enthalpy of the liquid; area 5'566', latent heat of vaporization; and 6'677', heat of superheat. Since enthalpies are given in tables for the properties of vapors for superheated and for dry and saturated conditions, it is unnecessary to calculate them. The point 10, however, represents wet vapor of a certain quality x. It is obvious that the enthalpy at point 10 would include all of the enthalpy of the liquid for that pressure, since that is unaffected by quality, and that portion of the latent heat which has been supplied and which, of course, is the proportion of the total latent heat represented by the quality. Thus

$$h_x = h_f + xh_{fg} \qquad\qquad (18)$$

The internal energy of vapors is not always given in tables of thermodynamic properties but may be calculated, from enthalpy, pressure, and specific volume, which are either directly tabulated or easily determined, by use of the fundamental equation for enthalpy:

$$u = h - APv \qquad\qquad (19)$$

Entropy values for superheated and dry saturated vapors are listed in tables. For wet vapors, the total entropy is made up of the sum of the entropies of the liquid and the proper proportion of that of vaporization,

$$s_x = s_f + xs_{fg} \qquad\qquad (20)$$

Specific volumes, like enthalpy and entropy, are tabulated only for superheated and dry saturated states and must be calculated for wet vapors. The form of simple equation is similar to those just given,

$$v_x = v_f + xv_{fg} \qquad (21)$$

In many instances, particularly with high quality and low pressure, the specific volume of the liquid is a negligible part of the whole and the equation may be written,

$$v_x = xv_g \qquad (22)$$

As previously noted, pressure and temperature, the other two important properties, are definitely related to each other for any given vapor within the saturated region and their corresponding values are listed in the tables.

11. Processes.—Vapors, in general, follow the polytropic path in compression and expansion subject to the limitations set forth in Sec. 5 regarding the variability of the exponent n. As mentioned, this variation may be sufficiently well compensated for, by successive integration of reasonably homogeneous portions of the curve, to render results of good accuracy.

In the saturated region, a constant pressure change is also an isothermal, but, unlike the perfect gas, is accompanied by a large change in internal energy since, during the vaporization process, by far the greater part of the heat supplied (total latent heat) is retained in the substance as energy of disgregation (internal latent heat).

Of all the adiabatic changes previously noted, the throttling and the isentropic processes stand out as the extremes of irreversibility and reversibility, respectively. In either case, with the initial condition of the vapor and one final property, usually the pressure, known, it may be required to determine the final condition by calculation from tables of thermodynamic properties. For the throttling process, the property which remains constant is enthalpy and

$$h_1 = h_2 = h_{f2} + x_2 h_{fg2} \qquad \text{or} \qquad x_2 = \frac{h_1 - h_{f2}}{h_{fg2}} \qquad (23)$$

which will hold if the process terminates in the saturated region. If the final condition is superheated, it is only necessary to find directly from the tables the condition at the second pressure for which the enthalpy is the same as it was initially. Throttling, being an irreversible adiabatic, always results in an entropy increase of the vapor. The isentropic change may be either a compression or an expansion with similar procedure in either case for determining the final conditions. For this process, with the final state saturated,

$$s_1 = s_2 = s_{f2} + x_2 s_{fg2} \qquad \text{or} \qquad x_2 = \frac{s_1 - s_{f2}}{s_{fg2}} \qquad (24)$$

If the final state is superheated, the conditions, as in the case for throttling, will be taken directly from the tables at the final pressure and the original entropy.

Until a clear conception is once obtained, there may be some confusion in differentiating between a "cycle diagram" and an "indicator card" since both may have much the same appearance on the P-V plane. A cycle diagram traces the state of the working substance, as represented by the two coordinate properties, throughout a complete thermal cycle showing, in their proper order, the effects of the reception or rejection of heat, of expansion or compression where work is involved, and of any other process which is included in the cycle. The indicator diagram, on the other hand, is simply a picture of the pressure-volume relationships in a cylinder during a certain series of operations. It represents a cycle of mechanical events, not a cycle of processes in the thermodynamic sense. A steam engine, for instance, may produce a closed P-V diagram in the form of an indicator card, but the steam engine itself is only a part of the heat engine system[1] and, as such, is capable of executing only a part of the heat engine cycle. This will also be true in the refrigeration cycles to be studied in which the compressor, although capable of producing a card, perhaps, is yet performing but one of the thermal processes pictured on the cycle diagram.

12. Joule-Thomson Effect.—The fundamental relationship for an adiabatic throttling process is that of constant enthalpy. It has been seen that, for a perfect gas, the enthalpy is dependent

---

[1] Reference to the steady-flow energy equation will show that, neglecting radiation, the steam engine itself neither receives nor rejects heat as such. That is the function of the boiler and the condenser, respectively, which, with the utilizer (the so-called steam engine), make up the complete heat engine.

only upon the temperature; hence throttling, for this fluid, takes place also at constant temperature.   This is true for actual gases, however, at only one temperature (depending somewhat upon the pressure), called the **inversion point,** which is a characteristic of the gas.   Below the inversion point the temperature drops as a result of throttling, while above the inversion point it rises.   Most commonly used gases have inversion temperatures so high that throttling, under service conditions, invariably produces a cooling effect.   The notable exception to this is hydrogen for which the inversion temperature, about $-112°F.$, is well below the ordinary range.   The cooling effect is evaluated by the **Joule-Thomson coefficient** $(\Delta T/\Delta P)_h$ expressed in any desirable units—degrees Fahrenheit per pound per square inch being a convenient English system.   This ratio is variable for any gas, depending upon the pressure and temperature at which throttling is undertaken and the range through which it is carried.   So long as the initial pressure of the gas does not exceed the critical, it is generally true that the Joule-Thomson coefficient decreases as the inversion point is approached.   With pressures in excess of the critical, the variability of the coefficient is likely to be erratic, particularly in the lower temperature ranges.

CHAPTER III

PRINCIPLES OF REFRIGERATION

In general, there are three principles by which a cooling effect may be procured. (1) By chemical means wherein a reaction is brought about which requires heat for its completion, this heat being supplied by the substance to be refrigerated. This method is not important from the standpoint of commercial refrigeration and does not come within the scope of this work. (2) By bringing in contact, either directly or indirectly, the substance to be cooled with a cooling medium, such as cold water or ice, from which heat has previously been removed either naturally or otherwise. (3) By supplying energy, in the form of work or as heat, to operate a "heat pump" by which heat may be abstracted from the substance of low temperature and rejected, together with the energy required to sustain the process, to a substance of higher temperature. To the last-named belong the mechanical refrigerating systems in general use today.

13. Ice Refrigeration.—Refrigeration by ice was the most common form of artificial cooling from the time when artificial cooling was first employed on a commercial scale to within a comparatively few years. Even now small unit refrigeration is largely, and railroad refrigeration almost entirely, carried on by means of ice, though the trend seems to be increasingly toward mechanical refrigeration for the former which includes domestic units.

The process of ice refrigeration is really divided into two distinct parts: (1) The preparation, or the abstraction of heat *from*, and the distribution of the cooling medium, ice; and (2) its consumption, or the abstraction of heat *by* the cooling medium in the home or plant. The preparation may take place in either of two ways, the respective products being known as "natural" and "manufactured" ice. These terms, however, apply rather to the method of production than to the product itself. By

27

natural ice is meant ice that has been frozen by natural means, harvested during the winter from the lakes and rivers of a country whose climate is sufficiently rigorous to permit it.   This ice is usually stored near by and, thence, it is transported to the points of consumption during the summer months according to the demand.   In communities located far from a natural source, it is usually cheaper to produce ice by mechanical means than to transport the natural product over the great distances necessary with the added loss due to melting en route to be considered.   In this case, a storage plant of moderate capacity

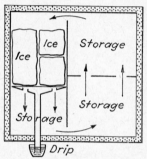

FIG. 4.—Direct ice refrigeration.

may be maintained at the ice plant to take care of peak demands while the refrigerating plant works steadily at a rate which will provide the average amount of ice required over a given summer period.   Manufactured ice possesses the advantages over natural ice of decreased loss in storage and transportation, and of purity from a chemical and bacteriological standpoint.   Natural ice can come from contaminated water, and may thus be a serious menace to the health of entire communities.

In the utilization of ice for cooling purposes, two general methods may be used, viz., the direct method and the indirect method.   In the direct method, the ice is placed in the same compartment with the articles to be cooled and, frequently, in contact with them.   Distribution of cooling effect is secured by air circulation alternately over the ice and the products to be cooled.   Such a method is illustrated in Fig. 4 and is similar in principle to the ordinary good household ice refrigerator.   In this case, there are four so-called compartments carefully opened to each other to permit the circulation of air.   Ice, in one of the upper compartments, so chills the surrounding air that its density is increased, and it descends to the compartment below displacing other and warmer air to surround the ice.   In the storage spaces the cool air is warmed, rises through the storage spaces, eventually returns to the ice, and repeats the circuit.   A continuous circulation is thus maintained so long as cooling of the air is carried on in the ice space.

In the indirect method, the ice is isolated from the storage space, cooling being carried on by means of a medium such as brine. This system is more satisfactorily applicable to large plants than is the direct method. Figure 5 illustrates a possible system. Chopped ice is supplied to compartment D where it surrounds the vertical tubes containing brine. The brine thus cooled is circulated, either by its own difference in density or by a small pump, through the storage spaces A, B, and C, and so back to D. A, B, and C may be held at any desired temperature above the minimum by regulating the quantity of brine passing through each.

Advantages of the indirect over the direct system are: better distribution of cold in the case of large installations, better

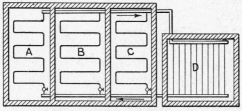

Fig. 5.—Indirect ice refrigeration

temperature regulation, possibility of various temperatures in different compartments, and no danger of food infection by impure ice. Disadvantages are: increased first cost, greater complexity, and larger space requirements.

Refrigeration by ice, in general, has the disadvantage of the lower temperature being limited by the comparatively high melting point of ice (32°F.). This results in a mean temperature in the storage spaces of about 50°F., in the case of the small household refrigerator, and probably not less than 40°F. in larger units. These temperatures are not sufficiently low for most cold storage purposes, and 50°F. has been shown to be too high for the proper preservation of food in the home.

14. Freezing Mixtures.—Lower temperatures than those attainable with ice alone may be had by the use of a "freezing mixture" composed of ice and some other substance, notably a salt. This phenomenon is due to four physical facts: (1) That heat is required by the process when salt dissolves in water. The heat involved is called the "heat of solution" and, supposing little or no heat to be supplied from without, will come from the sensible heat of the solution itself resulting in a lowering of the temperature.   (2) That a solid in melting will require its latent heat of fusion, and, again in the absence of outside heat, this will be derived from the sensible heat of the solution and will result in a drop in temperature.   (3) That when a saline solution freezes, the solvent, in more or less pure form, will precipitate out.   Thus a brine solution, partially frozen, will be partly in the form of pure ice and partly brine of increased concentration due to water having been precipitated out of solution.   (4) That the freezing point of a salt solution drops as the degree of concentration increases until the eutectic temperature is reached. Of these four facts, the last three are particularly important in the production of low temperatures by this method.   For purposes of explanation, consider a strong salt solution at a temperature of 32°F., the lowest temperature to be had with ice alone.   Suppose that a quantity of ice be added to the solution.   The mixture is now in precisely the state of partially frozen brine, composed of brine and some of the solvent in the form of ice.   Since the freezing point of the mixture will be below 32°F., the mixture exists at a temperature higher than its melting point.   This will result in a melting process taking the heat which it requires from the solution, and the temperature will drop.   This cooling process will continue until either the ice is melted or the freezing point of the solution is reached when no further melting will take place.   The "solution" in this case is weaker than the original for the reason that it is composed of the original solution diluted by water from the melting ice.   The freezing mixture process as a whole may be considered as the forced melting of ice, which requires heat, at temperatures below the normal melting point.

From what has been said, it may readily be seen that *the minimum temperature attainable with a freezing mixture is the freezing point of the final solution.*   It is obviously desirable, in order to obtain the greatest effect, to have the final solution strongly concentrated.   In practice, therefore, there is no original solution, as in the illustration, since that would only dilute the final solution and also make it necessary to abstract heat from the additional water.   Instead, salt is added directly to crushed ice resulting in a solution of much higher concentration.   As heat is added to the mixture from the substance which is being cooled, more ice and salt are supplied, and the resulting brine is drained off so that the process may be made to a certain extent continuous.

Sodium chloride or calcium chloride are the salts generally used with crushed ice. A mixture of one part of the former to three parts ice will give a temperature of about 0°F., and the latter may be mixed in the proportion of three parts to two parts ice for −27°F., or two parts to one of ice for −42°F.

This method of refrigeration, used to some extent on a small scale, is not readily applicable to commercial plants of any size.

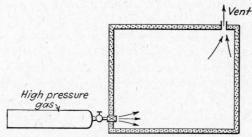

FIG. 6.—Cooling by Joule-Thomson effect.

15. Cooling by Gas.—Refrigeration may be produced by the expansion of a gas which has been previously compressed and cooled. Two types of expansion will reduce the temperature of a gas, *viz.*: throttling, utilizing the Joule-Thomson effect; or a reversible expansion in which the energy delivered as external work is supplied entirely or in part by the internal energy of the gas. These will be considered separately.

16. Cooling by Throttling.—During a throttling process there is no change in enthalpy, and, for a perfect gas, there is no change in temperature. Actual gases, however, diverge sufficiently from the perfect to show a substantial change, usually a decrease, in temperature when throttled (see Sec. 12).

Figure 6 shows a simple refrigeration system based upon this principle. A flask of air or some other gas at high pressure is throttled through a porous plug or an orifice into the refrigerator and escapes, after acquiring heat, to the outside air. The temperature of the gas leaving the plug will be a few degrees below that in the flask, the amount of the temperature drop depending upon the Joule-Thomson coefficient, the pressure drop, and the original state of the gas.   In any event, the resulting temperature will be too high for refrigerating purposes unless the original temperature is relatively low.   The system might be improved and the process made continuous if the air were supplied by a compressor directly and an air cooler used to provide as cool air as possible to the throttling valve.   A machine of this type would be unsatisfactory from the temperature stand-point unless the refrigerating temperature desired were close to that of the cooling water and, in any case, would require an excessive amount of work for a given cooling capacity.

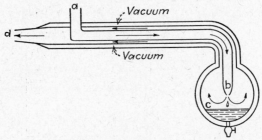

Fig. 7.—Liquefaction of gases.

Although the principle cannot be successfully applied to commercial refrigeration, the Joule-Thomson effect is readily utilized in the production of low temperatures and may be used effectively for cooling the gas stream itself by the use of regenera-tive cooling.   By this means it is possible to provide temperatures sufficiently low for the liquefaction of a portion of the gas. Hampson and Linde utilized this principle in the development of their liquid air machines.   Figure 7 shows diagrammatically the manner in which regenerative cooling operates.   The gas is supplied under pressure at a and flows through the small inner tube to the throttling valve at b.   Here it will be subjected to the Joule-Thomson effect and will leave the chamber c at a tempera-ture lower than that at which it entered.   In leaving c and passing to d, where it is discharged from the apparatus, the gas thus cooled is made to pass around the tube carrying the incoming gas, thereby cooling the latter before it is throttled.   Now, if the temperatures at a, b, and c be observed as the apparatus is started, its action may readily be seen. T_a is fixed by the precooler, and T_b (before throttling) is always greater than T_c owing to the Joule-Thomson effect. In starting, $T_b = T_a$, but T_c is less than T_b the moment gas is permitted to pass through the throttling valve. This gas at T_c will cool the incoming gas and constantly lower T_b which, in turn, results in a reduction in T_c, and this progressive cooling continues until the temperature reduction is checked either by heat leakage from the outside or by reaching the saturation temperature of the gas. If the latter, then any further cooling effect which takes place will withdraw the latent heat of vaporization from some of the gas and partial liquefaction will result. It should be noted that the operation

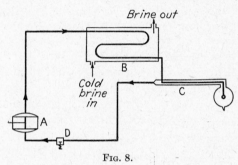

FIG. 8.

of the apparatus depends, not upon a great temperature drop during throttling since this remains relatively small, but upon precooling of the gas before throttling and then the *additional* temperature drop due to throttling. Because of the extremely low temperatures attained, the apparatus must be carefully insulated against heat from the surrounding atmosphere. This may be done on small laboratory machines by employing a vacuum jacket and by silvering.

A workable unit for the liquefaction of air is shown in diagram in Fig. 8. A machine of this type may produce liquid air continuously by simply compressing, cooling, and throttling. From 5 to 10 per cent of the air compressed may be liquefied, this being made up from the atmosphere through valve D as required.

Machines utilizing the principle of cooling of a gas by throttling, though simple and capable of producing extremely low temperatures with regenerative cooling, do not have sufficiently large capacities for heat abstraction, considering the work employed in compression, to be applicable to purposes of refrigeration on a large scale. Their use is therefore limited to such purposes as the production of low temperatures for laboratory work and the liquefaction of gases.

17. Cooling by Reversible Expansion.—Another method for the production of refrigerating temperatures with a permanent gas as the refrigerant is by means of an expansion with the accomplishment of external work. For the maximum temperature reduction in a given pressure range, the process should be, of course, the reversible adiabatic. Since, in this type of expansion, the energy removed in the form of work must largely come from the store of internal energy or sensible heat, which depends upon the temperature, it follows that any expansion bringing about a decrease in internal energy will also produce a temperature drop in the working substance. Such a process might be accomplished in a reciprocating engine or in a turbine.

A refrigerating system utilizing a process of this kind would circulate the gas thus cooled so that it might in turn provide the required cooling in the refrigerator. In order to render the operation continuous, the system would include a compressor to supply the expander continuously with gas under pressure.

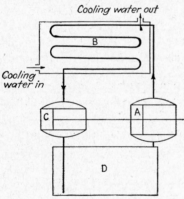

18. The Air System.—Figure 9 shows an air system composed of compressor A connected to a source of power; an air cooler B where some of the sensible heat due to compression is removed by cooling water; an expander or air engine C which, by expanding the air adiabatically, serves the double purpose of reducing its temperature greatly and of assisting in the work of compression; and the refrigerator or cold room D supplied at one end with cold air from the expander, the air leaving at the other, after accomplishing its cooling, to return to the compressor and repeat the cycle. Low temperature air in sufficiently large quantities for refrigeration on a reasonably large scale may be continuously produced in this manner with fair economy of power.

Fig. 9.—The air refrigerating system.

The system shown is a so-called "open" system inasmuch as the air used is openly circulated in the refrigerator room. A modification of this in which the cooling air is passed through the refrigerator room or brine cooler in pipe coils and does not mingle with the air of the room is called a "closed" system and has certain advantages that will be discussed later.

19. Cooling by Evaporation.—The application of this principle consists simply of the utilization of the latent heat of vaporization of some liquid which is put in such condition that, in vaporizing, it will abstract heat from the substance to be cooled. This may be effectively demonstrated by dipping the finger in a volatile liquid and holding it up in the air to dry. A very distinct cooling effect will be felt owing to evaporation of the liquid from the skin.

In many respects this type of artificial cooling is the oldest. Nature uses this means to maintain a proper body temperature in spite of high atmospheric temperatures or high rates of oxidation, with consequent generation of heat, occasioned by physical exertion. Perspiration forms on the surface of the skin in varying quantities, depending upon the cooling required, and is evaporated from the skin, thereby removing from the body a relatively large amount of heat. Humidity increases the suffering due to heat because high humidity retards evaporation of the perspiration. Another example of the cooling action resulting from evaporation is the porous earthen jar used by some primitive peoples in hot dry climates for preserving water at a more palatable temperature. Here some of the water seeps through the container and forms a light film on the outside which, in evaporating, removes a considerable amount of heat from the jar and its contents.

In both of the above cases, the refrigerant, *i.e.*, water, is evaporated at a temperature considerably below its boiling point at the atmospheric pressure to which it is subjected. This means that the rate of evaporation is dependent upon the vapor pressure of the surrounding atmosphere and will, in any event, be comparatively slow at this partial pressure. In other words, boiling does not take place, and the cooling effect, which is in proportion to the rate of evaporation, though great enough for the needs in the cases mentioned, would not suffice for producing refrigeration on a large scale. However, amongst the substances at our disposal today, many may be found of sufficient volatility to boil violently at pressures near atmospheric and temperatures highly suited to refrigeration requirements.

A crude application of one of these substances to evaporative cooling is shown in Fig. 10. This apparatus consists simply of a refrigerator room or box, a coil terminating on the one end in a vent through the top and on the other in a union, and a flask or container with a stopcock which connects to the lower end of the coil. Suppose now that this flask were filled with ammonia, NH_3, in the liquid state and the valve closed ready for installation in this apparatus. The pressure within the flask will be that

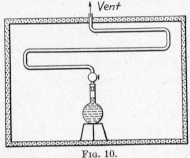

Fig. 10.

corresponding to the temperature at which it exists. If the temperature be 75°F., then the pressure within the vessel will be 140.5 lb. per sq. in. abs. in order to maintain the liquid state. Once installed, the cock will be opened, the pressure will decrease and so will the boiling point. This will continue until the liquid falls below the existing temperature of the flask and the surroundings, when boiling will commence, and it will continue as long as the saturation temperature is low enough so that heat may be absorbed from the surroundings. Thus the temperature within the flask, being the boiling point, may be fixed by regulating the pressure, controlled in this case by the valve. Supposing the valve to be opened wide, the flask pressure would be about atmospheric and the temperature around −28°F. Owing to the great difference in temperature between room and flask, much heat would be absorbed and boiling would be violent. If less refrigeration were desired, the valve might be partially closed, increasing the pressure and temperature within the flask and decreasing, because of reduced temperature difference, the absorption of heat by the ammonia from the room. This would, in turn, reduce the amount of ammonia evaporated, which would always be regulated by the heat supplied. The temperature of the room could, therefore, be held at any desired value above the minimum afforded by an ammonia temperature of −28°F. since the flask pressure could not be less than atmospheric.

Although a system of this sort would work and provide cooling, it is not practicable from several standpoints, the two principal objections being: the necessity of shutting down, when the supply of refrigerant becomes exhausted, in order to replenish it, *i.e.*, intermittent operation; and the expense involved in evaporating the refrigerant but once and then wasting it to the atmosphere.   Another objection is that those refrigerants requiring a vacuum in order to reach a sufficiently low temperature could not be used in this simple system.   In overcoming these difficulties, we have only to recover the vapor escaping from the refrigerator, liquefy it, return the liquid as required, and to make of this a continuous process.   The liquefaction may be carried out by compressing the vapor until its boiling point exceeds the temperature of the available cooling medium, water or air, and then cooling it by this medium below its boiling point, producing condensation.   There will thus be a compressor and a condenser in the system in addition to the vessel in which evaporation takes place.

Obviously there must be two terminal pressures in the system—the low pressure at which the refrigerant vaporizes, and the high pressure at which it condenses—which will require some type of apparatus for raising the pressure and some type of apparatus for again reducing it.   The first, as has already been seen, is accomplished by means of the compressor (in the compression system). The pressure reduction might be accomplished in either of two ways, *viz.*: by expansion in a cylinder with work done on a piston, or by expansion through a valve or orifice, *i.e.*, pure throttling. Since the fluid to be expanded is a liquid, the work derived by expansion in a cylinder would not be worth the added equipment and complexity and throttling is invariably used in vapor systems. This may be accomplished by any type of valve which will lend itself to close regulation.   An evaporator or refrigerating coil, in which the liquid may vaporize, after passage through the expansion valve, at low pressure and temperature, completes the essential apparatus of a vapor system.

20. The Vapor System.—An elementary compression system is shown in Fig. 11 and operates as follows.   Vapor at high pressure and temperature leaves the compressor A and enters the condenser B where heat is taken from the refrigerant and condensation occurs at the higher pressure.   The liquid refrigerant leaves the condenser and is stored temporarily in the receiver *C* which serves no thermodynamic purpose. From the receiver, the liquid is conducted to the expansion valve *D* located at the entrance to the refrigerating coils. Here a pressure reduction takes place, with a reduced boiling point as a consequence, and part of the liquid is immediately vaporized by virtue of the excess enthalpy of the liquid when throttled, so that the state of the refrigerant upon leaving the expansion valve is that of a vapor of low quality at a temperature corresponding to its low pressure. Upon entering the evaporator *E*, the vapor, being at a temperature below that of the refrig-

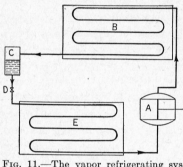

Fig. 11.—The vapor refrigerating system.

erator, absorbs heat from the latter for its further vaporization. It finally leaves the evaporator in a state either of saturation with high quality or of superheat and enters the compressor where the pressure is again increased and the cycle repeated.

21. Clearance and Clearance Factor.—Any reciprocating compressor, irrespective of the substance handled, must have clearance to a greater or a lesser degree owing to constructional considerations.

On the *P-V* diagram shown in Fig. 12, the theoretical indicator card without clearance would be *abefa*, in which the fluid is drawn in along *f-a*, compressed along the polytropic *a-b*, and discharged from the cylinder from *b* to *e*. In

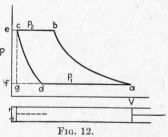

Fig. 12.

this case the piston displacement is equal to the cylinder volume, and a full piston displacement of fluid is drawn in on every suction stroke.

Consider now the case with clearance. The clearance volume is V_c or V_g. The piston displacement is now $V_a - V_g$. The fluid is compressed from *a* to *b* as before and is discharged from *b* to *c* but not fully discharged since the clearance volume V_c will remain in the cylinder. Upon the return stroke of the piston to the right, this volume of fluid—supposing it to be an elastic fluid—will reexpand along a polytropic *c-d* maintaining a sufficiently high pressure within the cylinder to prevent the entrance of fresh material until the point *d* is reached where the reexpansion has been carried to such a point that the pressure is reduced to normal suction pressure, and the induction of a fresh supply of fluid may begin. The actual volume of the fluid drawn in is, therefore, $V_a - V_d$ which is less than the piston displacement.

The ratio $(V_a - V_d)/(V_a - V_g)$, *i.e.*, the relation of that part of the piston displacement which is effective for suction to the total piston displacement, is called the **clearance factor** and may be found as follows:

$$V_a - V_d = (V_a - V_g) - (V_d - V_g)$$

Since *c-d* is a polytropic and $V_c = V_g$, $V_d = V_g(p_2/p_1)^{\frac{1}{n}}$.

Let $\dfrac{V_g}{V_a - V_g} = Cl$, then

$$V_a - V_d = (V_a - V_g) - Cl(V_a - V_g)\left(\frac{p_2}{p_1}\right)^{\frac{1}{n}} + Cl(V_a - V_g)$$

$$= (V_a - V_g)\left[1 - Cl\left(\frac{p_2}{p_1}\right)^{\frac{1}{n}} + Cl\right]$$

and

$$\frac{V_a - V_d}{V_a - V_g} = \text{clearance factor} = 1 + Cl - Cl\left(\frac{p_2}{p_1}\right)^{\frac{1}{n}} \qquad (25)$$

The exponent *n* for expansion may be assumed, in the absence of other data, the same as that for the corresponding compression.

It should be noted in passing that, although an increase in clearance decreases the capacity for a given piston displacement, it does not change the work done on the fluid discharged—other conditions remaining the same and neglecting mechanical friction—since the clearance volume, in reexpanding, returns the work that has been done in compressing it.

22. Volumetric Efficiency.—A compressor without clearance and without losses would draw into the cylinder, and discharge, a quantity of free gas equivalent to the piston displacement. No actual compressor does this, and the ratio of the volume of free gas actually delivered to the piston displacement in a given time is called **volumetric efficiency.**   This may also be expressed as the ratio of the weight of gas compressed to the weight of free gas represented by the piston displacement in the same time interval.

$$c_v = \frac{\text{volume of free gas delivered per unit of time}}{\text{piston displacement per unit of time}}$$

or

$$e_v = \frac{\text{weight of gas delivered per unit of time}}{\text{weight of piston displacement of free gas per unit of time}}$$

The factors influencing volumetric efficiency are clearance factor, change in pressure and temperature from outside conditions during the suction stroke, and leakage through valves or past the piston.   In further discussion here, leakage losses will be neglected.   The clearance factor expresses, volumetrically, the proportion of the piston displacement of gas which has been drawn in, and it is also an expression for volumetric efficiency provided the gas is still at outside pressure and temperature at the end of the suction stroke.   If, however, the condition of the gas in the cylinder at the end of the suction stroke differs from that of the free gas, the specific volume will be influenced, and the proportion represented by the clearance factor must be corrected to outside conditions.   Thus

$$e_v = \left[1 + Cl - Cl\left(\frac{p_2}{p_1}\right)^{\frac{1}{n}} \right] \times \frac{p_s}{p_o} \times \frac{T_o}{T_s} \qquad (26)$$

where subscript s denotes suction, and subscript o outside or free conditions.

In most cases, the pressure drop through the suction valve will be known from indicator card data, but the temperature rise of the gas during the suction stroke is not so readily determined.   Some heating will occur owing to exposure of the gas to cylinder walls which have been heated from previous compressions, but the amount of heating is dependent upon so many variables that no cognizance will be taken of it in ordinary cases in this work.   Also, since 1 lb. per sq. in. of wire-drawing has an effect approximately equivalent to a temperature rise of 40°F. during the suction stroke, the wire-drawing, for compressors, is probably of the greater importance.

Throttling of the gas through valves during suction and discharge, besides affecting volumetric efficiency, increases the work of compression for a given quantity of gas because of the greater range of pressure occasioned by it. In calculating work of compression and expansion, and also clearance factor, the terminal pressures within the cylinder should be used in order to include the work necessary to overcome friction through the valves.

23. Refrigerating Unit of Capacity.—The refrigerating unit of capacity is the **ton**, equal to 288,000 Btu per 24 hr., 12,000 Btu per hr., or 200 Btu per min.   This unit, as a *rate* of heat absorption by the refrigerant, is in nature comparable to the boiler horsepower which is a rate of heat absorption by the water and steam in a boiler.   The ton was originally derived from the average rate of heat absorption of 2000 lb. of ice at 32°F. in melting to water at 32°F. in a 24-hr. period.   Considering the latent heat of fusion of ice as 144 Btu per lb., the relationship is readily apparent.

Corresponding quantitative units of refrigeration are the **ton-hour** and the **ton-day,** equal, respectively, to 12,000 Btu and 288,000 Btu.

The refrigerating capacity of a machine may occasionally be referred to as the "ice melting" capacity expressed in tons. This is not to be confused with the ice making capacity of a machine which may be given in tons of ice per 24 hr.   The latter is, for a given machine, always less than the former because of the necessity of precooling the water to, and subcooling the ice below, the freezing point in addition to the actual freezing.

24. Efficiency.—In order to express the relative performance of refrigerating equipment, some criterion, comparable to the efficiency used for engines, is desirable.   Since the useful output of a refrigerating machine is the refrigerating effect, and the energy input to produce this effect, in the compression systems, is work, a suitable expression of performance is the ratio Q/AW, called the **coefficient of performance,** where Q is the refrigerating effect for the work input W.   This ratio is the efficiency of the unit.[1] Another widely used and favored criterion is **horsepower per ton** which expresses an inverse relationship as compared with the coefficient of performance.

[1] It is characteristic of refrigerating machines that the efficiency, in this sense, may exceed unity, while for heat engines it inherently may not.

CHAPTER IV

AIR REFRIGERATION SYSTEM

Although practically obsolete from the standpoint of commercial use, the air compression system of refrigeration is unique in its principle of operation and presents an interesting and instructive thermodynamic study. This system possessed two outstanding advantages over the vapor systems of its day. They were, first, the cheapness and availability of the refrigerant used, and, second, the safety of the refrigerant. These advantages made it a favorite, particularly for marine installation, the first rendering the renewal of the refrigerant easy and the second insuring safety in the event of leakage or serious mechanical failure.

Against these, the air system has the principal disadvantages, when compared to vapor machines, of larger size and higher cost for the same refrigerating capacity, and lower coefficient of performance, *i.e.*, greater power consumption. Furthermore, although the items listed in the preceding paragraph in favor of the air system are, strictly, inherent advantages, the progress in design and the general development of vapor systems and refrigerants have practically eliminated them as real points of superiority. It is thus easy to see why the air machine has been generally superseded for all types of service by the vapor system.

25. Carnot Cycle.—If the Carnot heat engine cycle be reversed, it becomes, in effect, a "heat pump" or refrigeration cycle. This represents the highest possible performance between two limiting temperatures and is therefore of value as an ideal. The reversed cycle is shown on P-V and T-s coordinates in Fig. 13, using a gas as the refrigerant. Starting from point 1, the gas within the cylinder undergoes successively, adiabatic compression, isothermal compression, adiabatic expansion, and isothermal expansion. It thus absorbs heat at low temperature and rejects it at high. Work is done on the gas during the compressions

42

and by the gas during the expansions, leaving, as the net work to be done, the difference. This is represented by the enclosed area, 12341, on the *P-V* diagram.

The *T-s* diagram gives a picture of the heat quantities supplied to or rejected from 1 lb. of the gas during the cycle. The heat rejected from the system at the higher temperature is the area 23562 and is equal to $T_2(s_2 - s_3)$. The heat supplied to the system, the refrigerating effect, is the area 41654, equal to $T_1(s_1 - s_4)$. The difference of the heat supplied and the heat rejected is the enclosed area 12341 which represents the energy

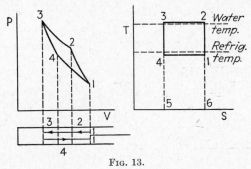

FIG. 13.

input in the form of work. Since for these three areas the change in entropy is the same, the energy quantities represented by them are proportional to the absolute temperatures. Thus, the coefficient of performance, being the refrigerating effect divided by the heat equivalent of the net work done in producing that effect, is

$$\text{Coefficient of performance} = \frac{T_1}{T_2 - T_1} \qquad (27)$$

It is obvious that the performance of the cycle may be improved either by lowering the higher temperature or by raising the lower temperature. This applies to all refrigerating machines, both theoretical and practical, just as a reduction in the head against which a pump may be forcing water will decrease the work required to handle a given quantity. It should be borne in mind, however, that these temperatures are fixed by the temperature at which the cooling water or air is available and the temperature that is to be maintained in the refrigerator, respectively. In order that there may be a transfer of heat in the right direction, the upper temperature must be in excess of that of the water or air to which heat is to be rejected, while the lower temperature must be below that of the substance to be cooled, as shown in Fig. 13.   Since, all other conditions remaining the same, the rate of heat transfer is directly proportional to the temperature difference, the temperature range of the refrigerant may in practice be somewhat increased at the expense of the coefficient of performance in order to obtain better heat flow in the heat exchangers, keeping both their size and cost within reason.

Although the Carnot cycle is commonly thought of as taking place within a single cylinder which accommodates itself succes-

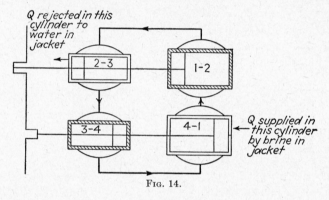

FIG. 14.

sively to the four processes, a clearer conception may perhaps be had by assuming each process to take place in its individual cylinder.   Such a layout for a reversed Carnot system is shown in Fig. 14.   In addition to the customary assumptions regarding the neglect of losses, all losses involved in the transfer of the working substance to and from the cylinders must also be neglected in this case.   Further, in this conception of the operation of the Carnot cycle, the steady-flow energy equation would have to be applied if the work in the individual cylinders were to be solved for, but this in no way affects the net work of the cycle or the heat quantities, and the diagrams of Fig. 13 are correct for this layout.

In cylinder 1-2, covered to prevent heat flow through the walls, the gas which is used as the refrigerant is compressed adiabatically.   Cylinder 2-3 further compresses the gas isothermally using a water jacket which removes energy in the form of heat as fast

as it is added in the form of work.   Cylinder 3-4 is also insulated
to provide adiabatic expansion, and cylinder 4-1 is jacketed
with brine from the refrigerator, the brine supplying heat to the
cylinder contents in amount equivalent to the work done by
the gas, thus giving an isothermal expansion.   The difference
between the work required by the compressions and the work
done by the expansions is supplied from some external source.

Example.—A refrigerating system operates on the reversed Carnot
cycle.   The higher temperature of the refrigerant in the system is
100°F., and the lower is 0°F.   The capacity is to be 10 tons.   Neglect
all losses.

Find: (*a*) Coefficient of performance; (*b*) heat rejected from the system per minute; (*c*) power required.

Solution:

(*a*) Coefficient of performance $= \dfrac{460}{560 - 460} = 4.6$

(*b*) Heat rejected $= {}^{560}\!/_{460}(10)(200) = 2435$ Btu per min.

or,

$\qquad S_1 - S_4 = {}^{2000}\!/_{460} = 4.35$

$\qquad$ Heat rejected $= 4.35(560) = 2435$ Btu per min.

(*c*) Net work $= 4.35(560 - 460) = 435$ Btu per min.

or

$\qquad$ Net work $= \dfrac{560 - 460}{460}(2000) = 435$ Btu per min.

or

$\qquad$ Net work $= 2435 - 2000 = 435$ Btu per min.

$\qquad$ Hp. $= \dfrac{435}{42.4} = 10.3$

It will be noted that in the example no refrigerant is specified
since, insofar as those calculations are concerned, the Carnot cycle
is independent of the working substance.

26. Theoretical Air System.—Although the Carnot cycle is
the most efficient between fixed temperature limits and is therefore useful as a criterion of perfection, it possesses undesirable
characteristics, particularly with a gaseous refrigerant such as
air, which render it objectionable from the practical viewpoint.
As will be seen later, the Carnot cycle may be applied to vapors
with comparatively few drawbacks, but the use of a permanent
gas as the working fluid produces both extreme pressures and

extreme volumes and would thus require a very large machine, judged by present standards, per unit refrigeration capacity. Also, for a gas, certain portions of the cycle, notably the isothermals, would be difficult of accomplishment. There have thus been evolved for practical application other theoretical cycles, less perfect thermally than the Carnot but more amenable to the requirements of actual use.

Practical refrigeration systems, therefore, for both air and vapors follow, with comparatively slight digressions, theoretical cycles other than the Carnot. The air refrigerating cycle is the reversed Brayton, or Joule, heat engine cycle. This system

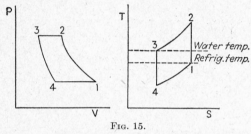

Fig. 15.

was shown diagrammatically in its fundamentals in Fig. 9 to consist of compressor, air cooler, expander or air engine, and refrigerator. The P-V and T-s diagrams for the theoretical cycle are shown in Fig. 15. No losses are considered in the elementary discussion of this cycle. Here, as in the Carnot cycle, the work of expansion assists in the compression, and both are adiabatics, but the isothermals have been replaced by constant pressure heat addition and heat rejection processes. No difficulty is experienced in practice in obtaining approximate constant pressure changes if it is so desired.

Referring to Fig. 15, the cycle proceeds as follows. Air is compressed isentropically from condition 1 to condition 2. The result is an increase in temperature, pressure, internal energy, and enthalpy; a decrease in specific volume; and no change in entropy. The compressor work for the steady-flow process may be expressed:

$$AW_{comp} = \frac{Ak}{k-1}(P_1V_1 - P_2V_2) = \frac{k}{k-1}(AMR)(T_1 - T_2)$$

but, since $R = (c_p - c_v)J = c_p\left(\frac{k-1}{k}\right)J$, or from the steady-flow energy equation for an adiabatic,

$$AW_{comp} = Mc_p(T_1 - T_2) \tag{28}$$

From 2 to 3, the air is passed, with no change in pressure, through a cooler with water usually used as the cooling medium. Here heat is rejected resulting in a decrease of specific volume, temperature, entropy, internal energy, and enthalpy. The heat which is rejected during this change is

$$Q = Mc_p(T_3 - T_2)^* \tag{29}$$

Adiabatic expansion takes place from points 3 to 4. Temperature, pressure, internal energy, and enthalpy decrease; specific volume increases; and there is no change in entropy. The work of the expander

$$AW_{exp} = \frac{Ak}{k-1}(P_3V_3 - P_4V_4) = \frac{k}{k-1}(AMR)(T_3 - T_4)$$
$$= Mc_p(T_3 - T_4) \tag{30}$$

Points 4 to 1 represents constant pressure passage through the cold room or the refrigerating coils, depending upon whether the system be open or closed. Temperature, specific volume, internal energy, entropy, and enthalpy increase in this process with the reception of heat by the air from the refrigerator. The heat supplied is

$$Q_{sup} = Mc_p(T_1 - T_4) \tag{31}$$

The net work of the cycle, being the difference between the compressor work and the expander work, may be expressed as an algebraic sum:

$$AW_{net} = \frac{Ak}{k-1}[(P_1V_1 - P_2V_2) + (P_3V_3 - P_4V_4)]$$
$$= \frac{k}{k-1}(AMR)[(T_1 - T_2) + (T_3 - T_4)]$$
$$= Mc_p[(T_1 - T_2) + (T_3 - T_4)] \tag{32}$$

* In general, a negative answer, when solving for an energy quantity, signifies heat *rejected* or work done *on* the substance. A positive answer denotes heat *supplied* or work done *by* the substance. The signs will usually be disregarded when numerical quantities are dealt with. However, in combining equations they must be taken into account, and what would be simply a numerical difference will then appear as an algebraic sum.

It is of interest to note that the last is also an expression for the difference between the heat rejected from, and the heat supplied to, the system as may be shown by a rearrangement of the terms:

$$AW_{net} = Mc_p[(T_3 - T_2) + (T_1 - T_4)] \qquad (33)$$

This is in accordance with the energy equation for the system which states, for this case,

$$AW_{net} = Q_{rej} - Q_{sup}$$

The coefficient of performance (C.P.) will be

$$\text{C.P.} = \frac{Q_{sup}}{AW_{net}} = \frac{Mc_p(T_1 - T_4)}{Mc_p[(T_1 - T_2) + (T_3 - T_4)]} = \frac{T_1 - T_4}{T_1 - T_2 + T_3 - T_4} \qquad (34)$$

The fact that this is negative has no significance, resulting simply from the negative sign given to work input. Rather than use the above equation for coefficient of performance, it is usually easier, since both the net work and the refrigerating effect will have been computed, to simply take the numerical ratio, expressing W_{net} in its heat equivalent.

Example.—An open air refrigerating system operating between pressures of 150 lb. per sq. in. abs. and 15 lb. per sq. in. abs. is required to produce 10 tons of refrigeration. Temperature of air leaving the refrigerator room is 20°F., and that leaving the air cooler is 60°F. No losses and no clearance.

Calculate the following for the theoretical cycle: (a) Temperature at points 1, 2, 3, and 4 (Fig. 15); (b) pounds of air circulated per minute; (c) theoretical piston displacement of compressor, cubic feet per minute; (d) theoretical piston displacement of expander, cubic feet per minute; (e) work of compressor, Btu per minute; (f) work of expander, Btu per minute; (g) net work of cycle, Btu per minute; (h) coefficient of performance; (i) horsepower required.

Solution:

(a) $T_1 = 20°F. = 480°F.$ abs.; $T_3 = 60°F. = 520°F.$ abs.

$T_2 = 480(^{150}/_{15})^{0.286} = 926°F.$ abs.

$T_4 = 520(^{15}/_{150})^{0.286} = 270°F.$ abs.

(b) Refrigerating effect $= 10 \times 200 = 2000$ Btu per min.

Refrigerating effect per lb. of air $= 0.24(480 - 270) = 50.5$ Btu

Lb. of air per min. $= \dfrac{2000}{50.5} = 39.6$ lb.

(c) Compressor piston displacement = volume of air per minute at suction or at point 1,

$$V_1 = \frac{39.6(53.35)(480)}{15(144)} = 470 \text{ cu. ft. per min.}$$

(d) Expander piston displacement = volume of air per minute at discharge or at point 4.

Since $P_1 = P_4$, $V_4 = 470(^{270}\!/_{480}) = 264$ cu. ft. per min.

(e) $AW_{comp} = 39.6(0.24)(926 - 480) = 4250$ Btu per min.

(f) $AW_{exp} = 39.6(0.24)(520 - 270) = 2380$ Btu per min.

(g) $AW_{net} = 4250 - 2380 = 1870$ Btu per min.

(h) Coefficient of performance $= {}^{2000}\!/_{1870} = 1.07$

(i) Hp. required $= \dfrac{1870}{42.4} = 44.1$

Hp. per ton $= 4.41$

As has been previously mentioned, the closed system operates upon the same cycle as does the open system just discussed. In the closed system, however, the air is not released to circulate freely in the cold room but is kept in pipes through which the heat is supplied to the low temperature air. These pipes may be placed in the cold room and absorb heat directly, or they may be in a brine cooler, the brine in circulating taking heat from the cold room and delivering it in turn to the air. The lower pressure in the open system is necessarily atmospheric since the cold room itself forms part of the system, but in the closed system, any desired pressure may be maintained on the low pressure side. The advantage in holding this pressure considerably above atmospheric is that both the specific volume and the total volume of the air are much reduced at the higher pressure permitting a very substantial reduction in piston displacement for the same refrigerating capacity. Because the air throughout the closed system is more dense than in the open system, the former is known as a **dense air** system.

In order to keep the piston displacement within reason, the open system must employ considerably greater pressure ratios than is necessary or desirable in the closed system. This results in greater temperature extremes for the former. According to the principles noted in the discussion of the Carnot cycle, this should react favorably for the dense air cycle in reducing the horsepower per ton.

The comparatively low air temperatures necessary in air machines are likely to cause trouble from frost formations unless

cylinder walls so as to preserve an effective oil film for lubrication, while its secondary, and almost incidental, function is that of removing heat from the cylinder contents in order to reduce the work of compression. In this the jacket is necessarily inefficient, and it succeeds in accomplishing only a small amount of cooling. The function of the expander, on the other hand, is to reduce the air temperature by the removal of energy in the form of work. This is best accomplished by isentropic expansion, and efforts are made to attain this by insulating the expander cylinder against inflow of heat from the relatively warm surroundings.

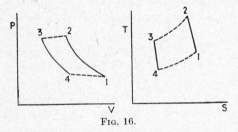

Fig. 16.

The actual cycle is shown on *P-V* and *T-s* coordinates in Fig. 16. To avoid unnecessary complexity, only four state points are indicated each representing the condition *within* its respective cylinder. Thus $P_2 - P_3$ represents the sum of successive pressure drops through compressor discharge valve, pipe to air cooler, air cooler, pipe to expander, and expander admission valve. Lines 2-3 and 4-1 are shown dotted since they represent partially irreversible processes, and the areas bounded by them have no significance. For this reason no attempt has been made in the diagrams to show the individual flow effects.

The heat rejected between compressor and expander, mostly in the air cooler, will be

$$Q_{rej} = Mc_p(T_2 - T_3)$$

and the heat supplied between expander and compressor, mostly from the refrigerator, will be

$$Q_{sup} = Mc_p(T_1 - T_4)$$

If precise data are desired concerning the heat quantities involved in the heat exchangers, air temperatures entering and leaving must be known.

Inspection of the steady-flow energy equation for the compressor will show that, with heat rejected to the water jacket, the work will no longer be the difference in enthalpies $(Mc_p\Delta T)$ as was the case in the theoretical cycle, but must be calculated from

$$AW_{comp} = \frac{n}{n-1}(A)(P_1V_1 - P_2V_2) = \frac{n}{n-1}(AMR)(T_1 - T_2) \tag{35}$$

or, since $R = Jc_p\left(\dfrac{k-1}{k}\right)$,

$$AW_{comp} = \frac{n}{n-1}\left(\frac{k-1}{k}\right)(Mc_p)(T_1 - T_2) \tag{36}$$

This is represented on the P-V plane by the area to the left of the curve 1-2. Similarly, the work of the expander is

$$AW_{exp} = \frac{n}{n-1}(A)(P_3V_3 - P_4V_4) = \frac{n}{n-1}(AMR)(T_3 - T_4)$$

$$= \frac{n}{n-1}\left(\frac{k-1}{k}\right)(Mc_p)(T_3 - T_4) \tag{37}$$

shown by the area to the left of the curve 3-4. As previously mentioned, the pressures at points 1, 2, 3, and 4 must be the terminal pressures *within the cylinders* in order to include the losses due to throttling through the valves.

Note that the work quantities as found by the above equations are work done by the compressor piston *on* the air and on the expander piston *by* the air, respectively, *i.e.*, *indicated* work. When mechanical friction is considered, therefore, the net input of work to the machine will be in excess of the difference between the indicated work of compression and of expansion by the amount necessary to overcome this friction. The mechanical efficiency of the machine will be the work output, *i.e.*, the indicated work of the compressor, or the work done *on* the air, divided by the work input to the machine which is the sum of the indicated work done by the expander and the net work from an outside source,

$$e_m = \frac{W_{comp}}{W_{exp} + W_{net}} \tag{38}$$

Then the net work required to drive the machine will be

$$W_{net} = \frac{W_{comp}}{e_m} - W_{exp} \tag{39}$$

and

$$AW_{net} = Mc_p\left(\frac{k-1}{k}\right)\left[\left(\frac{n_c}{n_c-1}\right)\left(\frac{1}{e_m}\right)(T_1 - T_2)\right.$$
$$\left. + \left(\frac{n_e}{n_e-1}\right)(T_3 - T_4)\right] \tag{40}$$

where n_c and n_e represent the exponent for compression and expansion, respectively.

Referring again to the T-s diagram of Fig. 16, it will be seen that there is a very definite area beneath the compression curve and a somewhat lesser area under the expansion curve. These areas represent in each case the heat supplied to or rejected from the cylinder contents in compressor and expander, respectively. The principal concern is to calculate the heat carried away by the compressor jacket rather than the heat added in the expander which should be the minimum possible, but either may be found by the use of the steady-flow energy equation. Applying this equation to the compressor,

$$AW_{in} = Q_{out} + (h_2 - h_1)M \tag{41}$$

which is to say that, of the energy supplied as work, a part increases the enthalpy of the air handled and the remainder is rejected as heat to the cylinder water jacket. Substituting known expressions for AW_{comp} and for $h_2 - h_1$,

$$_1Q_2 = \left(\frac{n}{n-1}\right)AMR(T_2 - T_1) - Mc_p(T_2 - T_1)$$
$$= M(T_2 - T_1)\left[AR\left(\frac{n}{n-1}\right) - c_p\right] \tag{42}$$

Example.—A dense air machine is to produce 10 tons of refrigeration. At the entrance to the compressor, the pressure is 60 lb. per sq. in. abs., and the temperature is 30°F. At the compressor discharge, the pressure is 220 lb. per sq. in. abs. A pressure drop of 10 lb. per sq. in. takes place in the air cooler and of 5 lb. per sq. in. in the refrigerating coils. Assume the following pressure drops due to wire-drawing through valves: compressor suction = 3 lb. per sq. in.; compressor discharge = 6 lb. per sq. in.; expander admission = 5 lb. per sq. in.; expander exhaust = 2 lb.

Energy out:
Heat rejected to compressor jacket.................. 1360
Heat rejected in air cooler........................ 2470
Indicated work of expander..................... 2995
Total.. 6825

If shown for the entire machine, instead of for the working
fluid alone, the work input to the machine and mechanical
friction must be included in the energy balance, thus:

Energy in:
Work input....................................... 2695
Heat absorbed by expander...................... 275
Refrigerating effect............................. 2000
Total.. 4970

Energy out:
Heat rejected from compressor................... 1360
Heat rejected from air cooler................... 2470
Heat rejected due to mechanical friction =
$$A W_{net} + A W_{exp} - A W_{comp} = \ldots\ldots\ldots\ldots 1140$$
Total.. 4970

It will be noted that, for this work, energy balances *for complete
systems* (closed cycles) need include only the two energy forms
indicated in the foregoing summations.

PROBLEMS

1. A theoretical open air refrigerating cycle operates with a high
pressure of 140 lb. per sq. in. abs. and a low pressure of 15 lb. abs. The
air may be water cooled to 60°F., and leaves the refrigerating room at
0°F.

Calculate: (*a*) Temperatures leaving expander and compressor; (*b*)
pounds of air to be circulated per minute per ton; (*c*) work of compressor,
Btu per minute per ton; (*d*) work of expander, Btu per minute per ton;
(*e*) net work, Btu per minute per ton and net horsepower per ton; (*f*)
coefficient of performance; (*g*) heat removed in air cooler, Btu per
minute per ton; (*h*) theoretical piston displacement of compressor,
cubic feet per minute per ton; (*i*) theoretical piston displacement of
expander, cubic feet per minute per ton.

2. A theoretical dense air refrigerating cycle operates with a high
pressure of 260 lb. per sq. in. abs. and a low pressure of 50 lb. abs. The
air may be water cooled to 60°F., and leaves the refrigerating room at
0°F.

Calculate: (*a*) Temperatures leaving expander and compressor; (*b*)
pounds of air to be circulated per min. per ton; (*c*) work of compressor,

Btu per minute per ton; (d) work of expander, Btu per minute per ton; (e) net work, Btu per minute per ton and net horsepower per ton; (f) coefficient of performance; (g) heat removed in air cooler, Btu per minute per ton; (h) theoretical piston displacement of compressor, cubic feet per minute per ton; (i) theoretical piston displacement of expander, cubic feet per minute per ton; (j) tabulate and compare the results of Probs. 1 and 2.

3. A dense air machine is to be designed for the following conditions: Pressure at compressor entrance = 60 lb. abs.; temperature at compressor entrance = 20°F.; pressure in compressor discharge line = 240 lb. abs.; depression through compressor suction valves = 1.5 lb.; depression through discharge valves = 3 lb.; pressure drop of 5 lb. in air cooler and the piping to the expander; temperature entering expander = 75°F.; pressure leaving expander = 67 lb. abs.; depression during admission = 2 lb.; compressor exponent n = 1.28; expander exponent n = 1.36; mechanical efficiency of unit = 87 per cent. Expander and compressor are each single-cylinder, double-acting with a piston speed of 300 ft. per min., and 3 per cent clearance. Capacity of machine = 6.6 tons.

Calculate: (a) Compressor cylinder diameter in inches; (b) expander cylinder diameter in inches; (c) horsepower necessary to drive the machine; (d) ihp. per ton, and coefficient of performance; (e) cooling water required per hour, for both cooler and compressor jacket, with a 15° rise, pounds and gallons; (f) system energy balance.

4. The following are test data from a dense air machine: compressor double-acting, 14 × 17 in.; expander double-acting, 12 × 17 in.; speed of both = 200 rpm; piston rod diameters = 1½ in.; clearances = 3 per cent; no tail rods.

Pressures: compressor suction line = 31 lb. gage, discharge line = 196 lb. gage; expander supply line = 188 lb. gage, discharge line = 37 lb. gage; barometer = 28.5 in.

Air temperatures: compressor inlet = 10°F., discharge = 198°F.; expander inlet = 70°F., exhaust = −90°F.; brine cooler inlet = −78°F.; brine cooler outlet = 2°F.

From indicator cards: compressor suction pressure = 29 lb. gage, discharge pressure = 200 lb. gage, ihp. = 194; expander admission pressure = 185 lb. gage, exhaust pressure = 40 lb. gage, complete expansion, ihp. = 126. The horsepower input to the machine = 90.

Calculate: (a) Compressor volumetric efficiency; (b) pounds of air circulated per minute; (c) useful capacity of machine, tons; (d) net ihp. per ton, and coefficient of performance; (e) mechanical efficiency; (f) exponents n for compression and expansion; (g) system energy balance.

CHAPTER V

VAPOR REFRIGERATION SYSTEM

The compression refrigeration system using a vapor as the refrigerant is the most important in use today. It has several inherent advantages over air refrigeration, the principal ones being smaller size for a given refrigerating capacity, higher coefficient of performance—*i.e.*, lower power requirements for a given capacity—and less complexity in both design and operation. The major disadvantages of the vapor system are being largely eliminated by improvements in design, which result in greater safety and the prevention of leaks, and by the development of nontoxic, noninflammable vapors for use as refrigerants.

It should be understood that, in using the term "vapor system" or "vapor cycle" throughout this book, restriction to the use of no particular vapor is implied. The principles upon which the vapor system works apply to any vapor, and the use of ammonia in most illustrations and examples is merely for the purposes of simplicity, because of the completeness of thermodynamic data, and uniformity. Any vapor for which a table of the thermodynamic properties is available may be treated in the same way as ammonia.

The outstanding difference in the theory and treatment of the vapor system as compared to the air system is that the vapor alternately undergoes a change of phase from liquid to vapor and vapor to liquid during the completion of a cycle. The latent heat of vaporization is thus utilized with a consequent reduction in temperature range when compared to a cycle, such as the air system, which depends largely upon the sensible heat of the refrigerant. The cooler of the air system becomes, for the vapor cycle, a condenser, and the refrigerating coils become also an evaporator.

28. Carnot Cycle.—This cycle for either gases or vapors consists of two adiabatic and two isothermal changes, which fact specifies that heat shall be supplied and rejected at constant temperatures. Inasmuch as an isothermal for a vapor within the saturated region is also a constant pressure change, the Carnot cycle for a vapor differs considerably on the P-V plane from that for a gas. The cycle for a vapor is shown in Fig. 17. Although superheat could be used by increasing the pressure reversibly during the rejection of heat in the superheat region, this would so complicate the cycle that it is practically confined to the saturated region. Compression may take place anywhere between the expansion line 3-4 and the line 1-2 such as at 1'-2'.

For a diagrammatic layout of the vapor cycle, Fig. 14 would be altered by the substitution of a condenser for cylinder 2-3 and of an evaporator for cylinder 4-1.

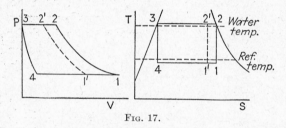

Fig. 17.

The energy quantities for this cycle may be determined, as for any Carnot cycle, by means of absolute temperatures and change in entropy, but for vapors it may be more conveniently done by the use of enthalpy since work and heat quantities for each process are shown by simple enthalpy changes during that process. The summation of these quantities would comprise an energy balance for a complete cycle.

29. Theoretical Vapor Cycle.—The diagrammatic arrangement of the apparatus composing the simple vapor compression system was shown in Fig. 11. It was also shown that an expansion valve, rather than a cylinder and piston, is used for reducing the pressure. This and the fact that superheat at constant pressure may be used are the principal deviations from the Carnot cycle. The state changes of the refrigerant in the cycle are shown in Fig. 18. Adiabatic compression may take place at any place but is shown, for the standard cases, as occurring along 1-2 or along 1'-2'. If the former, *i.e.*, from the saturation line into the superheat region, the process is said to be "dry compression"; if the latter, starting in the saturated region and terminating on the saturation curve, it is called "wet compression."

Inspection of the steady-flow energy equation for each of the processes or for the cycle as a whole will show that energy quantities may be solved for by the use of enthalpy alone. Thus, the work of compression per pound of vapor is the difference in enthalpy before and after the compression process, and the heat supplied to and rejected from the refrigerant may be found in a similar manner.

Passage of the refrigerant through the expansion valve takes place between points 3 and 4. This process is one of pure throt-

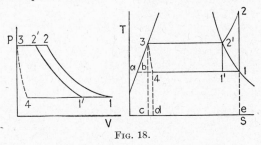

FIG. 18.

tling and, being irreversible, is shown in the diagrams as a dotted line which defines no significant area. The change is at constant enthalpy so that

$$h_{f3} = h_{x4} = h_{f4} + x_4 h_{fg4}$$

and

$$x_4 = \frac{h_{f3} - h_{f4}}{h_{fg4}}$$

For either wet or dry compression one of the terminal conditions is not fully known and must be solved for, in order to find the desired properties at that point. In the case of wet compression, the final condition is that of the dry and saturated vapor at the higher pressure, and the compression takes place without change in entropy so that the initial state may be readily found as follows:

$$s_{g2'} = s_{x1'} = s_{f1'} + x_{1'} s_{fg1'}$$

or

$$x_{1'} = \frac{s_{g2'} - s_{f1'}}{s_{fg1'}}$$

Having solved for $x_{1'}$ the other properties may be found as desired. For dry compression, the initial condition is known and the final may be found by use of the superheat tables for the refrigerant used.

The areas representing the energy quantities involved are easily distinguishable in Fig. 18. On the P-V plane, the work of the compressor is shown by the area to the left of the compression curve, that is, it is equal to $\int v dP$. On the T-s diagram, the area $e23ce$, or that beneath the curve 2-2'-3, represents the heat rejected in the condenser, and the area $e14de$, under the line 4-1, is the refrigerating effect. The difference between the heat rejected and the heat supplied is the heat equivalent of the work of compression and is shown by a simple subtraction of areas to be $123cd41$. This area may be shown to be equal to the area $123a1$ by proving the rectangle $d4bcd$ equal to the triangular area $b3ab$ as follows:

Area $d4bcd = h_4 - h_b$

Area $b3ab = (h_3 - h_a) - (h_b - h_a) = h_3 - h_b$

But $h_3 = h_4$ and $h_4 - h_b = h_3 - h_b$

Area $d4bcd = h_4 - h_b =$ area $b3ab$

Dry compression has the advantages over wet compression of lessening the probability that slugs of liquid will be drawn into the compressor, and of slightly smaller piston displacement. On the other hand, the coefficient of performance is likely to be somewhat lower for the dry compression. The following examples will tend to render a comparison of the two ideal cycles.

Example.—An ideal ammonia compression system, with wet compression, has a high pressure of 150 lb. per sq. in. abs. and a low pressure of 30 lb. per sq. in. abs.

Find: (a) Enthalpy at points 1', 2', 3, and 4 (Fig. 18); (b) pounds of ammonia circulated per minute per ton; (c) heat rejected to condenser per minute per ton; (d) work of compressor per minute per ton; (e) theoretical piston displacement of compressor, cubic feet per minute per ton; (f) coefficient of performance, and horsepower per ton.

Solution:

(a) $x_{1'} = \dfrac{1.2009 - 0.0962}{1.2402} = 0.89$; $h_{x1'} = 42.3 + 0.89(569.3) = 548$ Btu;

$h_{g2'} = 630.5$ Btu; $h_{f3} = 130.6$ Btu; $h_{x4} = 130.6$ Btu

(b) Refrigerating effect per lb. ammonia $= 548 - 130.6 = 417.4$ Btu

$$\text{Lb. ammonia per min. per ton} = \frac{200}{417.4} = 0.48$$

(c) Heat to condenser per min. per ton = 0.48(630.5 − 130.6) = 240 Btu

(d) AW per min. per ton = 0.48(630.5 − 548) = 39.6 Btu

(e) $v_{x1'} = 0.89(9.236) = 8.22$ cu. ft. per lb.

Theoretical compressor piston displacement = 0.48(8.22) = 3.95 cu. ft. per min. per ton

(f) Coefficient of performance = $\dfrac{200}{39.6} = 5.05$

Hp. per ton = $\dfrac{39.6}{42.4} = 0.935$

Example.—An ideal ammonia compression system, with dry compression, has a high pressure of 150 lb. per sq. in. abs. and a low pressure of 30 lb. per sq. in. abs.

Find: (a) Enthalpy at points 1, 2, 3, and 4 (Fig. 18); (b) pounds of ammonia circulated per minute per ton; (c) heat rejected to condenser per minute per ton; (d) work of compressor, Btu per minute per ton; (e) theoretical piston displacement of compressor, cubic feet per minute per ton; (f) coefficient of performance, and horsepower per ton.

Solution:

(a) $h_{g1} = 611.6$; $s_{g1} = 1.3364 = s_2$; $h_2 = 711.3$ ($t_2 = 204°\text{F.}$); $h_{f3} = 130.6 = h_{x4}$

(b) Refrigeration per lb. of ammonia = 611.6 − 130.6 = 481 Btu

Lb. of ammonia per min. per ton = $200/481 = 0.415$ lb.

(c) Heat to condenser per min. per ton = 0.415(711.3 − 130.6) = 241.5 Btu

(d) Work of compressor per min. per ton = 0.415(711.3 − 611.6) = 41.5 Btu

(e) Theoretical compressor piston displacement = 0.415(9.236) = 3.83 cu. ft. per min. per ton

(f) Coefficient of performance = $\dfrac{200}{41.5} = 4.82$

Hp. per ton = $\dfrac{41.5}{42.4} = 0.98$

30. Practical Simple Vapor Compression Cycle.—The practical cycle differs from those just discussed in a number of respects some of which are unavoidable and entail losses. There are two digressions from the theoretical cycles, however, which are desirable. One of these is the departure from adiabatic compression, and the other is the utilization of subcooling of the liquid. The undesirable deviations from the theoretical cycles are due to mechanical and fluid friction, the use of clearance, and heat absorption by communicating pipe lines and other cold surfaces.

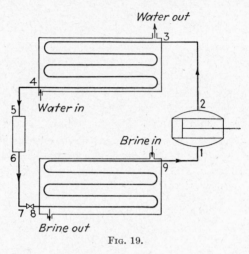

FIG. 19.

Because of the fact that the liquid state is involved, the pressure drop through condenser and evaporator is not serious and these operations may be assumed to take place practically at constant pressure.

Figure 19 shows the diagrammatic layout of the simplest form of practical vapor compression system. The pressure-

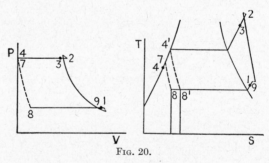

FIG. 20.

volume and temperature-entropy diagrams for the cycle, Fig. 20, indicate what takes place thermodynamically during the completion of a circuit by the refrigerant. The various processes will be discussed individually.

Compressor (1-2).—The compressor cylinder may or may not be water-jacketed. Jacketing serves the twofold purpose of cooling the cylinder walls for lubrication purposes and of cooling the cylinder contents during compression in order to reduce the work. However, the average temperature of the refrigerant may be so low during compression that a water jacket would have but little effect, in which case the cylinder would be left unjacketed. This may occur when the vapor is returned to the compressor at low temperature and when the pressure ratio is low as might be the case in compound machines. In other cases it may be necessary to jacket only the cylinder heads and a part of the cylinder barrel of single-acting compressors since the vapor temperature during the first part of the compression stroke is too low to be affected by water cooling.

The steady-flow energy equation, applied to the compressor, will take the form $Mh_1 + AW_{in} = Mh_2 + Q_{rej}$ where, with the suction and discharge conditions known, the enthalpies h_1 and h_2 are calculated or taken directly from a table of the thermodynamic properties of the vapor in question. But the solution of this equation further requires that either the indicated compressor work or the heat rejected from the refrigerant in the compressor be separately evaluated.

The compression curve will be, approximately, of polytropic form PV^n = const, subject to the deviations discussed in a previous chapter, for which an average value of n may be calculated from the terminal pressures and volumes without the introduction of very serious errors in the ordinary case. With the exponent known, the indicated work of the compressor will be $\int VdP$, for which the limits are the pressures at the beginning and end of the compression curve *within the cylinder*, not at points 1 and 2 which are just outside in suction and discharge lines, respectively, and which, owing to valve throttling and other effects, do not lie upon the compression curve at all. With the states at points 1 and 2 either known or readily predicted, consideration must now be given to the means for determining the conditions at beginning and end of compression with sufficient accuracy to make possible an approximation of the indicated work.

During the suction stroke the state of the incoming gas may be influenced simultaneously by three separate effects resulting, respectively, from flow through the suction valve, mixing with clearance gas, and exposure to the interior surfaces existing at a temperature different from that of the gas.   In the ordinary compressor the clearance gas has, in reexpanding, been reduced to substantially the condition of the entering gas, and this influence may be eliminated as a noticeable factor.   During discharge the state of the gas is affected successively by exposure to surfaces and by passage through the discharge valve.   Flow through both suction and discharge valves is a throttling action, when the subsequent dissipation of the kinetic energy is considered, taking place at constant enthalpy and, as such, is accompanied by a slight drop in temperature of the gas in each case.   But the effects of the heating and cooling to which the cylinder contents are subjected during suction and discharge are not so definitely apparent. At any time that a temperature difference exists between the gas and the interior surfaces to which it is exposed, a transfer of heat will occur.   The material of any compressor cylinder is subjected to cyclic temperature fluctuations, lagging behind, but following to a greater or lesser degree, the varying temperatures of the working fluid within.   There is very meager information concerning the amplitude of these temperature fluctuations, but the general statement may definitely be made that the surfaces exposed to the gas within the cylinder are, in the ordinary case, at higher temperature than the incoming gas and at lower temperature than the outgoing.   This would produce a heating effect upon the gas in the interval between passage through the suction valve and the beginning of compression, and a cooling effect between the end of compression and passage through the discharge valve.   This is shown in Fig. 20a which is an enlargement of the compressor action of Fig. 20.   Points 1 and 2 represent conditions immediately outside of the cylinder in suction and discharge lines, respectively, and p_{1s} and p_{2d} the corresponding suction and discharge pressures within the cylinder. The state change due to throttling through the suction valve at constant enthalpy is shown by the line 1-a.   This is followed by the reception of an unknown quantity of heat at constant pressure from a to b.   The point b represents the state of the gas at the beginning of compression.   The compression process is shown as the line b-c, with c marking the terminal condition. The gas is now at high temperature and is cooled, before passage through the discharge valve, to the state at *e*.   This is followed by valve throttling to the pressure p_2 outside the cylinder.

If the amount of heating and cooling of the gas during suction and discharge might be definitely evaluated, the terminal conditions at points *b* and *c* could be determined.   But there exist so many unknown and variable factors such as the heat transfer coefficients, the time and areas involved, and the temperature differences, that we must be satisfied with a compromise which, without being unduly laborious, will permit a reasonably accurate determination of the work without knowing with certainty the

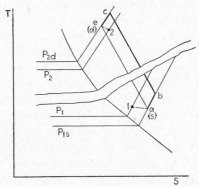

FIG. 20*a*.—Magnified temperature-entropy diagram.

exact terminal points of the compression curve.   With this aim in mind, let us weigh the effect upon work calculations of neglecting entirely the heat exchanges to and from the cylinder material during suction and discharge.   For this case, compression will be assumed to proceed from point *a* to point *e* as shown by the light line in Fig. 20*a*.   It is obvious that this compression, for superheated vapor, necessarily takes place between lower terminal temperatures than does the actual.   The effect of this upon the respective work quantities is best shown by a *P-V* plot of the two cases which immediately demonstrates that, keeping the heat quantities interchanged along *a-b* and *c-e* within reason, the two compression curves are practically indistinguishable and the areas are very nearly equal.   This points to the fact that, although the indicated work is greatly influenced by the pressure drop in the valve passages, it is not sensitive to such moderate heating effects as may be expected in compressors except as these may indirectly affect the capacity.   Exclusive of cases where a more accurate determination of compression terminal states may be desired for other purposes than the computation of work alone, the additional subscripts s and d will hereafter refer to the points a and e, respectively (Fig. 20a), which will be treated as the terminal points of the compression curve.

The temperature variation of the cylinder material in no way invalidates the steady-flow energy equation for the compressor. The material may be said to fluctuate above and below some mean temperature with each revolution of the compressor. Therefore the heat received by the cylinder walls and head and the piston during a part of the mechanical cycle, *exclusive of the heat transmitted through such material and disposed of on the outside,* is exactly balanced by the heat given up during the remainder of the cycle. This is an equal exchange taking place entirely within the machine and is not in any sense energy supplied to or taken from the compressor as a whole.

In view of the foregoing discussion, it will be appreciated that in practice in the reciprocating compressor there can be no such thing as a true isentropic compression, aside from thermal irreversibility, because there is no cylinder material which can avoid either the tendency to vary in temperature with the contents or the necessary heat exchanges that must follow. Unjacketed cylinders without excessive temperatures may produce practically adiabatic action which would simply indicate that the heat received by the gas from the metal is balanced by an equal return, the result being no net heat exchange. Strictly, an adiabatic cylinder would have a net heat rejection equivalent to the piston friction only. Again from the standpoint of the work involved, the degree of deviation from the isentropic or from the adiabatic with a negligible amount of heat leaving the cylinder is relatively unimportant, and the general plan previously outlined may be carried out using isentropic compression between the terminal points.

The compressor indicated work may be computed from

$$AW = \frac{An}{n-1}(P_sV_s - P_dV_d) \tag{43}$$

whence its substitution in the energy equation permits the heat rejected from the vapor during compression to be found by

$$Q = AW - M(h_2 - h_1) \tag{44}$$

An alternate method for the computation of the indicated work of compression is based upon the assumption that the compression is reversible and that the curve representing this process on the T-s diagram is a straight line, which, though not strictly true, is very nearly so. Then the heat rejected per pound of vapor during compression, being the area beneath this curve, is equal to the change in entropy times the mean absolute temperature, or

$$Q = M(s_s - s_d)\left(\frac{T_s + T_d}{2}\right) \qquad (45)$$

and the indicated work may be found by substitution in the energy equation as

$$AW = M(h_2 - h_1) + Q \qquad (46)$$

It should be here noted that work quantities computed by the methods just given assume that the compression is thermally reversible and also that there is no leakage of gas past piston or valves. The latter necessitates recompression of some of the gas following irreversible leakage to a lower pressure and may, in severe cases, greatly increase the work of compression per pound of gas delivered. For mechanically good compressors, the increased work from these causes should be slight. Notice should also be taken of the fact that, of the total quantity of heat passing through the cylinder walls, a part is contributed by the cylinder contents and a part is the result of mechanical friction, and that, while most of this heat will be absorbed by the jacket water, some may also be radiated directly or taken from the piston by lubricating oil. The heat quantity Q in the above equations takes account only of the heat rejected by the refrigerant which may not be the total quantity of heat received by the cooling water but which in ordinary cases is assumed to be so.

It may readily be seen that a fluid in passing through a compressor in which the compression is assumed to be adiabatic and isentropic would undergo an over-all entropy increase due to the introduction of the two irreversible processes occasioned by valve constrictions. This, with the heat supplied due to piston friction, also accounts for the increase in entropy noted, particularly in compound machines, when but a negligible amount of heat is either supplied to or taken from the cylinder.

Compressor volumetric efficiency is principally dependent upon clearance, the pressure ratio within the cylinder, wire-drawing through the suction valves, heating of the gas during the suction stroke, and leakage through the valves and past the piston. These factors as a whole may be closely evaluated, either by calculation or from experience in the prediction of volumetric efficiency, with the exception of leakage which is dependent upon many things. For compressors in a good state of repair and of good design, volumetric efficiencies from 73 to 88 per cent may be expected in average practice.

Mechanical efficiency is the ratio of the indicated compressor work, which is the useful output of the mechanism, to the work input at the shaft or pulley to drive the machine. For electrically driven machines, a combined mechanical and electrical efficiency might be used. This would be the compressor indicated work divided by the energy consumption of the motor.

Condenser (3-4).—The vapor enters the condenser at point 3 and is subjected to a cooling action throughout until the liquid leaves at point 4. The heat rejection process takes place substantially at constant pressure and involves the removal successively of the heat of superheat with a consequent lowering of temperature, the latent heat of vaporization with no change in temperature, and some of the heat of the liquid with a further temperature drop. The heat rejected in the condenser is the sum of these three heat quantities or, as was previously seen, simply the difference in enthalpy entering and leaving:

$$_3Q_4 = M(h_3 - h_4) \qquad (47)$$

In the actual condenser, only a part of this heat will be removed by cooling water, the remainder being rejected by radiation and by convection to the surrounding air. Without knowing the proportion of the heat rejected which goes to the cooling water, it is impossible to predict the exact quantity of water required, but computations based upon the assumption that the water carries away all the heat provide a reasonable margin of safety.

It will be seen from Fig. 20 that the liquid leaving the condenser at point 4 is at a temperature somewhat below that of the saturated liquid at condenser pressure. This additional cooling of the liquid is known as "subcooling" and is desirable inasmuch as it provides additional refrigerating effect without affecting the power required for compression. The increase in refrigerating effect by subcooling to point 7 is shown on the T-s diagram (Fig. 20) as the area beneath 8-8'. Except for the additional cooling water required, this is pure gain when the heat withdrawn from the liquid in subcooling is rejected from the system to the natural cooling medium. For this reason, liquid coolers are sometimes installed just before the valve in order to offset any heating which may have taken place in the receivers.

Expansion Valve (7-8).—The action in the expansion valve does not differ from that in the theoretical system. Both are pure throttling operations in which the refrigerant undergoes no change in enthalpy, $h_7 = h_8$, and the quality at point 8 after expansion may be found as before. The expansion valve is a direct means of regulating the flow of refrigerant into the evaporator, and, as such, controls the evaporator pressure and the amount of cooling effected.

Evaporator (8-9).—In this, the machine applies its useful refrigerating load. Evaporation, like condensation, takes place at almost constant pressure, and the energy equation again shows the heat supplied to each pound of the refrigerant to be the difference in enthalpy before and after the process. The vapor enters the evaporator at 8 in a condition of very low quality and leaves at 9 with, in this instance, a small amount of superheat. The condition of the vapor leaving the evaporator will vary considerably depending upon the type of system and the conditions under which it operates. In some cases, the vapor may be considerably superheated, though this is not advisable from the thermodynamic standpoint. Figure 20 is drawn to represent average good practice. The refrigerating effect is

$$_8Q_9 = M(h_9 - h_8) = M(h_9 - h_7) \qquad (48)$$

The vapor in passing through the evaporator may absorb heat either directly from the refrigerating room or from brine which, being thus cooled, is circulated through the cold room where it in turn absorbs heat. In the former case, the evaporator might be called the refrigerating coils; in the latter, it is called the brine cooler. The direct expansion system is best applied when the refrigerated space is concentrated near the machine since it is not considered advisable to circulate the refrigerant itself widely throughout an elaborate cooling system. Brine, on the other hand, may be safely circulated as desired while confining the vapor to the refrigerating machine proper. But the use of an intermediate medium such as brine, though necessary and desirable in many cases, entails losses due to the fact that the suction pressure must be held lower than for direct expansion in order to obtain good heat transfer in the brine cooler and also in the refrigerated space. In addition, a small amount of power is necessary to operate pumps for the circulation of the brine throughout the system.

Receiver and Piping.—A considerable exchange of heat is likely to take place between the interconnecting piping and the air of the room or rooms in which these are located or through which they pass. Some of the piping will be at a temperature higher than that of the room, resulting in the abstraction of heat from the pipe contents, whereas some will be below the temperature of the surrounding air with just the reverse effect. In general, it may be said of the high temperature vapor that the ultimate object is to remove as much heat as possible from it before passing it to the evaporator, while the purpose in the case of the low temperature vapor is to supply as much heat to it as possible as useful refrigerating effect *in the evaporator* which means as little as possible elsewhere. Thus heat absorption by the refrigerant in pipe lines or receiver is detrimental to efficiency and may be reckoned a loss, while heat rejection from piping is not but may actually be advantageous inasmuch as it relieves a small part of the cooling water load.

In the example illustrated, the cooling process in the pipe connecting compressor and condenser is shown as the line 2-3. All other extraneous heat exchanges are shown as losses, *i.e.*, heat absorptions. These are 4-5, between condenser and receiver (if separate receiver is used); 5-6, in the receiver; 6-7, from receiver to expansion valve; and 9-1, between evaporator and compressor. Of these losses, the first three, shown by 4-7 in Fig. 20, which occur only when the room temperature exceeds that of the liquid refrigerant, result in a decrease in the effective subcooling, and the last one results in increased work of compression and compressor displacement without compensating increase in useful refrigerating effect. The heat quantity involved in each case is represented by the area under the T-s curve for the change and is equal to the change in enthalpy during the action.

Obviously the above losses will be affected by the extent of and the rate of heat transfer through exposed surfaces. Therefore, all pipe lines carrying cool liquid or vapor should be as short as possible and all surfaces, including pipes, below the temperature of the surrounding air should be protected against undesired heat absorption.

Example.—An ammonia compression plant is to be designed for a capacity of 30 tons. The cooling water temperature requires a condenser pressure of 160 lb. per sq. in. abs. and the brine temperature a pressure of 25 lb. per sq. in. abs. in the brine cooler. The following temperatures will exist at the points designated: compressor suction, 0°F.; compressor discharge, 230°F.; entering condenser, 210°F.; leaving condenser, 60°F.; at expansion valve, 68°F.; leaving evaporator, −5°F. Wire-drawing through compressor valves: suction, 5 lb. per sq. in.; discharge, 10 lb. per sq. in. A two-cylinder, vertical, single-acting compressor is to be used at 400 ft. per min. piston speed. Mechanical efficiency = 0.8. Volumetric efficiency = 0.75. Ratio stroke/bore = 1.2.

Draw P-V and T-s diagrams and note the necessary properties at each point. Calculate: (a) Pounds of ammonia to be circulated per minute; (b) ihp. of compressor per ton and total; (c) power required to operate machine; (d) heat rejected to cylinder jackets per minute; (e) heat rejected in the condenser per minute; (f) compressor piston displacement per minute per ton and per minute; (g) bore, stroke, and rpm of compressor; (h) coefficient of performance.

Solution (Refer to Figs. 20, 20a):

$$p_1 = 25 \text{ lb. per sq. in. abs.}; t_1 = 0°\text{F.}; h_1 = 613.8 \text{ Btu.}; v_1 = 11.19 \text{ cu. ft.}$$
$$\text{per lb.}$$

The condition at the end of the suction stroke with a pressure reduction of 5 lb. per sq. in. and no change in enthalpy: $p_s = 20$ lb. per sq. in.; $t_s = -4°$F.; $h_s = 613.8$ Btu; $s_s = 1.3869$; $v_s = 14$ cu. ft. per lb. $p_2 = 160$ lb. per sq. in.; $t_2 = 230°$F.; $h_2 = 725.8$ Btu

The condition at the end of compression with a pressure drop of 10 lb. per sq. in. through the discharge valve and no change in enthalpy: $p_d = 170$ lb. per sq. in.; $h_d = 725.8$ Btu; $t_d = 231.5°$F.; $v_d = 2.437$ cu. ft. per lb.; $s_d = 1.3439$.

$$h_3 = 713.9; \qquad h_4 = 109.2; \qquad h_7 = 118.3; \qquad h_{x8} = 118.3;$$

$$x_8 = \frac{118.3 - 34.3}{574.8} = 0.146; \qquad h_9 = 610.9.$$

(a) Refrigerating effect in brine cooler $= 30 \times 200 = 6000$ Btu per min.
Refrigerating effect per lb. of ammonia $= 610.9 - 118.3 = 492.6$ Btu

Ammonia circulated per minute $= \dfrac{6000}{492.6} = 12.2$ lb. or 0.407 lb. per

min. per ton

(b) (First method)

Average $n = \dfrac{\log_{10}(P_d/P_s)}{\log_{10}(V_s/V_d)} = \dfrac{\log_{10} 8.5}{\log_{10} 5.75} = \dfrac{0.93}{0.761} = 1.225$

$AW = 0.407\left(\dfrac{1.22}{0.22}\right)(144)\left[\dfrac{20 \times 14 - 170 \times 2.437}{778.3}\right] = 55.5$ Btu per

min. per ton

Ihp. per ton $= \dfrac{55.4}{42.4} = 1.31$

Total ihp. $= 1.31(30) = 39.3$
(Second method)
$h_2 - h_1 = 725.8 - 613.8 = 112$ Btu
Q per lb. of ammonia $= (1.3869 - 1.3439)(574.2) = 24.7$ Btu
AW per min. per ton $= 0.407(112 + 24.7) = 55.6$ Btu

Ihp. per ton $= \dfrac{55.6}{42.4} = 1.31$

Total ihp. $= 1.31(30) = 39.3$.

(c) Power input to machine $= \dfrac{39.3}{0.8} = 49.1$ hp.

(d) Heat rejected to cylinder jackets:
(First method) $Q = AW - M(h_2 - h_1) = 39.3(42.4) - 12.2(112) =$
297 Btu per min.

(Second method) from part b, $Q = 24.7$ Btu per lb. ammonia
Q total $= 24.7(12.2) = 301$ Btu per min.

(e) Heat rejected in condenser $= 12.2(713.9 - 109.2) = 7360$ Btu per
min.

(f) Piston displacement $= \dfrac{0.407(11.19)}{0.75} = 6.08$ cu. ft. per min. per ton

or $6.08(30) = 182.4$ cu. ft. per min.

(g) Since this is a single-acting machine, the volume swept through by
the piston per cylinder $= 182.4$ cu. ft. per min.

Piston area $= \dfrac{182.4(144)}{400} = 65.7$ sq. in.

Cylinder bore $= \sqrt{\dfrac{4(65.7)}{\pi}} = 9.15$ in.

Stroke $= 1.2(9.15) = 11$ in.

Rpm. $= \dfrac{400(12)}{2(11)} = 218$

(*h*) Coefficient of performance $= \dfrac{6000}{49.1(42.4)} = 2.88$

Hp. input per ton $= \dfrac{49.1}{30} = 1.64$

PROBLEMS

5. An ammonia compression system with wet compression operates between pressures of 150 lb. abs. and 30 lb. abs. Base on the ideal cycle with vapor dry and saturated at the end of compression.

(*a*) Plot to scale the *T-s* diagram for this cycle, tabulating for each point specific volume, enthalpy, temperature, and entropy. Calculate: (*b*) horsepower per ton of refrigeration; (*c*) coefficient of performance; (*d*) compressor piston displacement per minute per ton (no clearance).

6. Same conditions as Prob. 5 except that the ammonia is dry saturated at the beginning of compression (dry compression). Superimpose this *T-s* diagram on the diagram for Prob. 5. In addition, show areas representing the difference in work of compressor per pound of ammonia and of the refrigerating effect per pound. Summarize the effect of wet and dry compression upon the various items calculated per ton of refrigeration.

7. A simple ammonia compression system has a compressor with a piston displacement of 62.8 cu. ft. per min., a condenser pressure of 172 lb. abs., and an evaporator pressure of 35 lb. abs. The liquid is subcooled to 75°F., and the temperature of the vapor leaving the evaporator and entering the compressor is 10°F. The temperature of the vapor leaving the compressor is 210°F. The heat rejected from the ammonia to the compressor jacket is 4860 Btu per hr. The volumetric efficiency of the compressor is 78.5 per cent.

Calculate: (*a*) Capacity of the machine in tons; (*b*) ihp. of the compressor; (*c*) coefficient of performance based on ihp.

8. A simple ammonia compression system has a two-cylinder, single-acting compressor. The compression exponent is 1.22. Condenser pressure is 170 lb. abs.; evaporator pressure, 26 lb. abs. Wire-drawing through the valves is as follows: suction = 4 lb., discharge = 10 lb. The liquid is subcooled to 76°F. The vapor leaves the evaporator at 0°F. There are 720 lb. of ammonia circulated per hour.

Neglect all surface losses and calculate: (*a*) Capacity of machine in tons; (*b*) ihp. of compressor; (*c*) heat from ammonia to compressor cylinder jacket, Btu per minute; (*d*) heat to condenser water, Btu per minute.

9. The following data were obtained from the test of an ammonia compression machine. Compressor is two-cylinder, single-acting, 6 × 7¾ in., 275 rpm. Ammonia temperatures: after expansion valve, entering brine cooler, −15°F.; leaving brine cooler, 0°F.; entering compressor, 20°F.; leaving compressor, 290°F.; entering condenser, 270°F.; leaving condenser, 72°F.; before expansion valve, 70°F. Pressures: condenser, 135 lb. gage; compressor suction line, 10.2 in. Hg gage; barometer, 30.5 in. Neglect pressure change between compressor discharge and expansion valve. There are 225 lb. of brine circulated per minute with a 12° drop in temperature through the brine cooler. Specific heat of the brine, 0.75. Electrical input to the motor, 17.9 kw. Motor efficiency at this load, 92 per cent. Jacket cooling water, 10.8 lb. per min. with 15° rise.

(a) Draw a T-s diagram, tabulating important data for necessary points; (b) calculate the quantity of ammonia circulated per minute and the capacity of the machine in tons, assuming 2 per cent of useful refrigerating effect lost by heat absorption by brine cooler from room; (c) find compressor ihp. and mechanical efficiency (assume all heat to jacket water to be from ammonia); (d) find compressor volumetric efficiency; (e) find the coefficient of performance; (f) make a system energy balance.

10. A simple ammonia compression system is to be designed with a useful ice melting capacity of 25 tons. This is to be represented in actual brine cooling and will be 95 per cent of the gross refrigerating effect. The following conditions are to be met. Ammonia pressures: condenser = 180 lb. abs.; brine cooler = 25 lb. abs.; cylinder discharge pressure = 190 lb. abs.; cylinder suction pressure = 21 lb. abs. Ammonia temperatures: compressor suction line = 20°F.; compressor discharge line = 260°F.; entering condenser = 240°F.; leaving condenser = 80°F.; entering expansion valve = 80°F.; leaving brine cooler = 10°F. Brine data: temperature entering brine cooler = 15°F.; leaving brine cooler = −5°F.; mean specific heat = 0.8 Btu per lb. per deg. Compressor data: two-cylinder, single-acting; piston speed 500 ft. per min.; ratio of stroke to bore = 1.2; volumetric efficiency = 0.84; mechanical efficiency = 0.8; flow through valves at constant enthalpy.

Calculate: (a) Brine per minute in pounds; (b) ammonia per minute in pounds; (c) ihp.; (d) horsepower input; (e) cylinder jacket water per hour with 10°F. rise; (f) piston displacement, cubic feet per minute; (g) bore and stroke, inches; (h) condenser water, pounds per hour with 15° rise; (i) coefficient of performance based on effective capacity; (j) a complete energy balance on the system.

CHAPTER VI

COMPOUND VAPOR COMPRESSION SYSTEMS

The motivating energy input to any compression refrigerating system is in the form of mechanical work, the cost of which constitutes a major operating expense. Therefore, any means which provides a saving in work while maintaining the same refrigerating output is advantageous so long as it does not involve too heavy an increase in other operating expenses, the initial cost of the plant, or maintenance.

The staging of air compressors effects a reduction in the work required to compress a given weight of air, and, in like manner, compounding the compressors of refrigerating machines may produce a saving in work per pound of refrigerant circulated. However, the added cost of compound over simple compressors is such that savings may be achieved only where the pressure ratio is considerable, as would be the case when low evaporator temperatures are desired or when the condenser pressure must be high owing either to warm cooling water or a limitation in quantity. It may be said further that compound compression is generally economical only in plants of considerable size.

Compound compression systems may be divided into two distinct classifications, the principal difference being the method used for intercooling. In the one, this is done as in air compressors by cooling water alone. In the other, some water is used but the main cooling effect is obtained by the evaporation of a portion of the refrigerant in an intermediate receiver. These will be considered separately.

31. Compound Compression with Water Intercooling.—In principle, the compressor for this system is the same as the compound, or two-stage, air compressor. The refrigerant is drawn from the evaporator by the low pressure cylinder, compressed to some intermediate pressure in this cylinder, and discharged to the intercooler. Here the gas is cooled by water to some temperature above the boiling point for that intermediate

77

pressure, and it is then compressed in the high pressure cylinder to condenser pressure. The process of heat abstraction in the

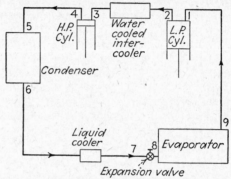

FIG. 21.—Compound vapor compression system—water-cooled intercooler.

intercooler is essentially one of constant pressure. A system of this type is illustrated diagrammatically in Fig. 21, and the

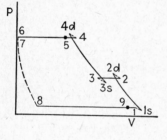

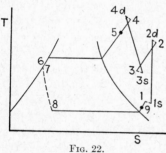

FIG. 22.

cycle is shown on *P-V* and *T-s* coordinates in Fig. 22. Aside from the compressor itself, the system is exactly similar to that for simple compression, and computations are carried out in the same manner. Calculations for the compressor may be done as for the simple compressor by considering the compound machine as two simple ones in series with the proper terminal conditions in each case. Owing to the fact that the average temperature of the gas within the low pressure cylinder is fairly low, this cylinder is usually not water-jacketed, and the actual compression may be very nearly adiabatic. The high pressure cylinder, being jacketed, withdraws some heat from the contents during compression, and the process is therefore likely to depart somewhat more from the adiabatic than is the case in the low pressure cylinder.

Example.—The following conditions apply to a 100-ton ammonia compound compression system with water intercooler. Condenser pressure = 200 lb. abs.; evaporator pressure = 22 lb. abs.; intercooler pressure = 70 lb. abs. Volumetric efficiency, low pressure = 85 per cent, high pressure = 78 per cent. Assume wire-drawing through compressor valves as follows: low pressure suction = 2 lb. per sq. in.; low pressure discharge = 5 lb.; high pressure suction = 4 lb.; high pressure discharge = 10 lb. Ammonia may be cooled to 90°F. in intercooler and subcooled as liquid to 85°F. Suction temperature = 0°F. Temperature leaving brine cooler = −5°F. Low pressure compression is adiabatic. High pressure compression, $n = 1.27$. Both cylinders double-acting.

Calculate: (a) Ammonia to be circulated per minute; (b) ihp. of low pressure cylinder; (c) ihp. of high pressure cylinder; (d) total ihp.; (e) heat rejected in intercooler, Btu per minute; (f) piston displacement of low pressure cylinder, cubic feet per minute; (g) piston displacement of high pressure cylinder, cubic feet per minute; (h) total piston displacement, cubic feet per minute; (i) coefficient of performance based on ihp.

Solution (Refer to Figs. 21, 22):

(a) $h_8 = h_7 = 137.8$; $h_9 = 612$.

$$\text{Ammonia circulated per min.} = \frac{100(200)}{(612 - 137.8)} = 42.2 \text{ lb.}$$

(b) Suction pressure $p_s = 22 - 2 = 20$ lb. abs.; $h_1 = 614.8 = h_s$;
$$v_1 = 12.77; \ s_s = 1.3895 = s_d; \ t_s = -1°.$$
Discharge pressure $p_d = 70 + 5 = 75$ lb. abs.; $h_d = 695.5 = h_2$.

$$\text{Ihp., low pressure} = \frac{42.2(695.5 - 614.8)}{42.4} = 80.5$$

(c) Suction pressure $p_s = 70 - 4 = 66$ lb. abs., $h_3 = h_s$, $v_3 = 4.72$,
$$v_s = 5.00$$

Discharge pressure $p_d = 200 + 10 = 210$ lb. abs.

$$v_d = \sqrt[1.27]{\frac{66(5)^{1.27}}{210}} = 2.01 \text{ cu. ft. per lb.}$$

$$\text{Ihp., high pressure,} = \frac{1.27(144)(42.2)(66 \times 5.00 - 210 \times 2.01)}{(1.27 - 1)(33,000)}$$
$$= 79.5$$

(d) Total ihp. $= 80.5 + 79.5 = 160$ Ihp. per ton $= 1.6$

(e) $h_2 = 695.5$, $h_3 = 654.6$

Heat rejected in intercooler $= 42.2(695.5 - 654.6) = 1728$ Btu per min.

(f) $v_1 = 12.77$

$$\text{Piston displacement, low pressure} = \frac{42.2(12.77)}{0.85} = 634 \text{ cu. ft. per min.}$$

(g) $v_3 = 4.72$

Piston displacement, high pressure $= \dfrac{42.2(4.72)}{0.78} = 255.3$ cu. ft. per min.

(h) Total piston displacement $= 634 + 255.3 = 889.3$ cu. ft. per min.

(i) Coefficient of performance $= \dfrac{20,000}{(42.4)(160)} = 2.95$

32. Compound Compression with Multiple Expansion Valves.

It has been previously noted in connection with the simple compression machine that the only useful subcooling of the liquid occurs when the heat thus removed from the refrigerant may be directly rejected from the system to the cooling medium employed. The lowest useful temperature of the liquid entering the expansion valve in the simple compression system is thus

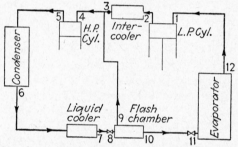

Fig. 23.—Compound system with multiple expansion valves.

the cooling water temperature. However, when stage compression is used, it becomes possible to expand the liquid successively from pressure to pressure into flash chambers which will remove the gaseous portion for recompression in the particular stage concerned. This method provides a liquid temperature at the last valve much below that attainable by the natural cooling medium with a consequent increase in refrigerating effect per pound of refrigerant entering the evaporator. In Fig. 23 is shown the compound system of the preceding section modified to include two expansion valves in series. It will be seen that this principle owes its efficacy entirely to the fact that the portion of refrigerant evaporated to cool the liquid need be compressed through only a part of the range of the entire system and is therefore applicable only in cases, such as stage compression, where an intermediate pressure exists and in which a means is provided for such partial compression. It is clear that the vapor used in subcooling will, in evaporating at the intermediate pressure, require less work for compression than will the refrigerant which vaporizes at the low pressure and that the transfer of a part of the refrigerating load to the former will have a beneficial effect upon the efficiency of the machine.

The calculations for this type of system are slightly complicated by the obvious fact that the quantities of refrigerant handled by each cylinder are different owing to the augmentation of the quantity leaving the low pressure cylinder by the gas from the flash chamber. The steady-flow energy equation for the flash chamber is (Fig. 23)

$$M_8 h_8 = M_9 h_9 + M_{10} h_{10}$$

But, since

$$M_8 = M_9 + M_{10}$$
$$(M_9 + M_{10}) h_8 = M_9 h_9 + M_{10} h_{10} \tag{49}$$

Now, for thermal equilibrium in the flash chamber h_9 is the dry saturated vapor enthalpy and h_{10} is the enthalpy of the saturated liquid at intermediate pressure. M_{10} is determined from the refrigerating effect, and h_8 is equal to h_7. The equation may thus be solved for M_9, and M_8 may be readily found by addition. In order to determine the high pressure cylinder work, the properties and condition at point 4 must be first known. This is simply the problem of adiabatic mixing of two gases under flow conditions, for which

$$M_3 h_3 + M_9 h_9 = M_4 h_4 = (M_3 + M_9) h_4$$

or

$$h_4 = \frac{M_3 h_3 + M_9 h_9}{M_3 + M_9} \tag{50}$$

Since the pressure at point 4 is the intermediate pressure, the determination of enthalpy fixes the state, and other properties may be determined at will.

Although it is theoretically desirable to carry the number of expansion valves and flash tanks to several, the practical limitations restrict the number, as the number of stages of compression are restricted, usually to two for ammonia systems and perhaps three valves in some cases of extreme pressure ratios with other refrigerants. As is frequently true for cycles of this general nature, the number of coolers or heaters, or stages of compression or expansion, as the case may be, are practically limited to the point where an additional number would thwart the purpose of the scheme by the introduction of losses or disadvantages in excess of the gain to be reasonably expected. The steam cycle utilizing extraction feed water heaters has many points of similarity, in the thermodynamic sense, to the compound cycle just discussed.

In the illustrative example which follows, the conditions, except for the use of two expansion valves, are exactly as in the preceding example. The results should be compared in the two cases, bearing in mind that, for the same refrigerating capacity, a reduction in power also means a decrease in the cooling water load.

Example.—The following conditions apply to a 100-ton ammonia compound compression system with water intercooler and series expansion valves. Condenser pressure = 200 lb. abs. Evaporator pressure = 22 lb. abs. Intercooler pressure = 70 lb. abs. Volumetric efficiency, low pressure = 85 per cent, high pressure = 78 per cent. Assume wire-drawing through compressor valves as follows: low pressure suction = 2 lb. per sq. in.; low pressure discharge = 5 lb.; high pressure suction = 4 lb.; high pressure discharge = 10 lb. Ammonia may be cooled to 90°F. in intercooler and water cooled as liquid to 85°F. Suction temperature = 0°F. Temperature leaving brine cooler = −5°F. Low pressure compression is adiabatic. High pressure compression, $n = 1.27$. Both cylinders are double acting.

Calculate: (a) Ammonia passing through evaporator and low pressure cylinder, pounds per minute; (b) ammonia passing through high pressure cylinder and condenser, pounds per minute; (c) ihp. of low pressure cylinder; (d) ihp. of high pressure cylinder; (e) total ihp.; (f) piston displacement of low pressure cylinder, cubic feet per minute; (g) piston displacement of high pressure cylinder, cubic feet per minute; (h) total piston displacement, cubic feet per minute; (i) coefficient of performance based on ihp.

Solution (Refer to Fig. 23):

$h_1 = 614.8 = h_{1s}$; $v_1 = 12.77$; $p_{1s} = 20$ lb. abs.; $t_{1s} = -1°$; $s_{1s} = 1.3891 = s_{2d}$; $p_{2d} = 75$ lb. abs.; $h_{2d} = 695.3 = h_2$; $h_3 = 654.6$; $h_7 = 137.8 = h_8$; $h_9 = 622.4$; $h_{10} = 84.2 = h_{11}$; $h_{12} = 612$.

(a) Low pressure ammonia per min. $= \dfrac{100(200)}{(612 - 84.2)} = 37.9$ lb.

(b) $M_{10} = 37.9$ lb. per min. $M_9 = \dfrac{37.9(137.8 - 84.2)}{(622.4 - 137.8)} = 4.2$ lb. per min.

High pressure ammonia per min. $= 37.9 + 4.2 = 42.1$ lb.

(c) Low pressure ihp. $= \dfrac{37.9(695.3 - 614.8)}{42.4} = 72.0$

(d) $h_4 = \dfrac{37.9(654.6) + 4.2(622.4)}{42.1} = 650$ Btu per lb.

$p_4 = 70$ lb. abs., $t_4 = 82°$F., $v_4 = 4.635$, $h_4 = h_{4s} = 650$ Btu
$t_{4s} = 81°$, $p_{4s} = 66$ lb. abs., $v_{4s} = 4.92$

$p_{5d} = 210$ lb. abs., $v_{5d} = \sqrt[1.27]{\dfrac{66(4.92)^{1.27}}{210}} = 1.98$ cu. ft. per lb.

High pressure ihp. $= \dfrac{1.27(144)(42.1)}{0.27(33,000)}$
$$\times (66 \times 4.92 - 210 \times 1.98) = 78.6$$

(e) Compressor ihp., total, $= 72.0 + 78.6 = 150.6$
Ihp. per ton $= 1.51$

(f) Piston displacement, low pressure $= \dfrac{37.9(12.77)}{0.85} = 570$ cu. ft. per min.

(g) Piston displacement, high pressure $= \dfrac{42.1(4.635)}{0.78} = 250$ cu. ft. per min.

(h) Total piston displacement $= 570 + 250 = 820$ cu. ft. per min.

(i) Coefficient of performance $= \dfrac{20,000}{42.4(150.6)} = 3.13$ based on ihp.

33. Compound Compression with Intermediate Receiver or Flash Intercooler.—It is not possible with water intercooling to reduce the gas temperature at entrance to the high pressure cylinder to the initial gas temperature, or even nearly to it as is done easily in the ordinary two-stage air compressor. This is, of course, due to the much lower initial temperatures encountered in refrigerating machines. The saving in work by the compound compressor with water intercooling, but without compound expansion, over the simple compressor is, therefore, not nearly so marked as in the case of air compression. In fact, there may be in some cases no saving whatever when the added mechanical friction and throttling losses of the compound machine are considered. The use of the multiple expansion valve principle improves the performance considerably, and a still greater improvement, both in performance and in piston displacement, might be expected if the principle were to be carried a step farther and the flash tank made to act as an intercooler as well as a subcooler. A system incorporating such an arrangement would retain the water-cooled intercooler, since it is always desirable to reject heat directly from the system when possible, but would follow it with a flash intercooler, or intermediate receiver, as shown in Fig. 24. The flash intercooler may be thought of as a vessel partially filled with liquid refrigerant at intermediate pressure, with the gas from the low pressure cylinder introduced below the surface of the liquid in order to accelerate the cooling effect, and with provision for removing both liquid at the bottom and accumulated gas at the top. The relatively warm liquid from the high side of the system and the gas from the water intercooler are cooled by the evaporation of liquid in the intermediate receiver until a condition of thermal equilibrium has been established and the contents are saturated, both liquid and vapor. The vapor then passes to the high pres-

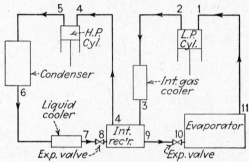

FIG. 24.—Compound system—water and flash intercoolers.

sure cylinder for compression to condenser pressure, and the liquid is expanded through the second valve to the evaporator.

Analysis will show that, insofar as quantities are concerned, there are two distinct circuits through which the working fluid travels. In the low pressure circuit, the refrigerant passes successively through second expansion valve, evaporator, low pressure cylinder, intermediate gas cooler, and intermediate receiver, producing in the evaporator the useful refrigeration output of the plant. The high pressure circuit comprises high pressure cylinder, condenser, receiver, liquid cooler, primary expansion valve, and intermediate receiver. This circuit is responsible for most of the heat rejected from the system. The quantities circulating in each part of the system are related to each other, but the relationship is dependent upon the conditions under which the machine operates, and the solution of the problem requires a knowledge of the conditions of the refrigerant entering the intermediate receiver and leaving the evaporator, and of the intermediate pressure. Assuming these as known and referring to Fig. 24 for notation, the solution may be carried out as follows. Obviously $M_8 = M_4$, since they are both quantities in the same circuit, and $M_3 = M_9$. The latter are directly determined by the capacity of the plant and the conditions of the refrigerant entering and leaving the evaporator. As the conditions leaving the gas cooler, point 3, and entering the expansion valve from the liquid cooler, point 7, are known, h_3 and h_7, or h_8, may be found. For thermal equilibrium within the receiver, the conditions at points 4 and 9 are, respectively, that of dry saturated vapor and saturated liquid, both at intermediate pressure, and the enthalpies at these two points h_4 and h_9 may be readily determined. Then, by application of the energy equation for steady flow, balancing the ingoing against the outgoing energy quantities and neglecting any heat which may be absorbed from the outside, which in practice is extremely small,

$$M_8 h_8 + M_3 h_3 = M_4 h_4 + M_9 h_9$$

and, since $M_3 = M_9$,

$$M_8 = M_4 = \frac{M_9(h_3 - h_9)}{h_4 - h_8} \tag{51}$$

The weights of refrigerant circulated in each part of the system being thus determined, it only remains to use the proper quantity when calculating data for either cylinder of the compressor or for any other portion of the system. In this type of compressor, as in other compound machines, the low pressure cylinder will not be water-jacketed, and in most cases the high pressure cylinder is also unjacketed owing to the fact that it too receives vapor at fairly low temperature from the flash intercooler. Data from actual machines of this type show the compression in both cylinders to be practically adiabatic. The term "adiabatic" in this case would indicate that the heat received by the gas during the first part of the compressor cycle is approximately balanced by the heat given up by the gas during the last part rather than the true adiabatic in the thermodynamic sense. However, the difference between the two insofar as this application is concerned is purely academic and, though worthy of note, need not affect computations.

Example.—The following conditions apply to a 100-ton ammonia compound compression system with both water and flash intercooling. Condenser pressure = 200 lb. abs.; evaporator pressure = 22 lb. abs.; intermediate pressure = 70 lb. abs.; volumetric efficiency, low pressure = 85 per cent, high pressure = 78 per cent. Assume wire-drawing through compressor valves as follows: low pressure suction = 2 lb. per sq. in., low pressure discharge = 5 lb. per sq. in., high pressure suction = 4 lb., high pressure discharge = 10 lb. Ammonia may be cooled to 90°F. in intermediate gas cooler and subcooled as liquid to 85°F. Suction temperature = 0°F. Temperature leaving brine cooler = −5°F. Adiabatic compression in both cylinders. Both cylinders are double acting.

Calculate: (a) Ammonia to be circulated per minute in low pressure circuit; (b) ammonia circulated per minute in high pressure circuit; (c) ihp. of low pressure cylinder; (d) ihp. of high pressure cylinder; (e) total ihp.; (f) piston displacement of low pressure cylinder, cubic feet per minute; (g) piston displacement of high pressure cylinder, cubic feet per minute; (h) total piston displacement, cubic feet per minute; (i) coefficient of performance based on ihp.

Solution (Refer to Fig. 24):

$h_1 = 614.8$; $v_1 = 12.77$; $t_1 = 0°F.$; $t_{1s} = -1°F.$; $p_{1s} = 20$ lb. abs.; $s_{1s} = 1.3891 = s_{2d}$; $h_{1s} = 614.8$; $p_{2d} = 75$ lb. abs.; $h_{2d} = 695.3 = h_2$; $h_3 = 654.6$; $h_4 = 622.4$; $v_4 = 4.15$; $t_4 = 37.7°F.$; $p_{4s} = 66$ lb. abs.; $s_{4s} = 1.2719 = s_{5d}$; $p_{5d} = 210$ lb.; $h_{5d} = 693.2 = h_5$; $h_7 = 137.8 = h_8$; $h_9 = 84.2 = h_{10}$; $h_{11} = 612$.

(a) Ammonia per min. in low pressure circuit $= \dfrac{100(200)}{612 - 84.2} = 37.9$ lb.

(b) Ammonia per min. in high pressure circuit $= \dfrac{37.9(654.6 - 84.2)}{622.4 - 137.8}$
$$= 44.65 \text{ lb.}$$

(c) Low pressure ihp. $= \dfrac{37.9(695.3 - 614.8)}{42.4} = 72$

(d) High pressure ihp. $= \dfrac{44.65(693.2 - 622.4)}{42.4} = 74.7$

(e) Total ihp. $= 72 + 74.7 = 146.7$
   Ihp. per ton $= 1.47$

(f) Piston displacement, low pressure $= \dfrac{37.9(12.77)}{0.85} = 570$ cu. ft. per min.

(g) Piston displacement, high pressure $= \dfrac{44.65(4.15)}{0.78} = 237.6$ cu. ft. per min.

(h) Total piston displacement $= 570 + 237.6 = 807.6$ cu. ft. per min.

(i) Coefficient of performance $= \dfrac{20,000}{42.4(146.7)} = 3.22$

In practice there is some difference of opinion regarding the economy of compound machines considering all costs, but in a number of instances it has apparently proved itself economical. In comparing this type of machine with that using simple compression, it should be remembered that the compound compressor is subject to greater throttling and mechanical friction losses, has a higher first cost, occupies more space, and is somewhat more expensive to maintain. These are disadvantages which must be overcome by a saving in power and water consumption if the compound machine is to be successful, and it may be repeated that whatever superiority it may possess is most pronounced in large installations where either the refrigerating temperature or the available cooling water, or both, compel a pressure range in excess of the ordinary. Severe operating conditions would probably justify the adoption of this type of machine for large capacities.

In compound systems of the types just discussed, the intermediate pressure value has some influence upon the power requirement per unit capacity. The effect of a change in intermediate pressure upon the relative work distribution between the stages is obvious, but the optimum pressure for minimum combined work of compression is more difficult to determine. With the ideal cycle as a basis, the total work does not appear to be highly sensitive to changes in intermediate pressure within rather wide limits on either side of the point for minimum work, nor does this point exactly coincide with that intermediate pressure which produces equal work distribution between the cylinders.[1] In the actual machine, the designed intermediate pressure will be varied by changing operating conditions, and particularly by variation in load, which are beyond the operator's control. The insensitivity of power requirements to moderate intermediate pressure changes is thus advantageous since it renders any attempt at precise control unnecessary for efficient operation.

A question frequently arises regarding the practicability of illustrating cycles, of which the ones just described are examples, with different quantities of working fluid flowing in various portions of the system. The answer is that they may be

[1] PETERS, W. H., and F. C. STEWART, *Southern Power Journal*, vol. 55, no. 9, September, 1937.

so shown but in such a manner that interpretations must be made with definite reservations. That is, we may, without difficulty, trace the state point of a given quantity of the refrigerant as it progresses around either the high or the low pressure circuit (Fig. 25), but the quantities actually are interchanged between circuits in the intermediate receiver. Consequently, although the cycle as a whole is closed, the individual circuits are not, in the strict sense, and the liquid leaving the flash cooler has in reality come from the high pressure circuit and is not the immediate condensate of the gas leaving the intermediate gas cooler.

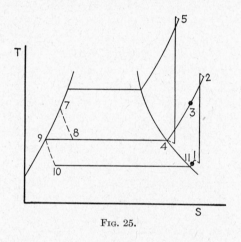

Fig. 25.

However, to represent each circuit as closed is accurate thermodynamically as may be seen by imagining the intermediate receiver to be a closed cooler with perfect heat transfer. The real difficulty with the diagram lies in the fact that the proportionate quantities of fluid circulating in each circuit may not easily be represented upon the conventional diagram which shows quantity for quantity. Thus, although the area beneath the line 10-11 (Fig. 25) shows the true refrigerating effect per pound of refrigerant circulated through the low pressure circuit, and the area under the line 5-7 is truly the heat rejected in the condenser and liquid cooler per pound circulated in the high pressure circuit, still the latter does not represent the heat rejected in the high pressure circuit for the amount of refrigerating effect shown by the diagram because, pound for pound, the quantities are not alike.

The alternative is a temperature-entropy diagram in which the proportional quantities flowing in each circuit are taken into consideration. This necessitates the displacement to the right of the high pressure diagram, since it represents the greater quantity, with respect to the low pressure diagram. The boundary curves are included in this shift and no longer match in the two diagrams, but the areas bear the correct relationship to each other. Such a diagram is shown in Fig. 26. The pressure-volume diagram may be shown in the same manner but with less apparent distortion because, for the processes involved,

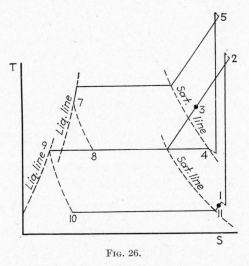

Fig. 26.

the difference in appearance in saturated and superheated regions is much less marked than on the temperature-entropy diagram. As before stated, a diagram of this kind, though correct and of use in certain applications, does not have the explanatory value of the simpler diagrams for the simpler systems. For this reason, complete diagrams will not usually be shown hereafter for cycles which circulate different quantities of working substance in various parts of the system.

34. Centrifugal Compression.—In certain instances, refrigerants may be used which characteristically require very large volumes to be handled per unit of refrigerating capacity. Machines with such refrigerants soon reach sizes where it is impracticable to use reciprocating compressors because of the prohibitive piston displacements which would be required. Such machines must therefore resort to other types of compressors which are better adapted to the handling of large quantities of gas. The centrifugal compressor is one of these which is extensively used, and since it is usually multistaged, the discussion of the general type properly belongs under compound or multistage compression. It may, however, have been noted in the previous discussion of compound systems that the importance of compounding lay more in the general arrangement of the system which it permitted than in the compression itself. Centrifugal compressors are multistaged through practical necessity in order to function satisfactorily, and it is not usual in refrigerating machines to provide intercoolers between stages. Consequently, from a thermodynamic viewpoint, the case is but little different from single-stage adiabatic compression, and the type of system may be classified as simple rather than as compound.

Centrifugal compressors depend upon the rotating impeller to impart to the gas a velocity which is subsequently transformed into pressure head. The velocity of the fluid leaving the vanes will be a component of the radial velocity of the gas and the peripheral velocity of the vane tip, the component, and thus the gas velocity, being considerably varied in different designs by the shape of the vanes in order to produce characteristics which are desirable in any particular case.

Inasmuch as the velocity of a fluid V (feet per second), due to the action of a differential head h (feet) of the fluid involved, is theoretically expressed by $V = \sqrt{2gh}$, where g is the acceleration of gravity in feet per second per second, then, conversely, the head resulting from the perfect utilization of velocity is

$$h = \frac{V^2}{2g}$$

which is no more than a simple statement of energy conversion. But, in order to express the theoretical pressure resulting from velocity when the fluid is efficiently brought to rest, the density, or specific weight, of the fluid must be considered thus

$$p = \frac{h \times d}{144}$$

where d is density, pounds per cubic foot, and p is pressure, pounds per square inch. Combining the two equations,

$$p = \frac{V^2 d}{288g} \tag{52}$$

It is clear from this expression that the pressure range through which a fluid may be raised is a function not only of the square of the velocity, but also of the density of the material. Hence, for a given velocity a rare fluid will undergo a much smaller pressure elevation than will a dense one. Now the velocity is a function of the tip speed of the impeller which in turn is limited by mechanical considerations so that the possible pressure boost, for a particular fluid, by a single impeller is limited. If this pressure increase is insufficient to satisfy the desired conditions, a second, or several, impellers may be operated in series to achieve the results wanted. This constitutes multistaging, and it may be seen to be a necessity for certain cases rather than a thermodynamic desirability as was the case in the staging of reciprocating compressors. Compound expansion similar to that already considered might be used with centrifugal machines by introducing the gas between stages, but the refrigerants requiring, or adaptable to, centrifugal compression are frequently used in a manner which would not permit easy application of the principle.

The losses to which the centrifugal machine is subject are principally those which are identified with flow at appreciable velocities, *i.e.*, turbulence, impact, and fluid friction. These all act to reduce the useful effect from an impeller of given size and speed, by decreasing the cubic capacity and the pressure rise, and to increase the necessary work to deliver a given weight of gas. Thus owing to these irreversible actions, the compression, while essentially adiabatic, causes the fluid to increase in entropy, and the final temperature may be considerably in excess of that which would result from isentropic compression. The efficiency of a centrifugal compressor may be considered as the ratio of the theoretical isentropic work of compression to the actual compressor input for the same weight of fluid discharged. Now the theoretical work to be done in isentropically compressing 1 lb. of refrigerant, being the enthalpy change during such compression, is readily determinable for the particular fluid from table or diagram, and the use of the efficiency term as defined permits easy conversion to the work input required at the shaft. The losses are not excessive in well-designed compressors of a moderate number of stages when working above 60 to 70 per cent of full capacity. For low loads the losses are likely to become proportionately severe and the power requirements excessive per unit weight of gas delivered.

The principal favorable characteristics of centrifugal compressors are the ability of a relatively small machine to handle very large volumes of gas, ease of control due to the fact that they are not positive displacement machines, adaptability to direct drive by motor or turbine, and simplified lubrication with the added advantage that the lubricant need not come in contact with the refrigerant. These machines are not adapted to the handling of small quantities of gas, nor can they ordinarily pump a gaseous fluid through a large pressure range without resorting to an excessive number of stages. The last mentioned characteristics are the direct opposites of those of reciprocating compressors, and the two types should therefore be regarded, not as competitors, but as being widely applicable in the services requiring their respective merits.

For further information dealing with the design and performance of centrifugal compressors, the reader is referred to works devoting more detailed attention to that subject than is possible here.

PROBLEMS

11. The following data are for a compound ammonia compression system with water intercooler. Capacity = 150 tons; cooling water available at 86°F.; condensation temperature in condenser = 96°F.; evaporation temperature in brine cooler = −10°F.; intercooler pressure = 70 lb. abs. Ammonia enters the compressor at 10°F. Ammonia gas may be cooled to within 10° of, and liquid may be cooled to the cooling water temperature. Wire-drawing through compressor valves = 2 lb., 4 lb., 4 lb., and 8 lb., respectively, from low pressure suction to high pressure discharge. Adiabatic compression in both cylinders. Heat losses to and from the air are negligible. Volumetric efficiencies, low pressure = 85 per cent, high pressure = 80 per cent.

Calculate: (a) Indicated horsepower; (b) ihp. per ton, and the coefficient of performance; (c) total piston displacement, cubic feet per minute, and cubic feet per minute per ton; (d) heat rejected by ammonia in condenser, Btu per minute; (e) heat rejected in intercooler, Btu per minute.

12. Data for a compound ammonia compression machine with both water and flash intercooling. Capacity = 150 tons; cooling water available at 86°F.; condensation temperature = 96°F.; evaporation temperature = −10°F.; intermediate pressure = 70 lb. abs. Ammonia gas enters the compressor at 10°F. Refrigerant may be cooled as a gas to 96°F. and as a liquid to 86°F. Wire-drawing through compressor valves = 2 lb., 4 lb., 4 lb., and 8 lb., respectively, from low to high pressure. Adiabatic compression in both cylinders. Volumetric efficiency, low pressure = 85 per cent, high pressure = 80 per cent.

Calculate: (a) Indicated horsepower; (b) ihp. per ton, and coefficient of performance; (c) total piston displacement, cubic feet per minute, and cubic feet per minute per ton; (d) heat withdrawn in intermediate gas cooler, Btu per minute; (e) heat withdrawn in condenser, Btu per minute.

13. During a test on a compound ammonia machine with both water and flash intercooling, the following average data were recorded:

Pressures: in brine cooler = 15.6 in. Hg gage; intermediate receiver = 71.7 lb. gage; condenser = 177 lb. gage; barometer = 29.1 in. Hg.

Temperatures: leaving brine cooler and entering low pressure cylinder = −9.3°; leaving low pressure cylinder and entering intermediate gas cooler = 181.2°; leaving intermediate gas cooler and entering flash cooler = 99.7°; vapor leaving flash cooler = 48.1°; entering high pressure cylinder = 50.8°; leaving high pressure cylinder = 181°; entering condenser = 156.5°; leaving receiver = 92.2°; leaving liquid cooler and entering first expansion valve = 78.2°; liquid from intermediate receiver to second expansion valve = 48.1°.

Ammonia leaving condenser was metered as 123.5 lb. per min.

Compressor data: dimensions = 22 × 13 × 24 in.; speed = 150 rpm; diameter of piston rods = 3.25 in.; cross compound (no tail rods). Both cylinders unjacketed, and heat transmitted through the walls as calculated is negligible.

Neglect all heat losses except as indicated by the data.

Calculate: (a) Ammonia supplied to brine cooler, pounds per minute; (b) refrigerating capacity in tons; (c) low pressure cylinder ihp.; (d) high pressure cylinder ihp.; (e) total ihp.; (f) net heat rejected in condenser, receiver, and communicating piping, Btu per minute; (g) heat rejected in liquid cooler, Btu per minute; (h) heat rejected in intermediate gas cooler, Btu per minute; (i) volumetric efficiency, low pressure cylinder; (j) volumetric efficiency, high pressure cylinder; (k) ihp. per ton, and coefficient of performance; (l) total piston displacement, cubic feet per minute, and cubic feet per minute per ton; (m) energy balance for the system.

CHAPTER VII

SOLID CARBON DIOXIDE

Solid carbon dioxide, known also as **dry ice,** has within the last few years become of considerable commercial importance for the preservation of perishables which require low temperatures while in process of transportation or distribution or while in isolated temporary storage. It possesses the advantages over water ice of lower temperature, the absence of objectionable liquid, and smaller space requirements for a given cooling capacity. The major disadvantage is its cost, which is several times that of water ice per pound, but the fact that solid carbon dioxide, weight for weight, provides almost twice the cooling helps materially to compensate for this. For some purposes the low temperature of dry ice may also be a disadvantage necessitating careful control in order to prevent damage by freezing.

The production of solid carbon dioxide naturally comprises two distinct processes—the manufacture of the gas; and its compression, liquefaction, and solidification. The first is a chemical process which will not be dealt with here. The second is a thermodynamic and mechanical problem involving principles which will now be discussed.

35. Solid CO_2 as a Cooling Medium.—Reference to Fig. 3 and to the adjacent text will show that the behavior of a solid under the influence of heat absorption is dependent upon the relation of the pressure at which it exists to the pressure of its triple point. If the existing pressure be below the triple point, the solid will be saturated (point a) and the heat supplied will produce vaporization directly from the solid phase without intermediate liquefaction. This sort of process is called **sublimation.** An example is solid CO_2 at standard atmospheric pressure, $-109°F.$ (triple point for CO_2, 75 lb. per sq. in. abs., $-70°F.$). If, on the other hand, the solid exists at a pressure in excess of that for the triple point, the addition of heat will first produce melting and then, if continued, vaporization following a rise in

94

temperature of the liquid to the boiling point. An example of this is water ice at atmospheric pressure (triple point for H_2O, 0.08 lb. per sq. in. abs., 32°F.). It is true that water ice at a temperature below freezing will evaporate at atmospheric pressure, but this is a slow process similar to the evaporation of water in an open vessel at room temperature, *i.e.*, it is an evaporation at the partial vapor pressure and is not comparable to the vaporization of dry ice. The latter may be in a state of saturation at any pressure below 75 lb. per sq. in. abs., while water ice, to be in a similar state, would have to be subjected to a high vacuum—a condition not likely to be met with naturally.

36. Principles of Production.—In general, a liquid may be solidified in either of two ways. The first method is by cooling without change of pressure to and below the freezing point as in the ordinary freezing of water. Applied to carbon dioxide, this method has not been successful for the reason that, in order to avoid very low temperatures, the liquid would have to be frozen under pressure and also that an exchange of heat would be necessary between the liquid and the refrigerant used to freeze it. Both of these produce difficulties and losses which render the scheme generally undesirable. It will not be further discussed except to note that it would involve little more than a conventional refrigerating system for which the heat abstracted from the liquid CO_2 would constitute the load. The second means of solidification is by the production of a saturated state at a pressure, and consequently a temperature, below the triple point. The saturated condition may range from saturated solid up through varying proportions of solid and gas to gas only. Now such a saturated state may be obtained either by cooling the superheated gas at a pressure below the triple point or by a satisfactory expansion to such a pressure from a higher pressure. The former is not favored and would again require only a straight refrigerating system, whereas the latter would provide a self-contained unit in which the carbon dioxide would be used as the working substance to provide the cooling effect upon itself directly without recourse to the transmission of heat through a surface. The type of expansion used is the simplest, throttling, and it is evident that the initial condition of the substance at high pressure should be liquid in order to derive the most benefit in the production of solid at the lower pressure.

The simplest possible system of this type is shown schematically in Fig. 27. Carbon dioxide gas is compressed to a pressure sufficiently high so that condensation may take place by means of the cooling water available. The liquid, subcooled as much as possible, is then throttled through an expansion valve into a snowchamber at atmospheric pressure. The material issuing from the valve or nozzle in the snowchamber is saturated at a quality which may readily be determined from tables or chart of thermodynamic properties. But there can be no liquid present below the triple point, and by "quality" is meant the proportion of vapor in a vapor-solid mixture. If the liquid entering the valve were at 80°F., for example, the resulting quality would be approximately 0.76. This would indicate that the substance is 76 per cent vapor and 24 per cent solid, or that the **yield** of

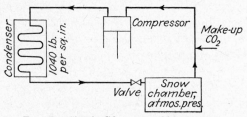

Fig. 27.—Simple CO_2 snowmaking system.

snow is 24 per cent, by weight, of the gas compressed. Following the expansion, the gas separates from the snow and returns to the compressor after the addition of sufficient make-up gas to compensate for that precipitated in the snowchamber. The snow itself is removed from the chamber and mechanically pressed into dense molded blocks.

37. Three-stage System with Water and Flash Intercooling.— Among the costly ingredients which go into the manufacture of dry ice are the carbon dioxide itself, the necessary equipment, and mechanical energy to operate the machine. As for many refrigerating plants, cooling water may also be an item of considerable expense. Bearing in mind that a saving in power directly effects a decrease in the cooling water demand, it is our particular problem to investigate means for reducing the necessary expenditure of work for the production of a given quantity of snow.

The layout shown in Fig. 27, simplified so as to illustrate the underlying principles, would be extravagant in power consumption—400 to 500 ihp.-hr. per ton of snow produced.   This is primarily due to two things: (*a*) the excessive amount of work required per pound of gas compressed and (*b*) the comparatively large quantity of gas which must be compressed per unit weight of snow, *i.e.*, the small yield.   In dealing with the first factor, the exceedingly large pressure ratio of compression, about 70, is at once apparent.   This suggests the use of stage compression, and three stages are in this case feasible.   With straight water intercooling, the pressure ratio in each stage could be approximately $\sqrt[3]{70}$, or 4.1.   The pressures would thus be: snow-chamber, 14.7 lb. abs.; low intermediate pressure, 65 lb. abs.; high intermediate pressure, 260 lb. abs.; and condenser pressure, 1040 lb. abs.   This system would require from 300 to 350 ihp.-hr. per ton of snow on the same basis of computation as the preceding simple case.

Consider now the use of flash intercoolers in conjunction with the water intercoolers.   This change operates to decrease the total work per unit weight of snow principally by increasing the yield due to more effective subcooling of the liquid before expansion.   The pressure in the low pressure flash cooler must now be increased to some value above the triple point in order to avoid the formation of solid in that tank which would block the subsequent flow to the snowchamber.   In practice this pressure must be considerably above the triple point in order to avoid stoppage within the expansion valve or nozzles due to too early solidification in the expansion process.   The necessity for this, by forcing an increase in pressure ratio in the low pressure stage, upsets the pressure relation of the preceding case, but this is somewhat compensated for, insofar as equal stage works are concerned, by the larger quantities handled in the higher pressure cylinders at lower pressure ratios.   Equality of work in each stage is less to be desired, however, than is the avoidance of excessive temperature at the end of compression in any one stage over another.   Since the final temperature is a function of the initial as well as of the pressure ratio, the first stages, receiving cold gas, can stand higher pressure ratios than can the last stage.

Figure 28 shows a diagrammatic layout of this type of system. In view of the previous discussion of all principles involved, it is unnecessary to describe the operation further.   In the following illustrative example, the consideration of certain losses has been omitted in order to simplify the problem and avoid undue repetition, but the results may be profitably compared with other cycles treated in a similar manner. Adiabatic compression is nearly true of actual CO_2 compressors in which, because of the weight of metal required to withstand high pressure, water jackets may be less favorably located and distributed than in some other types.

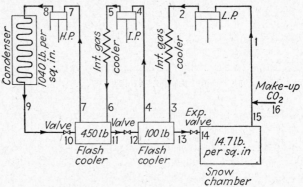

FIG. 28.—Three-stage solid CO_2 machine with flash and water intercooling.

Example (Refer to Fig. 28).—It is desired to determine power and piston displacement requirements for a solid CO_2 machine using three-stage compression with water and flash intercooling. The pressures are as follows: snowchamber, 14.7 lb. abs.; low intermediate, 100 lb. abs.; high intermediate, 450 lb. abs.; condenser, 1040 lb. abs. Liquid CO_2 may be water-cooled to 80°F., gas to 90°F. Make-up gas enters the system at 80°F. and atmospheric pressure. Adiabatic compression in all cylinders. Neglect losses.

Calculate: (a) Ihp.-hours per ton of solid CO_2 (ihp. for 1 ton per hr.); (b) theoretical piston displacement in cubic feet per minute for 1 ton of snow per hour.

Solution (Enthalpy values based on $h_f = 0$ at $-40°F.$):

$h_3 = 170$; $h_4 = 136$; $v_4 = 0.88$; $h_5 = 165$; $t_5 = 110°F.$; $h_6 = 159$; $h_7 = 138$; $v_7 = 0.19$; $h_8 = 153$; $t_8 = 137°F.$; $h_9 = 69 = h_{10}$; $h_{11} = 32 = h_{12}$; $h_{13} = -8 = h_{14}$; $h_{15} = 133$; $h_{16} = 170$.

Quality after final expansion $= \dfrac{-8 - (-113)}{246} = 0.426$

Yield $= 1.000 - 0.426 = 0.574$ lb. snow per lb. low pressure gas compressed

$h_1 = 0.574(170) + 0.426(133) = 154$; $t_1 = 0°F.$; $v_1 = 7.6$ (approximately); $h_2 = 203$; $t_2 = 230°F.$

Low pressure circuit:

Weight through low pressure cylinder per ton of snow per hour =

$$\frac{2000}{60(0.574)} = 58.1 \text{ lb. per min.}$$

Low pressure ihp. $= \dfrac{58.1(203 - 154)}{42.4} = 67.2$ ihp. per ton snow per hour.

Low pressure theoretical piston displacement $= 58.1(7.6) = 442$ cu. ft. per min. for 1 ton snow per hour

Intermediate pressure circuit:

$$M_4 = \frac{M_3(h_3 - h_{13})}{(h_4 - h_{12})} = \frac{58.1(170 - -8)}{136 - 32} = 58.1(1.71) = 99.5 \text{ lb. per}$$

min. for 1 ton snow per hr.

Intermediate pressure ihp. $= \dfrac{99.5(165 - 136)}{42.4} = 68$ ihp. per ton snow per hr.

Intermediate pressure theoretical piston displacement $= 99.5(0.88) = 87.5$ cu. ft. per min. for 1 ton snow per hr.

High pressure circuit:

$$M_7 = \frac{M_6(h_6 - h_{11})}{h_7 - h_{10}} = \frac{99.5(159 - 32)}{138 - 69} = 99.5(1.84) = 183 \text{ lb. per}$$

min. per ton snow per hr.

High pressure ihp. $= \dfrac{183(153 - 138)}{42.4} = 65$ ihp. per ton snow per hr.

High pressure theoretical piston displacement $= 183(0.19) = 34.8$ cu. ft. per min. for 1 ton snow per hr.

(a) Ihp.-hr. per ton snow $= 67 + 68 + 65 = 200$

(b) Total theoretical piston displacement per ton snow per hr. $= 442 + 87.5 + 34.8 = 564.3$ cu. ft. per min.

38. The Pressure Snowchamber.

38. The Pressure Snowchamber.—In order to decrease the large over-all pressure ratio (71) of the cycle discussed in the preceding article, the possibility of precipitating CO_2 snow at or just below the triple point suggests itself. Solid will be readily formed at a snowchamber pressure of, say, 70 lb. per sq. in. abs. thus apparently enabling the pressure ratio to be reduced to 15. This is not wholly true, however, when it is considered that, since the snow must eventually be lowered from 70 lb. per sq. in. ($-72°F.$) to atmospheric pressure ($-109°F.$) with consequent cooling by sublimation, the gas thus evolved must be compressed together with the make-up CO_2 which is introduced into the system at atmospheric pressure. A low pressure cylinder must be provided to compress these two quantities of gas to the low intermediate pressure.

This is plainly a modification of the system just dealt with wherein the low intermediate pressure is set at such a point that snow is precipitated before undergoing a further expansion to atmospheric pressure. A moderate saving in power requirements may be expected owing to the fact that the residual gas, left after precipitation of snow, need not in this case be compressed through the entire range. This may be put somewhat differently by saying that a smaller proportion of gas is reduced to atmospheric pressure. The subcooling of the liquid is considerably less effective in this system, with the usual high intermediate pressure, than in the previous plan and there would be more benefit derived from the application of a regenerative precooler. This will be discussed later after consideration of the cycle in its simpler form.

The principle of the pressure snowchamber is shown in the schematic layout of Fig. 29. No attempt is made to demonstrate the actual manipulation of the snowchamber. For the purposes of explanation, two snowchambers are shown. These will be operated alternately—the pressure being reduced in one while the other is filling with snow. Consider chamber I to be filling at 70 lb. absolute pressure and chamber II to be cooling its contents and reducing the pressure to atmospheric. For this condition, valve A will admit liquid to I which will separate into solid and gas, the latter passing through B to the intermediate pressure cylinder. Valve C, communicating to atmospheric pressure, will be closed. Chamber II will be cut off from pressures higher than atmosphere by valves D and E. Valve F will be open to reduce the chamber pressure to atmospheric and to pass the gas which vaporizes in cooling the charge of snow from saturated solid at $-72°F$. to saturated solid at $-109°F$. This gas, augmented by the make-up, will be compressed in the low pressure cylinder to low intermediate pressure and delivered through an intercooler to the suction of the intermediate pressure cylinder along with the gas from I.

Although time would have to be taken to remove the snow, it will be proper to consider constancy of flow, from one chamber or the other, past the points designated 13 and 14, without regard to the instantaneous status of either chamber since both are operating similarly. This imposes the condition that sublimation take place in the atmospheric chamber at a uniform rate and over a period of time equal to that required for the pressure tank to fill with snow, also at a steady rate. The condition at 11 would be known from the high intermediate pressure, and the yield may be determined in the ordinary manner. But this will not be the ultimate yield because the subsequent sublimation, before mentioned, will reduce the quantity of solid prior to removal from the machine. The quantities passing

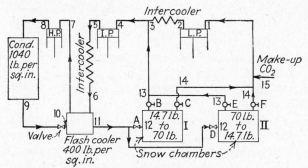

FIG. 29.—Solid CO_2 pressure snowchamber system.

points 11 and 13 may nevertheless be determined per unit weight of high pressure snow formed.

It now becomes necessary to calculate the useful yield, the relative quantity at point 14, and the amount of make-up required. A snowchamber cut off from the CO_2 supply may be considered to undergo a gradual decrease in pressure with a uniform rate of vaporization during the cooling of the contents until atmospheric pressure and the corresponding temperature are reached. It will thus be seen that the enthalpy of the escaping saturated vapor, point 14, will vary from that for the low intermediate pressure to that for atmospheric pressure. Because the enthalpy of the solid and the enthalpy of vaporization are changing inversely in this range, the enthalpy of the vapor does not vary radically during the pressure drop and may be assumed constant at a mean value between the two limiting conditions. Considered in this way, a simple energy balance is sufficient to determine the weights. With the snowchamber at low intermediate pressure just prior to sublimation, the energy possessed by the solid contents is internal energy. This is so nearly equal to the enthalpy of the solid (within 0.14 Btu) that the latter will be used for simplicity. At the completion of vaporization, the saturated solid remaining possesses internal energy at atmospheric pressure, and there has left the chamber the quantity of energy represented by the mean enthalpy of the gas evolved. If the process has been carried out with no reception of heat from without, as would practically be the case, then the energy equation may be expressed

$$M_{12}u_{f12} = M_y u_{f14} + M_{14}h_g \text{ (mean)} \tag{53}$$

or, approximately,

$$M_{12}h_{f12} = M_y h_{f14} + M_{14}h_g \text{ (mean)} \tag{54}$$

where M_{12} is the weight of snow originally present, M_y the weight of snow finally remaining, and M_{14} the weight of gas evaporated. The weight relationship is

$$M_{12} = M_y + M_{14} \tag{55}$$

which permits solving for either the useful yield or the gas returned in terms of the primary or pressure yield. The make-up is, without loss by leakage, equal to the quantity of snow removed from the machine.

Adiabatic mixing may be assumed to occur at gas junctions, points 14 and 15 to 1 and points 3 and 13 to 4. The calculation of data for the remainder of the system conforms to theory previously discussed and need not be repeated here.

Example (Refer to Fig. 29).—It is desired to determine power and piston displacement requirements for a solid CO_2 machine of the type just discussed. The pressures are as follows: low, 14.7 lb. abs.; low intermediate, 70 lb. abs.; high intermediate, 400 lb. abs.; condenser, 1040 lb. abs. Liquid CO_2 may be water-cooled to 80°F., gas to 90°F. Make-up gas enters the system at 80°F., atmospheric pressure. Adiabatic compression in all cylinders. Compute on the basis of the previous example.

Calculate: (a) Ihp.-hours per ton of solid CO_2; (b) theoretical piston displacement in cubic feet per minute for 1 ton of snow per hour.

Solution:

$h_3 = 171$; $h_6 = 161$; $h_7 = 138.5$; $v_7 = 0.218$; $h_8 = 156$; $t_8 = 143°F.$; $h_9 = 69 = h_{10}$; $h_{11} = 28 = h_{12}$; $h_{13} = 136$; $h_{14} = 134.6$ (mean); $h_{15} = 170$; $h_{f12} = -98$; $h_{f14} = -113$.

For 2000 lb. per hr. useful yield (M_y):

$M_{12}(-98) = 2000(-113) + M_{14}(134.6)$

$M_{12} = 2000 + M_{14}$. $(2000 + M_{14})(-98) = 134.6M_{14} - 226,000$

$-196,000 - 98M_{14} = 134.6M_{14} - 226,000$

$M_{14} = 129$ lb. per hr. or 2.15 lb. per min.

$M_{12} = 2129$ lb. per hr. or 35.5 lb. per min.

Make-up $= 2000$ lb. per hr. or 33.33 lb. per min.

Weight through low pressure cylinder, $M_1 = 33.33 + 2.15 = 35.48 = M_{12}$

$$h_1 = \frac{33.33(170) + 2.15(134.6)}{35.5} = 167 \text{ Btu per lb.}; t_1 = 65°F.; v_1 = 8.7;$$

$h_2 = 208; t_2 = 250°F.$

Low pressure ihp. $= \dfrac{35.5(208 - 167)}{42.4} = 34.4$ ihp. per ton snow per hr.

Low pressure theoretical piston displacement per ton per hr. = $35.5(8.7) = 308$ cu. ft. per min.

Quality, $x_{12} = \dfrac{28 - (-98)}{234.7} = 0.535$

Primary yield $= 1.0 - 0.535 = 0.465$ lb. snow per lb. CO_2

CO_2 through intermediate pressure cylinder $= \dfrac{35.5}{0.465} = 76.5$ lb. per min.

$M_{13} = 76.5 - 35.5 = 41$ lb. per min.

$$h_4 = \frac{41(136) + 35.5(171)}{76.5} = 152 \text{ Btu per lb.}; t_4 = 5°F.; v_4 = 1.6;$$

$$h_5 = 194; t_5 = 218°F.$$

Intermediate pressure ihp. $= \dfrac{76.5(194 - 152)}{42.4} = 76$ ihp. per ton per hr.

Intermediate pressure theoretical piston displacement per ton per hr. = $76.5(1.6) = 122$ cu. ft. per min.

$M_7 = \dfrac{76.5(161 - 28)}{138.5 - 69} = 146.2$ lb. per min.

High pressure ihp. $= \dfrac{146.2(156 - 138.5)}{42.4} = 60.5$ ihp. per ton per hr.

High pressure theoretical piston displacement $= 146.2(0.218) = 31.9$ cu. ft. per min.

(*a*) Total ihp. $= 34.4 + 76 + 60.5 = 171$ for 1 ton snow per hr.

(*b*) Total theoretical piston displacement $= 308 + 122 + 32 = 462$ cu. ft. per min. for 1 ton per hr.

Because it is possible in this cycle to reduce the quantity of atmospheric gas compressed, the reduction of piston displacement over the preceding system is very noticeable (18 per cent).

The greatest saving is, of course, in the low pressure cylinder size, but this is partially offset by the necessary increase in the intermediate pressure cylinder.   A corresponding saving of 15 per cent in indicated work is effected for the reasons previously set forth.

39. Regenerative Liquid Precooler.—Precooling, or subcooling, the liquid CO_2 before entering the final expansion valve or nozzle serves to increase the yield by producing a lower quality after throttling.   The gas leaving the snowchamber may be used for

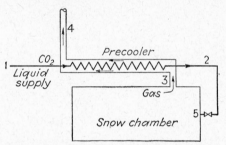

FIG. 30.—Regenerative liquid precooler.

this purpose in a regenerative cooler such as is diagrammatically illustrated in Fig. 30.   The cold gas leaving the snowchamber is passed through a heat exchanger counterflow to the incoming liquid.   Because the gas is always less in quantity than the liquid and also because it has the smaller specific heat, it must undergo a much greater temperature rise than does the liquid a temperature drop.   In the case of a perfect heat exchanger, the temperatures of the entering liquid t_1 and the leaving gas t_4 would be the same.   Actually there will exist a temperature difference at this point, t_4 being 15 to 30° less than t_1.   This temperature difference forms the basis on which the energy equation may be used to determine the yield after expansion.

The fundamental energy equation is

$$M_1 h_1 + M_3 h_{g3} = M_2 h_2 + M_4 h_4$$

or, since $M_1 = M_2$ and $M_3 = M_4$,

$$M_1(h_1 - h_2) = M_3(h_4 - h_{g3}) \qquad (56)$$

Two unknowns appear in this equation, h_2 and either M_1 or M_3, but they are not independent.   The two weights are related as

$$M_3 = x_5 M_1 \tag{57}$$

where x_5 is the quality resulting from expansion into the snow-chamber. Since we are interested only in the weight proportion, M_1 may be assumed to be unity, and the energy equation becomes

$$h_1 - h_2 = x_5(h_4 - h_{g3}) \tag{58}$$

If point 5 represents the condition following expansion, it may be seen that x_5 and h_2 are dependent according to

$$x_5 = \frac{h_2 - h_{f5}}{h_{fg5}} \quad \text{or} \quad h_2 = x_5 h_{fg5} + h_{f5} \tag{59}$$

Substituting this expression for h_2 in Eq. (58) and for h_{g3} its equivalent $h_{f5} + h_{fg5}$,

$$x_5 = \frac{h_1 - h_{f5}}{h_4 - h_{f5}} \tag{60}$$

The yield is then, as previously, $1 - x_5$.

Example.—Taking data from the preceding example, determine the primary yield when using a regenerative precooler with a temperature difference of 20°F. between entering liquid and leaving gas. Compare with the yield before using a precooler.

Solution (Refer to Fig. 30):

$h_{f1} = 28$; $t_1 = 17°F.$; $h_3 = 136$; $p_4 = 70$; $t_4 = 17 - 20 = -3°$;
$$h_4 = 150; \; h_{f5} = -98.8.$$

$$x_5 = \frac{28 - (-98.8)}{150 - (-98.8)} = 0.509$$

Primary yield $= 1.000 - 0.509 = 0.491$ lb. per lb. CO_2

(Primary yield without precooler $= 0.465$ lb. per lb. CO_2)

CO_2 to be handled by the intermediate pressure cylinder $= \dfrac{35.5}{0.491}$
$$= 72.2 \text{ lb. per min.}$$

This is a reduction of 4 lb. per min. as compared to the system without precooler, but will be practically offset, insofar as intermediate cylinder work or volume is concerned, by the increased temperature of the suction gas.

The foregoing statement, however, applies only to the intermediate pressure cylinder. The low pressure work and piston displacement per unit weight of snow will be unaffected by the addition of the precooler since neither quantities nor conditions are altered in this circuit. The weight of CO_2 circulated in the high pressure circuit will be decreased and conditions remain unchanged with a consequent proportional reduction of work and volume for this cylinder. Inasmuch as the high pressure cylinder is the only one affected, from the standpoint of power and piston displacement, and this only slightly, but little saving for the system as a whole may be expected. This is particularly true of displacement because the high pressure cylinder provides only 7 per cent of the volume while doing 35 per cent of the work in the original cycle. The high pressure ihp. would, with pre-cooler, be 57.1 and for the system would be 167.5 ihp.-hr. per ton snow—a saving of 2 per cent.

The limit of liquid precooling in all cases is either the freezing point, when cooled at high pressure, or the triple point, when flash tanks are used, because any formation of solid other than in the snowchamber will clog the system and prevent the necessary flow. In the three-stage atmospheric snowmaking cycle first discussed, the low intermediate pressure was such that the liquid was flash cooled nearly to the triple point eliminating the necessity for or the possibility of further precooling.

40. Binary Vapor Snowmaking Cycle.—Although the efficiency of a Carnot heat engine or refrigeration cycle is independent of the nature of the working substance, this is not true for most cycles in actual use—vapor cycles in particular. In vapor refrigeration cycles, the character of the working fluid influences to a considerable degree the performance of the machine from the standpoint of energy required to operate the system, and it is therefore important that relative power consumption be considered as a basic characteristic of a refrigerant. The variation in efficiency among commonly used substances is due to fundamental characteristics, but, in general, it may be said that fluids become less suitable, on an efficiency basis, for use as refrigerants as the operating range approaches the critical condition. It may be seen at once that carbon dioxide is very bad in this respect because its critical temperature (about 88°F.) occurs very close to the usual condensation temperature encountered in water-cooled condensers. On the other hand, there are many refrigerants with critical conditions sufficiently high so that it is unnecessary to approach them in ordinary operation.

In the snowmaking cycles just discussed the high pressure stages were, for the reason just mentioned, operating in a particularly inefficient range considering the refrigerant used. An improvement in power consumption might therefore be expected to result from the substitution for CO_2, in the high pressure stage, of a refrigerant which is better adapted to the higher temperatures encountered. Such a dual refrigerant or binary cycle is shown in Fig. 31, using a pressure snowchamber. In this cycle there are two stages of CO_2 compression topped by a single-stage NH_3 system. The low pressure CO_2 circuit is similar in all respects, both weights and conditions, to that previously discussed (Fig. 29). The intermediate pressure stage is also similar in layout but the high intermediate pressure has been reduced

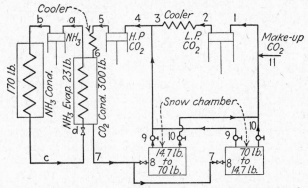

Fig. 31.—Binary CO_2 snowmaking cycle with pressure snowchamber.

to 300 lb. per sq. in this instance. This reduction is more feasible for the binary system but is not necessarily an inherent feature of it. The intermediate circuit now contains a low temperature carbon dioxide condenser which is at the same time an ammonia evaporator. Thus the useful refrigerating effect of the NH_3 cycle is the heat removed in desuperheating, condensing, and subcooling the CO_2. Other than this, the ammonia system does not differ from the simple compression system already discussed.

Inasmuch as the condensation temperature of the carbon dioxide is in this case $-1°F.$, it is well removed from the critical temperature, while the ammonia, with a comparatively high critical temperature ($271.4°F.$), may also be operated within a range which does not approach the critical condition. In Fig. 31, the numbered points are for CO_2 and the lettered points for NH_3.

Many refrigerants other than ammonia might be successfully used in the high temperature stage of machines of this kind. Ammonia is considered in this illustration because it is the most likely industrial refrigerant and because the tabulation of its properties is, next to water vapor, most complete. The principle would be the same for any vapor refrigerant which could be used.

In the example which follows, the basis of computation is the same as for the other solid carbon dioxide cycles for purposes of comparison. A temperature difference of about 10° between NH_3 and CO_2 in the CO_2 condenser has, however, been properly considered since a heat transfer loss at this point is inevitable in systems using dual refrigerants and constitutes one of their inherent faults.

Example.—A binary solid CO_2 system, with NH_3, is to be used in conjunction with a pressure snowchamber as shown in Fig. 31. The pressures are: low, 14.7 lb. abs.; low intermediate, 70 lb. abs.; CO_2 condenser, 300 lb. abs.; NH_3 evaporator, 23 lb. abs.; NH_3 condenser, 170 lb. abs. Liquids may be water-cooled to 80°F., gases to 90°F. Make-up CO_2 enters the system at 80°F., atmospheric pressure. Adiabatic compression in all cylinders. Compute on the basis of previous examples.

Calculate: (*a*) Ihp.-hours per ton of snow; (*b*) theoretical piston displacement in cubic feet per minute for 1 ton snow per hour.

Solution (Refer to Fig. 31):

Conditions affecting the low pressure circuit remain unchanged and, from the example of Fig. 29, $h_3 = 171$; $h_9 = 136$.

Weight through low pressure cylinder $M_1 = 35.5$ lb. per min.

Low pressure ihp. $= 34.4$ per ton snow per hr.

Low pressure piston displacement per ton per hr. $= 308$ cu. ft. per min.

$h_6 = 164$; $h_7 = 18.4 = h_8$.

Quality, $x_8 = \dfrac{18.4 - (-98)}{234.7} = 0.495$

Primary yield $= 1.0 - 0.495 = 0.505$ lb. snow per lb. CO_2

CO_2 through intermediate pressure cylinder, $M_4 = \dfrac{35.5}{0.505} = 70.4$ lb.

$$\text{per min.} = M_7$$

$M_9 = 70.4 - 35.5 = 34.9$ lb. per min.

$h_4 = \dfrac{34.9(136) + 35.5(171)}{70.4} = 154$; $t_4 = 13°F.$; $v_4 = 1.65$; $h_5 = 190$;

$$t_5 = 190°F.$$

Intermediate pressure ihp. $= \dfrac{70.4(190 - 154)}{42.4} = 59.8$ ihp. per ton

$$\text{snow per hr.}$$

Intermediate pressure piston displacement per ton per hr. =
$$70.4(1.65) = 116 \text{ cu. ft. per min.}$$

Heat removed from CO_2 in condenser $= 70.4(164 - 18.4) = 10,230$
$$\text{Btu per min.}$$

Ammonia circuit: $h_a = 608.1$, $v_a = 11.85$; $h_b = 736$, $t_b = 250°$;
$$h_c = 132 = h_d$$

NH_3 circulated per min. $= \dfrac{10,230}{608 - 132} = 21.5$ lb. for 1 ton snow per hr.

NH_3 ihp. $= \dfrac{21.5(736 - 608)}{42.4} = 65$ ihp. per ton snow per hr.

NH_3 piston displacement per ton snow per hr. $= 21.5(11.85) = 255$
$$\text{cu. ft. per min.}$$

(a) Total ihp. $= 34.4 + 59.8 + 65 = 159.2$ for 1 ton snow per hr.

(b) Total theoretical piston displacement $= 308 + 116 + 255 = 679$
$$\text{cu. ft. per min. for 1 ton snow per hr.}$$

The principal advantages and disadvantages of the binary cycle, compared to the straight CO_2 system, are readily apparent. There is a distinct thermal gain resulting from the use of two fluids despite the fact that the binary principle makes it necessary to interpose an additional heat exchange surface with its attendant losses. The saving in power over the preceding system is 7 per cent. There is also the advantage of lower operating pressures. Against these is the undesirable feature of greatly increased piston displacement. However, since the increase in size results solely from the addition of the ammonia system, this is not so objectionable as it at first appears except on the basis of space requirement.

Other arrangements for the solid carbon dioxide machine are possible, but the principles discussed in this chapter provide the greatest gains and are the most easily adapted to practice. Minor rearrangements may produce further slight thermal or operating improvements.

The following tabular summing up of power and piston displacement requirements, as determined in the examples, for cycles from the elementary to the more economical types serves to illustrate the savings possible by the application of correct thermodynamic principles. Additional small gains could be had by the use of regenerative liquid precooling in cases where it is applicable.

Comparison of Ideal Carbon Dioxide Snowmaking Cycles

Type of cycle	Theo. ihp.-hr. per ton snow	Power in %. #1 = 100%	Theo. p. d. cu. ft./min. per ton/hr.	P.d. in %. #1 = 100%
1. Simple, single-stage.....	410	100	895	100
2. 3-stage, water coolers, atmospheric snow-chamber..............	320	78	1055	117.9
3. 3-stage, flash coolers, atmospheric snow-chamber..............	200	48.8	564	63
4. 3-stage, flash coolers, pressure snowchamber..	171	41.7	462	51.6
5. Binary, 2 CO₂ stages, 1 NH₃ stage, pressure snowchamber..........	159	38.8	679	75.9

PROBLEMS

14. A solid CO_2 machine is to be designed to produce 1000 lb. of snow per hour. The cooling water is such that liquid carbon dioxide may be cooled to 80°F., gas to 95°F. Make-up gas is at 90°F. Condenser pressure will be 1060 lb. abs.; atmospheric pressure is standard. Allow 20 per cent greater piston displacement than the theoretical and 15 per cent greater ihp.

Using several different combinations of intermediate pressures in each case, compute the piston displacement for each cylinder, and total, and the total ihp. for the following types of machine: (*a*) Three-stage with water intercooling; (*b*) three-stage with water and flash intercooling; (*c*) three-stage with water and flash intercooling and pressure snowchamber; (*d*) two-stage CO_2 with water and flash intercooling, and single-stage ammonia at the high temperature, for both atmospheric and pressure snowchamber; (*e*) regenerative liquid precooler in conjunction with those systems to which it will apply.

CHAPTER VIII

MULTIPLE EFFECT VAPOR COMPRESSION

It has been seen that, for best performance, the two ruling temperatures, that at which condensation takes place and that at which vaporization occurs, should be as near together as circumstances will permit. This necessitates the operation of condenser and evaporator at as low and as high a temperature, respectively, as possible while maintaining a sufficiently great temperature difference between the heat exchange fluids in each as to keep the size of the apparatus within reasonable limits.

Consider now the case wherein it is desired to maintain two coolers at different temperatures. The cooling could be accomplished by a plant using a simple compressor, but it is obvious that, if this were done, the evaporator temperature would have to be such as to take care of the lowest temperature irrespective of the temperature or capacity of the higher temperature cooler. The latter would be cooled by a plant, the evaporator of which would be operated at a temperature much lower than necessary to maintain its comparatively high temperature requirements, the consequence being a lower coefficient of performance for that part of the refrigerating load due to widely diverging temperature limits as noted in the preceding paragraph. Since the higher temperature load is likely to constitute a large part of the plant capacity, the efficiency of the entire system would be seriously impaired.

One solution to this problem would be the use of two complete machines. Each system would carry its load independent of the other, and each would be able to operate under conditions which would produce best individual performance. This would enable the plant as a whole to work more efficiently while, at the same time, providing the required evaporator temperatures for each storage space. The principal objections to this system would be the high first cost and the complexities of such a plant embodying, as it does, two complete machines.

111

An alternative scheme can, however, be worked out, the object being to combine those parts of each system which in any way will lend themselves to a combination without sacrificing performance in too great a degree.   Thus, it may be seen that the two condensers might readily be replaced by one unit of proper capacity since the condenser pressure is governed by the temperature of the cooling water which is common to both systems. Because the evaporators must operate at different pressures in order to fulfill the object of the arrangement, these cannot be combined, and the revised system will have to be provided with two coolers to be operated at pressures suitable for the main-

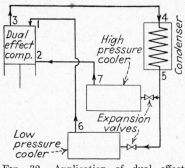

FIG. 32.—Application of dual effect compressor.

tenance of their respective temperatures.   O b v i o u s l y a separately controlled expansion valve will also be necessary for each evaporator.   Of the principal organs of the systems, there now remain only the compressors to be considered. These have a common discharge pressure, and, although they operate at different suction pressures, an ingenious modification of the ordinary compressor permits the combination of these two units into a single compressor.   This **multiple effect** or **dual** compressor shows considerable variation in design, particularly with regard to the location of and the method of operating the valves, and in application, where the evaporation of the lower pressure gas may fulfill different functions.   One application, a system incorporating the combinations just discussed, is illustrated diagrammatically in Fig. 32.

41. The Compressor.—For the present purpose, the simplest form of the dual compressor will suffice in which the higher pressure suction valve is a cylinder port opened and closed by the piston.   This type is shown schematically in Fig. 33, and Fig. 34 is an indicator card such as a machine of this kind might produce.

Assuming the compressor to be in operation, the action is as follows.   Let p_1, p_2, and p_3 represent, respectively, the lower pressure suction, higher pressure suction, and discharge pressures

immediately without the cylinder. On the suction stroke, the
clearance gas will first reexpand until, reaching the lower suction

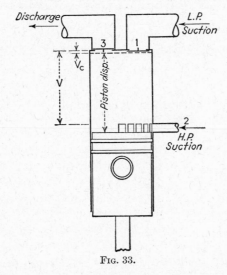

Fig. 33.

pressure, the suction valve will open admitting gas from the lower
pressure suction line as would be the case in the conventional type
of compressor. Wire-drawing will result in a slight lowering of

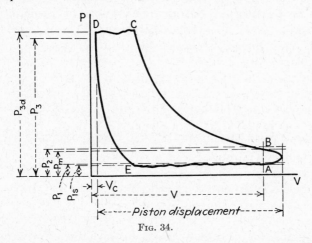

Fig. 34.

pressure during admission so that the suction pressure within the
cylinder will be less than p_1, or p_{1s}. Near the end of the stroke,

the piston uncovers the port through which gas is admitted
from the higher pressure line where it exists at p_2. The effect
of this is to raise the pressure within the cylinder, causing the
lower pressure suction valve to close, until either the pressure
p_2 is established or the piston closes the port with a somewhat
lesser pressure p_{2s} or p_m, existing because of throttling. In
either case, the influx of higher pressure gas has ceased with the
closing of the port. The piston, having covered the port,
compresses the cylinder contents to the cylinder discharge
pressure, p_{3d}, and finally discharges a part of them to the discharge line at p_3, the clearance gas remaining in the cylinder.

So long as conditions do not vary, the compressor will handle
a definite amount of gas from each suction during each revolution
or during each interval of time. The determination of the
relationship between these two quantities for a given condition
constitutes a problem which must be solved if the load distribution and the indicated work are to be determined. As will be
seen presently, this solution involves the finding of the state, at
the beginning of compression, of the cylinder contents which are
composed of clearance, lower pressure suction, and higher
pressure suction gases of unknown quantities and initially
possessing each its individual properties. These three quantities
will be considered separately.

At the beginning of the suction stroke and throughout the
reexpansion process, the cylinder contents consist entirely of the
gas that occupied the clearance space at the end of the stroke
and was not discharged. The weight of this clearance gas will
be designated as M_c. At the point near the end of the suction
stroke where the piston is about to uncover the higher pressure
suction port, the admission of lower pressure gas has taken
place and is about to be terminated by the rise in pressure
incident to the opening of the port. Let M_1 represent the
weight of lower pressure vapor drawn in. With the piston in
this position, then, the material in the cylinder is the sum of
the constituents from these two sources, or $M_c + M_1$ lb. From
this position, the piston proceeds to the end of its stroke, reverses
its direction of motion, and returns to the point last considered
which may now be termed the point of closure of the higher
pressure port. In the meantime, higher pressure suction gas
has entered the cylinder raising the pressure therein to approxi-

mately that existing in the higher pressure suction line. Denoting the weight of higher pressure gas admitted as M_2, the total weight of material in the cylinder at the beginning of compression is $M_c + M_1 + M_2$ lb. Neither the individual weights nor the condition of the vapor are known at this juncture. Furthermore, the weights involved are dependent upon the condition because the specific volume is concerned in both, and a solution for the quantities would necessitate the incidental determination of the state.

42. Adiabatic Case.—Consider the problem in which it is desired to determine the suction gas weights handled by the compressor and the work of compression with the following data known: the piston displacement per unit of time; the clearance; the per cent stroke at which the auxiliary port opens; the state of the vapors in their respective suction lines (p_1, p_2, and the temperatures or qualities); the discharge line pressure (p_3); and the pressure drop occurring through each port or valve. In addition, let adiabatic compression be assumed in this initial case.

Now the lower pressure gas is, during suction, subjected to three distinct influences which act to change its properties. These are the throttling process through the valve, mixing with the clearance gas, and exposure to the relatively warm internal surfaces. The first of these will tend to produce a small temperature drop without change in enthalpy. The second, differing in effect from that in the conventional compressor, will also result in a decrease in temperature, if the gas be superheated at entrance, because the clearance gas, having reexpanded through a greater pressure ratio than that through which it was adiabatically compressed, will be at a lower temperature than that of the incoming gas. The third definitely has a heating effect but is difficult to evaluate. However, since none of these effects is likely to be of sufficient magnitude to greatly affect the results, it is reasonable to consider that the first two effects approximately compensate for the third and, therefore, that the temperature of the cylinder contents at the time of port opening is that of the lower pressure gas in the suction line, or t_1.

Let V be the cylinder volume per unit of time at the point of port opening and closure. This may be computed from the data given. Also, since the state of the gas within the cylinder at port opening is known, its specific volume v_{1s} may be found and

$$M_c + M_1 = \frac{V}{v_{1s}} \qquad (61)$$

Note that, although the sum of these two quantities may be so determined, neither M_c nor M_1 is as yet known.

During the short time that the port is open, M_2 lb. of higher pressure suction gas have entered the cylinder and mixed with the contents already present. Owing to the small time consumed in admission and mixing, this process will be considered as adiabatic but, nonetheless, carried to the completion of thermal equilibrium. At port closure, the weight of the volume V of the mixture is $M_c + M_1 + M_2$, and the state or condition is designated by the subscript m. Then

$$(M_c + M_1) + M_2 = \frac{V}{v_m} \qquad (62)$$

or

$$M_2 = \frac{V}{v_m} - (M_c + M_1) \qquad (63)$$

It will at once be seen that, as M_2 and v_m are here independent variables, another equation is required for their solution.

Considering by themselves the higher pressure gas admission together with the subsequent mixing process, taken as adiabatic, the energy equation for this may be written:

$$(M_c + M_1)u_{1s} + M_2 h_2 = (M_c + M_1 + M_2)u_m \qquad (64)$$

This is based upon the premise that the gas already within the cylinder, $M_c + M_1$, being static, possesses only internal energy, while the incoming gas M_2, being in a state of flow, brings in energy in the form of both internal energy and flow work (APv), the sum being represented by enthalpy. While this equation properly represents the initial and incoming *gas* energies, it neglects the net input of mechanical energy occasioned by the movement of the piston from the point of port opening to the bottom dead center, and its return to the point of port closure *against an increased pressure*. This energy input, constituting a very small part of the compressor work, takes place during the mixing process and, strictly, belongs in the energy equation, Eq. (64), whence it will be seen to influence the condition of the mixture. The net work accomplished by the piston while the port is open may be expressed as

$$AW = CA(P_m - P_{1s})(\text{total cylinder volume} - V)$$

in which C is the proportion of the "toe" of the diagram (Fig. 34) that is effective and depends upon the relative rate of entrance of the higher pressure suction gas. The work quantity may also be seen to be a function of the difference between the suction pressures $P_m - P_{1s}$ and of the location and size of the cylinder port with respect to piston travel. Including the piston work, the energy equation for adiabatic mixing is

$$(M_c + M_1)u_{1s} + M_2h_2 + CA(P_m - P_{1s})(V_{\text{cyl}} - V) = (M_c + M_1 + M_2)u_m \quad (64a)$$

Because the inclusion of the additional term complicates the solution of the problem to a degree ordinarily unwarranted by the effect upon the results and by the accuracy of assumptions already made, the development will be carried through neglecting the influence of the piston work upon the mixture condition, but attention will be directed from time to time to the more rigorous solution in order that its significance may be fully understood.

Continuing with the development of the approximate method, the substitution of $h_m - AP_mv_m$ for u_m in Eq. (64) gives

$$(M_c + M_1)u_{1s} + M_2h_2 = [(M_c + M_1) + M_2](h_m - AP_mv_m) \quad (65)$$

Writing for M_2 its equivalent $\dfrac{V}{v_m} - (M_c + M_1)$, from Eq. (63),

the energy equation becomes

$$(M_c + M_1)u_{1s} + \left[\frac{V}{v_m} - (M_c + M_1)\right]h_2$$

$$= \left[(M_c + M_1) + \frac{V}{v_m} - (M_c + M_1)\right](h_m - AP_mv_m) \quad (66)$$

or

$$(M_c + M_1)u_{1s} + \frac{V}{v_m}(h_2) - (M_c + M_1)h_2 = \frac{V}{v_m}(h_m) - AP_mV \quad (67)$$

Collecting unknown terms on the left of the equation and known terms on the right, simplifying, and changing signs,

$$\frac{h_m - h_2}{v_m} = AP_m - \frac{1}{V}(M_c + M_1)(h_2 - u_{1s}) \quad (68)$$

This equation contains two dependent variables v_m and h_m and may be solved most readily by plotting a curve, from tables of thermodynamic properties, of the quantity $(h_m - h_2)/v_m$ versus temperature for the pressure P_m. With the condition of the mixture thus determined and with $M_c + M_1$ known, M_2 may be found by Eq. (63).

For the more exact method, including the work input during admission of the higher pressure suction gas, Eq. (68) becomes

$$\frac{h_m - h_2}{v_m} = AP_m - \frac{1}{V}(M_c + M_1)(h_2 - u_{1s})$$
$$+ \frac{CA}{V}(P_m - P_{1s})(V_{cyl} - V) \quad (68a)$$

where C is the same as in Eq. (64a).

The states of the gas after isentropic compression to cylinder discharge pressure, point $3d$, and in the discharge line following valve throttling, point 3, may now be determined without difficulty. The condition of the clearance gas at the time that it occupies only the clearance volume is that of the cylinder contents following compression but prior to discharge, and, the clearance volume being known,

$$M_c = \frac{V_c}{v_{3d}} \quad (69)$$

where V_c is the volume of the clearance space in the unit time corresponding to volume V. M_1 may now be found by applying Eq. (61).

An alternate means for solving M_1 is suggested by the use of the clearance factor, but this method is not recommended in cases where the other may be used because of the uncertainty of the value of the exponent n for the reexpansion when adiabatic conditions do not exist.

The indicated compressor work is calculated by application of the steady-flow energy equation:

$$AW = M_3 h_3 - M_1 h_1 - M_2 h_2 + Q \quad (70)$$

in which $M_3 = M_1 + M_2$, and Q is the heat rejected from the cylinder contents. If, as is usual, the weights are per unit of time, then the work and the heat rejected in the above equation are also rates for the same time interval. In the adiabatic case under consideration, Q is, of course, zero. Equation (70) applies to both the approximate and the more exact methods, but not with equal significance. For the latter, the equation gives directly the total indicated work of the compressor, while in the case of the former it should be noted that the term AW does not include the piston work done during the time that the cylinder port is open. In cases where an appreciable error would otherwise result, this may be compensated for by simply adding the small mechanical energy input in question to AW as determined from the energy equation.

The indicated work may also be computed from the net area of the probable indicator card (Fig. 34) and requires only the compressor data, the cylinder pressures, and a knowledge of the equations of the compression and the reexpansion curves. This method is subject to the same inaccuracy as that previously mentioned in connection with the determination of clearance factor but should prove reasonably accurate in the adiabatic case and, in any case, would serve as a valuable check upon the results obtained by the method first described. In the following example, the computation of the card area will be demonstrated at the end in order to check the indicated work.

Example.—The following are data for an adiabatic multiple effect ammonia compressor. Cylinder: single-acting; 10 × 12 in.; 175 rpm; 2 per cent clearance; cylinder port opens at 93 per cent of stroke. Wiredrawing: low pressure valve, 1 lb. per sq. in.; high pressure port, 2 lb. per sq. in.; discharge valve, 6 lb. per sq. in. Suction line conditions: Low pressure suction: pressure $p_1 = 10$ lb. abs.;[1] temperature $t_1 = -30°F$. High pressure suction: pressure $p_2 = 40$ lb. abs.;[1] temperature $t_2 = 20°F$. Discharge line pressure $p_3 = 170$ lb. abs.

Calculate the ammonia quantities in pounds per minute from each suction line, and the ihp.

Solution.—Approximate method (use notation previously described):

$h_1 = 603.2$ Btu at 10 lb. abs. and $-30°F$.;
$h_{1s} = 603.6$ Btu at 9 lb. abs. and $-30°F$.; $v_{1s} = 29.6$ cu. ft. per lb.;
$h_2 = 620.4$ Btu at 40 lb. abs. and $20°F$.;
$p_m = 38$ lb. abs.; $p_{3d} = 176$ lb. abs.

Piston displacement $= \dfrac{\pi(10)^2(12)(175)}{(4)(1728)} = 95.5$ cu. ft. per min.

---

[1] Extreme suction pressures are here selected for illustration.

Clearance volume = 0.02(95.5) = 1.91 cu. ft. per min.
Cylinder volume at port opening, V = 0.93(95.5) + 1.91 = 90.7 cu. ft. per min.

$$\text{Cylinder contents at port opening} = \frac{90.7}{29.6} = 3.06 \text{ lb. per min.} =$$

$$M_c + M_1$$

$$u_{1s} = 603.6 - \frac{9(144)(29.6)}{778} = 554.2 \text{ Btu per lb.}$$

By Eq. (68),

$$\frac{h_m - 620.4}{v_m} = \frac{38(144)}{778} - \frac{3.06(620.4 - 554.2)}{90.7} = 4.81$$

Plotting the quantity $(h_m - 620.4)/v_m$ versus temperature for a pressure p_m of 38 lb. abs. from the ammonia tables, as shown in Fig. 35, it is seen that the temperature after mixing is 96.5°F. for which state $h_m = 663.5$ and $v_m = 9.01$.

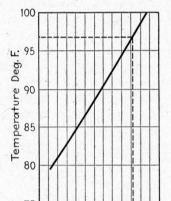

$$M_2 = \frac{90.7}{9.01} - 3.06 = 7.01 \text{ lb. per min.}$$

Condition at point $3d$ after isentropic compression to 176 lb.:

$$s_{3d} = s_m = 1.4128; \; t_{3d} = 322°F.;$$
$$h_{3d} = 779.3 = h_3; \; v_{3d} = 2.71.$$
$$\text{Clearance gas } M_c = \frac{1.91}{2.71} = 0.705 \text{ lb. per min.}$$
$$M_1 = 3.06 - 0.705 = 2.355 \text{ lb. per min.}$$
$$M_3 = M_1 + M_2 = 2.355 + 7.01 = 9.365 \text{ lb. per min.}$$

FIG. 35.

From Eq. (70), AW = 9.365(779.3) − 2.355(603.2) − 7.01(620.4) = 1528 Btu per min.

Considering three quarters of the rectangular area at the toe of the diagram as effective, this area is (0.07)(95.5)(38 − 9)(144)(0.75) = 21,000 ft.-lb. per min., or 27 Btu per min.

Total indicated work = 1528 + 27 = 1555 Btu per min. or 36.7 ihp.

In solving for the work from the indicator diagram (Fig. 34), the enclosed area will be calculated by the algebraic summing of the areas involved. For compression, $k = 1.276$; for reexpansion, $k = 1.272$.

$$p_A = 9 \text{ lb. abs.}; \; p_B = 38 \text{ lb. abs.}; \; p_C = 176 \text{ lb. abs.}; \; V_A = 90.7 \text{ cu. ft. per min.} = V_B$$

For the figure axis labels:
Temperature Deg. F.

100
95
90
85
80
75

4.0 4.2 4.4 4.6 4.8 5.0

$\dfrac{h_m - h_2}{v_m}$, at $p_m = 38$ Lb. per Sq. In. Abs.

$$V_C = 90.7\left(\frac{38}{176}\right)^{\frac{1}{1.276}} = 27.3 \text{ cu. ft. per min.; } V_D = 1.91 \text{ cu. ft. per}$$

$$\text{min.; } V_E = 1.91\left(\frac{176}{9}\right)^{\frac{1}{1.272}} = 19.7 \text{ cu. ft. per min.}$$

Area to left of A-B = $(38 - 9)(144)(90.7)$ = 378,800 ft.-lb. per min.

Area to left of B-C = $\dfrac{1.276(144)}{0.276}(176 \times 27.3 - 38 \times 90.7)$ =

904,100 ft.-lb. per min.

Effective area while port is open = 21,000 ft.-lb. per min. (from above)

Area to left of D-E = $\dfrac{1.272(144)}{0.272}(176 \times 1.91 - 9 \times 19.7)$ =

107,000 ft.-lb. per min.

Net area = 378,800 + 904,100 + 21,000 − 107,000 =

1,196,900 ft.-lb. per min., or 1538 Btu per min. (36.3 ihp.)

In evaluating the area of the indicator diagram, the adiabatic exponents were determined from the conditions found by the other calculation. They are, therefore, somewhat more accurate than would usually be the case when the conditions are unknown. It will be noted that, while this method gives a close approximation of indicated work, it does not provide a means of determining the weights of the respective suction gases. The other analysis must therefore be resorted to if information regarding the load distribution is desired.

Using the more accurate method, the results will be changed to the following:

By Eq. (68a), $\dfrac{h_m - 620.4}{v_m} = 5.1$

$t_m = 102.5°\text{F.; } h_m = 666.95; v_m = 9.117; s_m = 1.4187.$

$M_2 = \dfrac{90.7}{9.117} - 3.06 = 6.89$ lb. per min.

$t_{3d} = 330°\text{F.; } h_{3d} = 783.9; v_{3d} = 2.74.$

$M_c = \dfrac{1.91}{2.74} = 0.697$ lb. per min.; $M_1 = 2.363$ lb. per min.; $M_3 = 9.253$

lb. per min.

$AW = 9.253(783.9) - 2.363(603.2) - 6.89(620.4) = 1553$ Btu per min., or 36.6 ihp.

From the indicator diagram, the net work is 1541 Btu per min. (36.3 ihp.)

43. Dual Compression with Cylinder Water Jacket.—Because of the relatively high temperature at the beginning of compression in the multiple effect compressor, the discharge temperature will be particularly high considering the pressure ratio of direct compression. This renders the use of a cylinder water jacket imperative if moderate piston, valve, and wall temperatures are to be maintained.

The discussion in the preceding section concerning the various effects on the lower pressure gas during the suction stroke was not strictly correct for the case of the adiabatic cylinder since such a cylinder would produce no heating effect upon the contents. However, rather than set up a particular procedure for adiabatic action which would be applicable to no other case, the discussion was made to conform to actual conditions, and the assumption of constant temperature induction of the lower pressure gas applies more accurately to the actual than to the adiabatic cylinder. The mixing process of lower and higher pressure suction gases occurs rapidly, but, since compression starts immediately after the termination of flow through the port, the final portion of the mixing is undoubtedly completed during the early part of the compression rather than prior to its beginning. The effect of this slight lag upon the computations previously made is small and the mixing will here be considered as adiabatic and instantaneous. The method of calculation is thus the same to this point as for the adiabatic case previously considered.

The effects of withdrawing heat during compression are decreased work and greater density of material at discharge as compared to adiabatic compression between the same pressure limits and with similar initial conditions. The increased density will result in a larger proportion of the gas remaining in the clearance space at the end of the discharge stroke, but this is at least partially compensated for by the lower temperature of reexpanded clearance gas which in turn produces the cooling effect assumed to maintain the incoming gas at constant temperature against the influence of heating.

Reference to the example of the preceding section will show that the only changes necessary to make this applicable to the non-adiabatic case are the consideration of the heat quantity Q in the energy equation and the revision of discharge conditions and such weights as are affected by them. The weight of clearance gas M_c will be increased, and that of the lower pressure gas M_1 will be correspondingly reduced, while the quantity of higher pressure gas M_2 will be unaffected.

Example.—Data as for the preceding example except that the temperature in the discharge line t_3 has been reduced to 270°F. by a cylinder water jacket.

Calculate the ammonia quantities in pounds per minute from each suction line, and the ihp.

Solution.—Use pertinent data from previous example.

$h_1 = 603.2$; $h_{1s} = 603.6$; $v_{1s} = 29.6$; $h_2 = 620.4$

$M_c + M_1 = 3.06$ lb. per min.; $t_m = 96.5°F.$; $h_m = 663.5$; $v_m = 9.01$; $s_m = 1.4128$; $h_3 = 748.7 = h_{3d}$; $t_{3d} = 271°F.$; $v_{3d} = 2.51$; $s_{3d} = 1.3723$.

$M_2 = 7.01$ lb. per min.

Clearance gas $M_c = \dfrac{1.91}{2.51} = 0.76$ lb. per min.

Low pressure gas $M_1 = 3.06 - 0.76 = 2.30$ lb. per min.

Gas discharged $M_3 = 2.3 + 7.01 = 9.31$ lb. per min.

Heat to jacket water $Q = 643.6(1.4128 - 1.3723) = 26$ Btu per lb.
or 242 Btu per min.

Indicated work $AW = 9.31(748.7) + 242 + 27 - 2.3(603.2) -$
$7.01(620.4) = 1489$ Btu per min.

Ihp. $= \dfrac{1489}{42.4} = 35.1$

The saving in power effected by the jacket is, in this instance, about $4\frac{1}{2}$ per cent. At the same time, it will be noticed that the lower pressure suction is reduced 2 per cent in quantity. The thermodynamic gain from cylinder cooling is thus shown to be slight and, from this standpoint only, could not be economically justified. This is also true for most types of compressors. From practical considerations, however, jacketing would be not only desirable but necessary for the cooling of cylinders, pistons, and valves even if there were no thermodynamic advantage to be derived.

Regarding economy of power, it may be said that the dual compressor will show considerable improvement over the conventional system which carries an equal load entirely at the low pressure. On the other hand, two simple independent machines will have a somewhat smaller power consumption while carrying the same relative loads than will the multiple effect system. These statements apply only when the individual high pressure and low pressure loads are a substantial proportion of the whole.

44. Dual Compressor with Flash Precooler.—With certain refrigerants, such as CO_2, the refrigerating effect is greatly improved by precooling the liquid just before final expansion into the evaporator. This is due to the fact that, with substances working near the critical point, the enthalpy of the liquid entering the expansion valve under ordinary conditions is a very large proportion of the enthalpy of the vapor leaving the evaporator. The difference in these enthalpies, which is the refrigerating effect, is therefore in such cases substantially increased by subcooling of the liquid. In order to illustrate, consider simple cases for three refrigerants, ammonia, Freon 12, and carbon dioxide. The condensation temperature in each case is 80°F., and the evaporation temperature is 0°F. These refrigerants are first considered without subcooling, then with subcooling to 20°F. For each case the refrigerating effect per pound of refrigerant is given together with the percentage improvement in refrigerating effect due to precooling in the following tabulation.

Refrigerant	No precooling			Precooling to 20°F.			
	h_f at 80°	h_g at 0°	Refrig. effect/#	h_f at 20°	h_g at 0°	Refrig. effect/#	Per cent gain
Ammonia................	132	611.8	479.8	64.7	611.8	547.1	14
Freon 12................	26.3	78.2	51.9	12.5	78.2	65.7	26.6
Carbon dioxide..........	73.9	138.9	65.0	29.4	138.9	109.5	68.5

The percentage improvement noted in the foregoing table is not pure gain since precooling exacts a toll, but the cost may be less than the gain if the cooling can be carried out by the evaporation of a gas which does not have to be compressed through the entire range. This principle was fully demonstrated in Chap. VI during the discussion of multiple expansion valves in conjunction with compound compression. Where stage compression would not ordinarily be used, however, compound expansion may be employed by utilizing the multiple effect compressor as shown in

Fig. 36. Here the gas which is evaporated in precooling the liquid in the flash cooler constitutes the higher pressure suction gas for the compressor and need be compressed through only part of the pressure range of the system.

The principles involved in a system of this type have already been discussed under multiple expansion valves and the dual

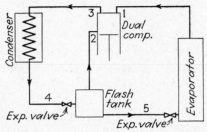

Fig. 36.—Use of the dual compressor for liquid precooling.

compressor, but the combination of the two in this manner evolves further a problem of balance. Assuming that the condenser and evaporator pressures remain constant, the quantity of higher pressure suction gas handled by the compressor is a function of the precooler pressure as is also the quantity of gas evaporated in the flash cooler. These quantities are obviously the same, and in practice that flash cooler pressure which will produce a weight balance will be automatically selected. But it may be desirable in some instances to predict this pressure in order to compute the probable performance characteristics of the machine. The solution is essentially

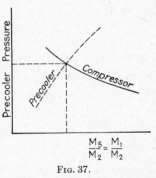

Fig. 37.

one of trial and error, but the labor may be considerably reduced by the consideration of cooler and compressor separately. With conditions at points 1 and 4 (Fig. 36) fixed by external requirements, and considering the flash cooler alone, the weight ratio M_5/M_2 may be determined for several flash cooler pressures (or temperatures). These values will establish a curve showing the relation of M_5/M_2 to cooler pressure. This would be similar to the broken curve in Fig. 37. Given the compressor data, the relation of M_1/M_2 may be calculated for the compressor for various high suction pressures and a curve plotted as shown solid in Fig. 37. Since M_2 is common to both cooler and compressor and $M_1 = M_5$, it is clear that the ratios must be the same in both cases and that the intersection of the curves indicates the balancing pressure, or temperature, for the precooling flash tank. At the same time, of course, the proper weight ratio is also shown. Following these determinations, the problem may be carried through to its conclusion by methods previously discussed.

The inherent inflexibility of the dual compressor does not constitute a major disadvantage in this type of system because, as stated before, the flash cooler pressure will be automatically selected for any particular load condition. This is brought about by the necessity for the cooler pressure to adjust itself to the higher pressure suction capacity of the compressor. The machine is thus controlled in the same manner as a conventional simple system. The degree of subcooling will, however, vary with the load and evaporator pressure and is not under the direct control of the operator or designer.

The actual gain to be derived from a machine of this type with its added complexity is probably insufficient to warrant such an installation except in the case of carbon dioxide where the benefit may be considerable.

PROBLEMS

15. Air from a pipe line at 150 lb. per sq. in. abs. and 100°F. flows into an initially evacuated adiabatic tank of 5 cu. ft. capacity. When the tank pressure reaches 150 lb. abs., flow will cease. At this time, what will be the air temperature in the tank and how many pounds of air will have entered? Neglect kinetic energy of flow.

16. Same as Prob. 1 except that the tank is initially filled with air at 20 lb. abs., 60°F. Find the temperature of air in the tank and the weight of air which has entered at the time that the tank pressure reaches 150 lb. abs.

17. A vessel of 10 cu. ft. internal volume contains steam at 40 lb. abs., 300°F. Steam at 200 lb. abs., 600°F., is permitted to enter from a pipe line. Assuming adiabatic mixing, calculate the weight of steam which has entered from the pipe line when flow stops.

18. A dual effect ammonia compressor operates two brine coolers, A and B, at pressures of 25 lb. abs. and 40 lb. abs., respectively. Discharge pressure is 154 lb. abs. The layout is similar to that shown in Fig. 32. The lower pressure suction gas comes to the compressor at

0°F., higher pressure suction at 20°F. Liquid enters the expansion valves at 70°F.

Compressor data: single cylinder, single acting; dimensions = 12×14 in.; speed = 200 rpm; 2 per cent clearance; cylinder port opens at 94 per cent of stroke. Wire-drawing through low pressure valve = 2 lb.; high pressure port = 3 lb.; discharge valve = 6 lb.

a. With cylinder port closed and all refrigerant passing through cooler *A*, calculate the refrigerating capacity in tons, the ihp., the ihp. per ton, and the coefficient of performance. Assume adiabatic compression.

b. Using both coolers, calculate the weight of ammonia passing through cooler *A*, the weight through cooler *B*, capacity of each cooler in tons, the ihp., the ihp. per ton, and the coefficient of performance. Assume adiabatic compression.

c. Same as part *b* except that a cylinder water jacket reduces the compression exponent to 1.22. Find also the quantity of jacket water necessary with a 15° temperature rise.

19. A multiple effect ammonia compressor is to operate two brine coolers at 15 lb. abs. and 30 lb. abs., respectively. The high pressure cooler is to provide 25 tons of refrigeration. Liquid temperature to expansion valves = 80°F. Condenser pressure = 180 lb. abs. Assume isentropic compression and no wire-drawing. Clearance = 2 per cent. Port opens at 94 per cent of stroke. Low pressure suction gas is at −20°F., high pressure suction at 20°F.

Calculate: (*a*) The compressor piston displacement, cubic feet per minute; (*b*) refrigerating effect in low pressure cooler in tons.

20. A carbon dioxide refrigerating machine is to have a dual compressor with flash precooling (Fig. 36). Condenser pressure = 1000 lb. abs. Evaporator pressure = 300 lb. abs. Temperature of liquid entering first expansion valve = 70°F., of gas leaving evaporator = 10°F. Clearance = $1\frac{1}{2}$ per cent. Port opens at 95 per cent of stroke. Assume isentropic compression and no wire-drawing.

Calculate: (*a*) The precooler pressure for the conditions stated; (*b*) the ihp. and the piston displacement if the capacity of the machine is 25 tons; (*c*) the ihp. and the piston displacement for a conventional machine of 25 tons capacity under similar conditions.

CHAPTER IX

ABSORPTION REFRIGERATION SYSTEM

All of the mechanical cycles of refrigeration heretofore considered have been heat pumps in which the energy input to operate the system has been in the form of mechanical work. In certain circumstances it may be desirable to use heat directly as the operating energy, for instance, in a plant where there is exhaust or process steam available.

Probably the most successful system operating almost wholly on an input of heat is the **absorption system,** and of the various

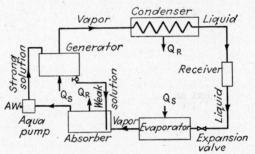

Fig. 38.—Basic absorption system.

refrigerants possible in this type of machine, ammonia is the most generally used. Because of this, as well as for other reasons previously mentioned, the *ammonia* absorption system will be principally discussed here, but the theory which follows is in general applicable to other fluids which are adaptable for use in absorption systems.

The absorption system differs fundamentally from the vapor compression system only in the method employed for compressing the refrigerant, so that if, in Fig. 19, the compressor be removed and there be substituted therefor an absorber, generator, and pump, as in Fig. 38, we have the basic absorption machine. The operating principle in this system is simply to dissolve or absorb the refrigerant, after leaving the evaporator, in a solution in the absorber at relatively low temperature and pressure; to mechanically pump the solution thus formed into the generator at higher pressure; and to distill from the solution, by the application of heat in the generator, the refrigerant received in the absorber and pass it to the condenser after which the weakened solution returns to the absorber to repeat its cycle. The refrigerant which goes to the condenser follows the usual course of events until it emerges from the evaporator to be again absorbed, pumped to higher pressure, and released to the condenser. If ammonia is the refrigerant, water is usually used as the absorbing agent and the solution is known as **aqua ammonia.** The only mechanical energy used is that required to operate the pump, and, inasmuch as the fluid handled is liquid, this energy is but a small fraction of the work which would be necessary to compress the refrigerant in the gaseous state. The energy which must be considered as the important quantity in operating the machine is the heat supplied in the generator for the distillation of the refrigerant, and the system may be said to be operated essentially by the heat so supplied.

45. Characteristics and Properties of Aqua Ammonia.—In order to be able to analyze the ammonia absorption system, a knowledge of the characteristics and properties of aqua ammonia solutions is necessary. Unfortunately there exist both an insufficiency of, and considerable conflict between, data concerning the properties of this solution, but the fundamental characteristics appear to be sufficiently in harmony to permit reasonable accuracy.

Aqua ammonia solutions may vary in strength, or **concentration,** from pure water (0 per cent concentration) to anhydrous ammonia (100 per cent concentration). The concentration is expressed in terms of the quantity of ammonia present in the solution, either as a **molal concentration** x_m—mols of ammonia per mol of solution—or as a **weight concentration** x_w—pounds of ammonia per pound of solution. Since the molal weights of ammonia and water are, respectively, 17 and 18 lb., the conversion from molal to weight concentration is

$$x_w = \frac{17x_m}{17x_m + 18(1 - x_m)} \qquad (71)$$

and, conversely,

$$x_m = \frac{x_w/17}{\dfrac{x_w}{17} + \dfrac{(1 - x_w)}{18}} \qquad (72)$$

When an aqua ammonia solution existing at a homogeneous temperature and pressure in the presence only of its own vapors has the tendency neither to increase nor to decrease its concentration, it is said to be, together with the vapors above it, in **equilibrium** or to have an **equilibrium concentration.** For each particular equilibrium concentration the pressure of the solution must be accompanied by a specific temperature in order that equilibrium may be maintained. Curves of constant equilibrium concentration may thus be plotted on pressure-temperature coordinates as shown in the accompanying aqua ammonia chart (Fig. 39). The 0 per cent concentration line (pure water) may be plotted directly from steam table data for saturated conditions, and the 100 per cent concentration line (anhydrous ammonia) may be correspondingly taken from ammonia tables. It should be noted that the effect of increased pressure is to increase the equilibrium concentration, while an increase in temperature has the opposite effect. The heating of an equilibrium solution without a corresponding rise in pressure will result inevitably in the positive evolution of ammonia vapor and a decreased concentration of the remaining solution. Thus a concentration *stronger* than equilibrium, for the conditions, may exist only momentarily. The cooling of the solution, however, produces no such positive action, and, while the tendency is to increase the concentration, this may not be carried out if ammonia is not supplied or if insufficient time is allowed for absorption. A concentration *lower* than equilibrium (subcooled solution) may therefore readily exist.

The vapors naturally existing above an equilibrium aqua ammonia solution within a closed vessel, or during boiling, are the vapors of both constituents at their respective partial pressures. Inasmuch as neither of the vapors is saturated under these conditions, the partial pressures may only be found experimentally. The *p-t-x* chart presented in this chapter shows also the partial pressures of water vapor above the solution for any particular equilibrium condition.[1] To illustrate the use of

---

[1] Both *p-t-x* relationships and partial water vapor pressures plotted from data in *Bulletin* 146, *University of Illinois Engineering Experiment Station.*

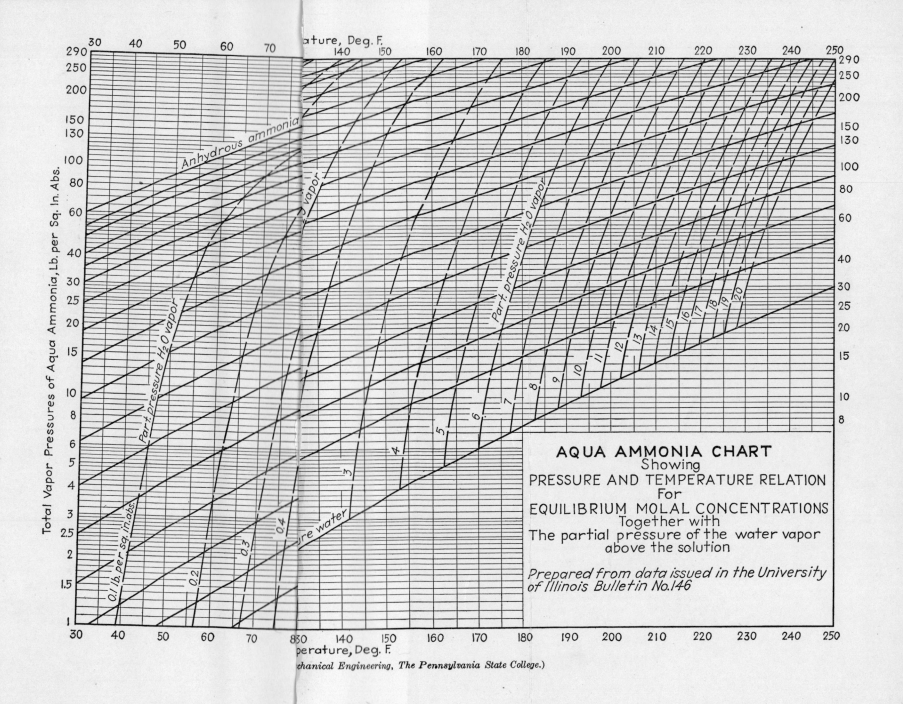

AQUA AMMONIA CHART
Showing
PRESSURE AND TEMPERATURE RELATION
For
EQUILIBRIUM MOLAL CONCENTRATIONS
Together with
The partial pressure of the water vapor
above the solution

Prepared from data issued in the University
of Illinois Bulletin No.146

(chanical Engineering, The Pennsylvania State College.)

the chart, suppose an equilibrium solution to be at 200 lb. per sq. in. abs., 195°F. The molal concentration is seen to be 40 per cent ($x_w = 0.386$), and the partial pressure of water vapor above the solution is 6 lb. per sq. in. abs. The partial pressure of the ammonia vapor is accordingly $200 - 6 = 194$ lb. per sq. in. abs., while the temperature of both water and ammonia vapors is 195°F.

The absorption of anhydrous ammonia liquid by water or by an aqua ammonia solution of low or medium concentration is accompanied by the evolution of heat which is variously termed **heat of absorption, heat of solution, heat of admixture,** etc. Conversely, heat is required in order to separate the components of the solution. The magnitude of the heat of absorption depends upon the concentration of the solvent, and, according to H. Mollier,[1] may be expressed by the equation

$$q = 345(1 - x_w) - 400x_w^2 \qquad (73)$$

in which q is the heat of absorption in Btu per pound of anhydrous ammonia absorbed. In this equation, x_w is evidently the average weight concentration of the absorbing solution since the first fraction of ammonia will be taken up or given off at one concentration and the final fraction at a different one. The arithmetic mean concentration is satisfactory for use in Eq. (73) when the change in concentration during the absorption process is small, but it is obvious that, since the equation is quadratic, the arithmetic mean may be somewhat in error for large ranges of concentration.[2] Mollier's equation is not in close agreement

---

[1] Mollier, Hilde, Lösungswärme von Ammoniak in Wasser, *Mitteilungen über Forschungsarbeiten,* heft 63 and 64, 1909.

[2] The true mean heat of solution, using Mollier's equation, is

$$\frac{\int_{x_1}^{x_2} q\,dx}{x_2 - x_1} = \frac{345\int_{x_1}^{x_2} dx - 345\int_{x_1}^{x_2} x\,dx - 400\int_{x_1}^{x_2} x^2\,dx}{x_2 - x_1}$$

The integral heat of solution, with $x_1 = 0$, therefore is

$$q_{mean} = 345\left(1 - \frac{x_2}{2}\right) - 133.3x_2^2$$

where x_2 is the final weight concentration of the solution.

In actual fact, the use of the arithmetic mean concentration makes so little difference as to be in all probability within the limits of accuracy of the equation itself.

with some later data, but it is simple to use and, being empirical, its correctness will not seriously interfere with the development of the general theory. It will be noticed that this equation becomes zero for an average concentration of approximately 0.594, and it is said that the heat of absorption is zero for all higher concentrations.

The enthalpy of a solution, such as aqua ammonia, where the formation of a new compound is not involved, may be explained by reference to the diagram of Fig. 40. Water, or a weak aqua ammonia solution, is flowing from A, while liquid ammonia is flowing from B. Adiabatic mixing takes place at C resulting in the formation of a solution which leaves at D. Neglecting the kinetic energy of flow, which may be made very small, the

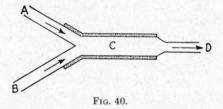

Fig. 40.

relevant energy entering the mixing chamber is composed of the sum of the enthalpies of the liquids from A and B. During the absorption process, the heat of absorption will be evolved, resulting in a considerably elevated temperature at D. The energy leaving the system is the enthalpy of the solution at D, and, since $H_D = H_A + H_B$, it may be seen that the enthalpy of a solution formed adiabatically is the sum of the enthalpies of the liquid constituents *at their original temperatures* irrespective of the temperature of the solution after absorption.

In order to evaluate the enthalpy of an aqua ammonia solution in a more general manner, consider the diagram of Fig. 41. Here the mixing chamber, instead of being adiabatic, is provided with a cooling coil which removes only the heat of absorption. Assume, further, that the liquids at A and B exist at a common temperature lower than the equilibrium temperature of the solution to be formed. Then it is evident, since the heating effect is removed from the system and is not applied to the solution, that the mixing process will be isothermal and that the temperature of the solution at D will be the same as the temperature of the constituents at A and B, or $T_D = T_A = T_B$. Considering 1 lb. of solution with x_w lb. of ammonia liquid at B and $1 - x_w$ lb. of water at A, the energy equation for this case is

$$x_w h_B + (1 - x_w)h_A = h_D + x_w q$$

Expressing the enthalpy of the solution,

$$h_D = x_w h_B + (1 - x_w)h_A - x_w q$$

or for the general case,

$$h_{\text{sol}} = x_w h_f' + (1 - x_w)h_f'' - x_w q \qquad (74)$$

where h_f' is the enthalpy of liquid ammonia, and h_f'' is the enthalpy of water, both at solution temperature. That is, in general, the enthalpy of an aqua ammonia solution is equal to the sum of the enthalpies of the pure liquid constituents, taken at solution

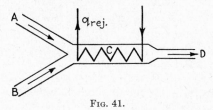

FIG. 41.

temperature, minus the heat of absorption of the solution. The pressures encountered in the ammonia absorption machine are sufficiently low to permit consideration of the enthalpy of each of the pure liquids as a function of the temperature only. In this connection it is convenient to make use of existing tables of thermodynamic properties for water and ammonia. The fact that values in these tables are based, respectively, on 32°F. and −40°F. is immaterial when dealing with enthalpy changes. To demonstrate that the enthalpies of the *liquid* constituents are the properties involved in the enthalpy of the solution, were the ammonia at B in Fig. 40 vapor instead of liquid, and the temperatures still the same at A, B, and D, the heat removed by the cooler would include not only the heat of absorption but also the heat necessary to reduce the ammonia vapor to the liquid phase at the temperature concerned.

The specific volume of aqua ammonia is not exactly the sum of the individual volumes of the liquid constituents. For medium concentrations at moderate temperatures, about 15 per cent of the ammonia liquid present appears to be absorbed within the volume occupied by the water. The specific volume of the solution is thus approximately the volume of the water present plus 85 per cent of the volume of ammonia liquid present, or

$$v_{sol} = 0.85x_w v_f' + (1 - x_w)v_f'' \qquad (75)$$

where v_f' is the specific volume of ammonia liquid and v_f'' is the specific volume of water. In calculating solution volumes it is permissible to use specific volumes of the saturated liquids at the temperature desired. The density, or specific weight, is the reciprocal of the specific volume; and the specific gravity is the ratio of the specific volume of water to that of the solution at the same temperature.

46. Simplified Treatment of Aqua Ammonia Energy Quantities.—The expression in the preceding section representing the enthalpy of ammonia water solutions, Eq. (74), is not well adapted to direct use in engineering problems because of the necessity for calculating the heat of absorption for every concentration encountered. Such heat of absorption being that emitted in bringing the solution from 0 per cent concentration up to the particular strength in question, the finding of enthalpy involves the use, in our case, of Mollier's equation [Eq. (73)] over a wide range of concentrations with the introduction of the error, previously mentioned, incident to using the arithmetic mean concentration. Tabular and graphical representations of solution enthalpies and other properties for various temperatures and concentrations have been recently prepared,[1] but it will be well here to investigate the means for carrying out accurate computations by the use of steam and ammonia tables only. Consider first the simple heating of a solution at constant pressure without change in concentration from condition 1 to condition 2. The energy equation for this process, per pound of solution, is

$$h_{sol1} + Q_{sup} = h_{sol2}$$

[1] Stickney, A. B., Supplement to *Refrigerating Engineering*, vol. 30, no. 4, October, 1935; Jennings, B. H., and F. P. Shannon, *Journal of the A. S. R. E.*, May, 1938.

or

$$x_w h'_{f1} + (1 - x_w)h''_{f1} - x_w q + Q_{sup} = x_w h'_{f2} + (1 - x_w)h''_{f2} - x_w q$$

Expressing the heat supplied,

$$Q_S = x_w h'_{f2} + (1 - x_w)h''_{f2} - x_w q - x_w h'_{f1} - (1 - x_w)h''_{f1} + x_w q$$

Obviously for this case the term $x_w q$ is the same for the outgoing as for the incoming solution, and the equation may be simplified to

$$Q_S = x_w(h'_{f2} - h'_{f1}) + (1 - x_w)(h''_{f2} - h''_{f1})$$

The procedure would, of course, apply equally well to a cooling process. It has thus been rendered unnecessary to deal with the heat of solution in cases of this kind, and the only enthalpies required are those of the liquid constituents. These are readily obtainable from steam and ammonia tables.

In cases where there is a change in concentration, with ammonia either evolved or absorbed, the problem may be solved on the above basis provided the *differential* heat of absorption be taken into account. This is the additional heat of absorption concerned in the distillation or absorption of the quantity of ammonia involved in a decrease or an increase in the concentration of the solution. Since the generator and absorber of the absorption system deal with relatively small ranges of concentration, the differential heat of absorption may be closely approximated by Eq. (73) using the arithmetic mean concentration. As will be seen later, this treatment renders the terms in the energy equations for various parts of the system very easy to determine. In general, in the analysis of the absorption system, it will be convenient to consider the enthalpies of the individual constituents in this manner, taking separate account of the differential heats of solution as they apply.

47. Aqua Ammonia Vapors.—The vapors above an aqua ammonia solution will, as mentioned in a preceding section, be composed of a mixture of water vapor and ammonia vapor at their respective partial pressures. There is no reason for treating this vapor mixture differently from any other vapor mixture except as it may be influenced by the solution beneath it. Inspection of the partial vapor pressures existing above an equilibrium concentration of aqua ammonia and reference to steam and ammonia tables will demonstrate the fact that both vapors are superheated, *i.e.*, the solution temperature exceeds the saturation temperature of either of the constituents and the vapors are thus distilled as superheated vapors. Similarly, the vapors may be absorbed into solution directly from the superheat state without definite intermediate liquefaction.

The accurate determination of the properties of vapor mixtures is dependent upon a knowledge of the partial pressures of the constituent vapors. For aqua ammonia vapors these pressures have been variously determined indirectly by laboratory methods in which the direct results were the total vapor pressure and the proportion of water or ammonia vapor present by weight in a given mixture. From the weight concentrations so determined, the molal proportions are easily calculated and from these, in turn, the partial pressures were computed by the use of Avogadro's and Dalton's laws. However, since these laws are strictly valid for ideal gases alone,[1] the partial pressures found in this manner are only approximate and may be in considerable error in regions of high vapor pressure. This fault applies to the data from which partial pressures were plotted in the chart presented with this chapter. For the sake of illustrating the principles, it will nevertheless be assumed that the partial pressures indicated on the chart are correct.

With the basic partial pressure data known, the specific volume of each constituent may be found from tables. The inverse ratio of specific volumes is then the ratio of weights of the respective vapors present. As an example, consider an equilibrium vapor mixture at 110 lb. per sq. in. abs., 210°F. From the chart, the partial pressure of the water vapor is 10 lb. abs. The partial pressure of the ammonia vapor is therefore $110 - 10 = 100$ lb. abs. Specific volume of water vapor at 10 lb. and 210°F. is 38.97 cu. ft. per lb. Specific volume of ammonia vapor at 100 lb. and 210°F. is 4.09 cu. ft. per lb.

$$\text{Lb. of ammonia vapor per lb. water vapor} = \frac{38.97}{4.09} = 9.53$$

---

[1] Avogadro's and Dalton's laws may also be applied without appreciable error to vapors under certain low pressure conditions when perfect gas characteristics are simulated.

or

$$\text{Lb. water vapor per lb. ammonia vapor} = \frac{4.09}{38.97} = 0.105$$

In a similar manner, the enthalpy of each constituent vapor may be found for use in energy equations, and with total quantities known, it is unnecessary to combine these into an expression of enthalpy per unit weight of the vapor mixture. In general, other properties than those mentioned will not be required.

48. The Practical Ammonia Absorption System.—The ammonia absorption system shown in Fig. 38 was said to be of the simplest form. That is, it possessed only the bare essentials for none too satisfactory operation. There are two principal drawbacks to the use of a basic system of this kind, both of which may be satisfactorily corrected by the addition of relatively simple apparatus.

It has been seen that the vapors distilled from an aqua ammonia solution contain a considerable amount of water vapor. The vaporization occurring in the generator would thus pass on to the condenser a large quantity of water vapor with the ammonia. This would result in the formation, in the condenser, of an aqua ammonia solution of high concentration which would continue through the system as the refrigerant instead of the dry ammonia desired. It is impracticable to attempt to remove all of the water vapor from the mixture, but all except a very small fraction may be condensed out or absorbed by the simple process of cooling. In the generator vapors, the ammonia vapor is superheated to a considerably greater degree than is the water vapor, which would indicate that, in cooling, the water vapor would be the first to condense, followed, if the temperature were carried low enough, by ammonia vapor. A trial calculation would show that only a negligible quantity of water vapor would remain in a mixture cooled to not less than 20° above the saturation temperature of the ammonia. A moment's thought, however, will show that the process of dehydration of the vapors is not so straightforward as this. The water condensate will immediately seek to form a solution of equilibrium concentration for the existing temperature and pressure and, in so doing, will absorb the requisite quantity of ammonia vapor. The condensate, or drip, leaving any cooler which may be interposed between the generator and the condenser will thus be an aqua ammonia solution. Furthermore, owing to the high pressure and relatively low temperature existing in such a cooler, the concentration will be high. The cooling process accordingly condenses, in effect, both water and ammonia from the vapors—considerably more of the latter than of the former. In the ultimate analysis, it is simply the fact that there happens to be a greater preponderance of ammonia present in the vapor mixture than in the drip that makes dehydration possible by means of cooling alone.

Two different types of vapor coolers are usually used in series. The first is of the "open" type utilizing the comparatively cool strong solution from the absorber, just before it enters the generator, to cool the outgoing vapors by direct contact. This has the additional beneficial effect of preheating the strong aqua and of distilling some ammonia from it. This first cooler, called an **analyzer,** is incorporated with or placed near to the generator. The second cooler through which the vapors are made to pass is of the "closed" type, is liquid-cooled, and is called a **rectifier** or **dehydrator.** This provides the final drying effect and, under favorable conditions, delivers practically anhydrous ammonia to the condenser. The drip from the rectifier is returned to the generator by way of the analyzer.

The second of the two principal improvements mentioned in the first paragraph concerns the conservation of heat within the system. It should be appreciated that, as heat must be constantly supplied in the generator to maintain the high temperature desired during evaporation, so heat must be constantly withdrawn from the absorber in order to maintain the lower temperature desired for the formation of the strong solution. With consideration given to this, it becomes evident that, in the basic system, the hot weak solution from the generator must be cooled in the absorber while the cool strong solution from the absorber must be heated in the generator in addition to the legitimate functions of these units. This constitutes an unproductive heating and cooling load of considerable magnitude which is highly detrimental to good economy. The obvious remedy lies in an exchange of heat between the weak and the strong solutions whereby the one will be heated by the cooling of the other. Such an interchange of heat is made to take place through a heating, or cooling, surface in a heat exchanger which is customarily called simply an **exchanger.** Complete conservation of the sensible heat of the solutions cannot be realized in practice, but a sufficient saving may be made to render the exchanger very effective.

The schematic layout of an absorption system incorporating the additions mentioned is shown in Fig. 42. A weak aqua cooler is frequently used between the exchanger and the absorber to further cool the solution by water, but this cooling load may, for our purpose, be combined with that of the absorber without individual treatment.

Because of the higher input of motive energy, the cooling water load is much heavier in the absorption system than in a compres-

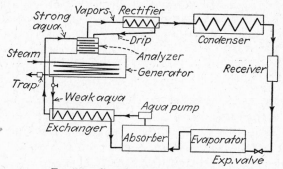

Fig. 42.—Complete absorption system.

sion machine of the same refrigerating capacity. This encourages the use of series water connections between some of the parts in an attempt to reduce the quantity of water necessary by increasing the effective temperature rise. The fact that the portions of the system which require cooling operate at different temperatures lends itself to the plan. The condenser will usually receive water first, after which the water will be directed through the rectifier or the absorber or both in the required quantities.

It will be preferable from this point to deal separately with the major parts of the system. In each case, that portion of the solution of the following example which applies will be carried out.

Example.—An ammonia absorption refrigerating system is to have a capacity of 100 tons. The cooling water temperature is such that a condenser pressure of 170 lb. abs. exists. The brine temperature requires an evaporator pressure of 30 lb. abs.

Pressures throughout the system are as follows: generator, 175 lb. abs.; rectifier entrance, 174 lb. abs.; rectifier exit, 171 lb. abs.; absorber, 29 lb. abs.; aqua pump suction, 25 lb. abs.; aqua pump discharge, 185 lb. abs.

Temperatures are as follows: generator, 220°F.; vapors and drip from rectifier, 110°; liquid from condenser and to expansion valve, 76°; evaporator exit, 10°; weak aqua from exchanger and to absorber, 100°; strong aqua from absorber, 80°.

The aqua pump handles 570 lb. of strong aqua per minute. Steam is supplied to the generator coils at 20 lb. abs., dry saturated.

Calculate: (*a*) The heat supplied to the generator, and the heat removed from absorber, rectifier, and condenser in Btu per pound of anhydrous ammonia circulated, Btu per minute per ton, and Btu per minute; (*b*) the pump horsepower required, per ton and total, if the combined hydraulic and mechanical efficiency is 65 per cent; (*c*) the pump piston displacement, cubic feet per minute per ton and cubic feet per minute, with 20 per cent slip; (*d*) pounds of steam required per minute per ton and per minute; (*e*) an energy balance on the system on the basis of Btu per minute per ton.

Absorber.—The absorber consists essentially of a vessel containing cooling water coils or tubes. In operation, the absorber is filled with aqua ammonia solution. The weak aqua and the gas from the evaporator are introduced at the bottom, and the strong aqua is removed from the top. The flow diagram is shown in Fig. 43 in which the weak aqua at *A* has come from the exchanger, the ammonia at *B* is from the evaporator, and the strong aqua at *C* is going to the pump. The weak aqua concentration depends upon the temperature and pressure to which it was subjected in the generator and will be an equilibrium solution for those conditions. If sufficient time were allowed in the absorber for the complete absorption of ammonia, the strong solution would leave with equilibrium concentration. In practice, however, the full strength is seldom reached, and the strong aqua leaves with a somewhat lower ammonia content than would correspond to the conditions. The small amount of water vapor which enters with the ammonia from the evaporator will be neglected in calculations for the evaporator and absorber.

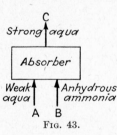

Fig. 43.

Three equations may be written which deal with the mass flow through the absorber.   These are

$$M_A + M_B = M_C$$

for the total quantity passing;

$$x_{wA}M_A + M_B = x_{wC}M_C$$

for the ammonia alone; and

$$(1 - x_{wA})M_A = (1 - x_{wC})M_C$$

for the water.   The unknowns are usually either M_A and M_C or x_{wC}, depending upon the data given.   By solving two of the above equations simultaneously, either of these cases may be satisfied.   In solving for the strong aqua,

$$M_C = \frac{(1 - x_{wA})M_B}{x_{wC} - x_{wA}} \tag{76}$$

or, for the weak aqua,

$$M_A = \frac{(1 - x_{wC})M_B}{x_{wC} - x_{wA}} \tag{77}$$

and, for the concentration of the strong aqua,

$$x_{wC} = \frac{x_{wA}M_A + M_B}{M_C} \tag{78}$$

In working with the energy quantities it will be convenient, as previously suggested, to deal with the individual components rather than with solutions or mixtures as such.   Letting the primed symbols represent ammonia in the solution or mixture and double-primed symbols represent the water, the energy equation for the absorber is

$$x_{wA}M_A h_A' + (1 - x_{wA})M_A h_A'' + M_B h_B + M_B q = x_{wC}M_C h_C' +$$
$$(1 - x_{wC})M_C h_C'' + Q_R$$

or, more simply,

$$M_A' h_A' + M_A'' h_A'' + M_B h_B + M_B q = M_C' h_C' + M_C'' h_C'' + Q_R$$

and, for the heat rejected to the cooling water,

$$Q_R = M_A' h_A' + M_A'' h_A'' + M_B h_B + M_B q - M_C' h_C' - M_C'' h_C'' \tag{79}$$

In this equation, the enthalpies at A and C are those of the particular liquids at their existing temperatures, and q is the differential heat of absorption for which the average concentration is used as before explained.

Solution (For absorber).—For application to all parts of the problem:

Enthalpy of liquid entering the expansion valve at 76°F. = 127.4
Enthalpy of vapor leaving evaporator at 30 lb. and 10°F. = 617.8
Refrigerating effect per lb. of ammonia = 617.8 − 127.4 = 490.4 Btu
Lb. of anhydrous ammonia per min. per ton = $\dfrac{200}{490.4}$ = 0.408
Lb. of anhydrous ammonia per min. = 0.408(100) = 40.8

For the following, refer to Fig. 43 for notation.

M_B = 40.8 lb. per min., or 0.408 lb. per min. per ton
M_C = 570 lb. per min., or 5.7 lb. per min. per ton, or 14 lb. per lb. anhydrous ammonia
M_A = 570 − 40.8 = 529.2 lb. per min., or 5.29 lb. per min. per ton, or 13 lb. per lb. anhydrous ammonia
t_A = 100°F.; h'_A = 155.2; h''_A = 68; t_C = 80°F.; h'_C = 132; h'' = 48; h_B at 30 lb., 10°F. = 617.8.

From generator conditions (175 lb., 220°F.), x_{mA} = 0.32.

$$x_{wA} = \frac{0.32(17)}{0.32(17) + 0.68(18)} = 0.308$$
$$x_{wC} = \frac{0.308(13) + 1}{(14)} = 0.357$$

Average concentration = $\dfrac{0.308 + 0.357}{2}$ = 0.3325

q = 345(0.6675) − 400(0.3325)^2 = 185.7 Btu per lb. of anhydrous ammonia absorbed
M'_A = 0.308(13) = 4 lb. per lb. anhydrous ammonia
M''_A = M'_A = 9 lb. per lb. anhydrous ammonia
M'_C = 5 lb. per lb. anhydrous ammonia
Q_R = 4(155.2) + 9(68) + 617.8 + 185.7 − 5(132) − 9(48) = 944.3 Btu per lb. anhydrous ammonia, or 944.3(0.408) = 385.3 Btu per min. per ton, or 944.3(40.8) = 38,527 Btu per min.

Aqua Pump.—The work input necessary to drive the aqua pump, whether of the reciprocating or centrifugal type, is the sum of the energies required to overcome mechanical friction and hydraulic losses, and to force the desired quantity of solution against the existing head.   In the absorption system the aqua pump will be required to operate against a head considerably in excess of the pressure difference between the generator and the absorber owing to the fluid friction introduced in the exchanger, piping, and valves.   The velocity head may usually be neglected.

The power representing the useful work actually done upon the fluid may be termed the hydraulic horsepower, and the ratio of this to the power input to the pump is the combined hydraulic and mechanical efficiency.   The hydraulic work is simply the product of the weight of fluid pumped and the head expressed in feet of fluid, or

$$W = M \times H$$

Since the head is customarily expressed in pounds per square inch, it is necessary to know the specific volume or density of the fluid in order to make the conversion to feet.   If the fluid be considered as incompressible and v is the specific volume, then the density d is $1/v$ and the head in feet

$$H = Pv = 144pv = \frac{144p}{d}$$

where p is the head in pounds per square inch.   The work is

$$W = 144Mpv = \frac{144Mp}{d} \tag{80}$$

Since the pressure head p is the difference between the discharge pressure p_d and the suction pressure p_s, Eq. (80) obviously becomes also

$$W = 144M(p_d - p_s)v = \frac{144M(p_d - p_s)}{d} \tag{81}$$

Expressing M in pounds per minute, the equation for hydraulic horsepower is

$$\text{Hp.} = \frac{144M(p_d - p_s)v}{33,000} = \frac{144M(p_d - p_s)}{33,000d} \tag{82}$$

In reciprocating pumps the liquid delivered is theoretically equivalent in volume to the piston or plunger displacement but actually a lesser quantity is discharged.   The difference between theoretical and actual volumetric discharge expressed in terms of the piston displacement is called **slip** which is thus the proportion of the displacement which is unproductive insofar as the output of the pump is concerned.

Solution (For aqua pump):

The weight of strong aqua to be pumped is given as 570 lb. per min.
$x_w = 0.357$; $p_d = 185$ lb. abs.; $p_s = 25$ lb. abs.
v_f' at 80°F. = 0.0267; v_f'' at 80°F. = 0.0161.

From Eq. (75),

$v_{sol} = 0.85(0.357)(0.0267) + 0.643(0.0161) = 0.0184$ cu. ft. per lb.

Hydraulic hp. $= \dfrac{144(570)(185 - 25)(0.0184)}{33,000} = 7.33$

Hp. input $= \dfrac{7.33}{0.65} = 11.3$ or 0.113 hp. per ton

Piston displacement $= \dfrac{570(0.0184)}{0.8} = 13.1$ cu. ft. per min., or 0.131 cu. ft. per min. per ton.

Heat equivalent of the work input to the aqua pump, $AW = 11.3(42.4)$ = 479 Btu per min., or 4.79 Btu per min. per ton, or 11.7 Btu per lb. anhydrous ammonia.

Of the energy supplied to drive the pump, all but a fraction of that converted to heat by mechanical friction is represented in the strong aqua by an increase in enthalpy. Although this increase is small per pound of solution, it becomes noticeable when expressed in energy units per minute or per minute per ton, or when appearing in an energy balance for the system. In the exchanger calculations which follow in the next section, it will be noted that the enthalpy of the strong aqua leaving the absorber has been augmented by the heat equivalent of the pump work before entering the exchanger. This is assuming that all of the energy input to the pump is taken up by the liquid.

Exchanger.—The exchanger may be of either the double pipe or the shell and coil type. In any case, the counterflow principle will be utilized in order to provide a more complete heat interchange. For the sake of simplicity, a double pipe exchanger is shown diagrammatically in Fig. 44 with the weak aqua from the generator flowing through the inner pipe and with the strong aqua from the absorber passing through the annular space between the pipes. The strong solution, in addition to having the higher heat capacity pound for pound, is also greater in quantity than the weak aqua; therefore, with a perfect heat exchanger, temperature equalization would occur at AB and not at CD. In the actual exchanger the temperature difference at AB is dependent upon the extent of the surface provided and on the coefficient of heat transfer.

The weight relationships for the exchanger are simple since there is no change in concentration of either fluid. The weights at A and at D are equal, both total fluid and components, and the same relation holds for the weights at B and C.

The process for the weak solution is that of simple cooling. The heating of the strong aqua, however, may be accompanied by vaporization of a small portion of the constituents if the temperature is carried high enough. This will tend to repress

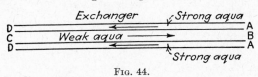

Fig. 44.

the temperature rise of the strong aqua and will make the final temperature somewhat difficult to predict. When this temperature is desired it may be found by trial and error, but in problems involving energy quantities alone the temperature is unimportant so long as the energy of the solution leaving the exchanger may be determined for application to the generator. This may be done, irrespective of any vaporization which may occur, by adding to the energy of the strong aqua entering the exchanger the heat removed from the weak aqua. Since in the strong aqua the relative quantities of ammonia and water have not changed during the heating, the heat of absorption need not be considered until the generator calculations are carried out.

The energy equation is

$$M_C' h_C' + M_C'' h_C'' + M_A' h_A' + M_A'' h_A'' = M_B' h_B' + M_B'' h_B'' + M_D' h_D' + M_D'' h_D''$$

or

$$M_D' h_D' + M_D'' h_D'' = M_C' h_C' + M_C'' h_C'' + M_A' h_A' + M_A'' h_A'' - M_B' h_B' - M_B'' h_B'' \quad (83)$$

where $M_D' h_D' + M_D'' h_D''$ may be considered as the energy of the strong solution entering the analyzer if the differential heat of absorption be subsequently taken into account. The heat exchanged through the surface

$$Q = M'_C h'_C + M''_C h''_C - M'_B h'_B - M''_B h''_B = M'_{CB}(h'_C - h'_B) + M''_{CB}(h''_C - h''_B) \quad (84)$$

Solution (For exchanger):

Per lb. of anhydrous ammonia circulated in the system, $M'_A = M'_D = 5$ lb.; $M'_C = M'_B = 4$ lb.; $M''_A = M''_D = M''_C = M''_B = 9$ lb. h'_f at 80°F. $= 132$; h''_f at 80°F. $= 48$.

$M'_A h'_f + M''_A h''_f$ at absorber exit $= 5(132) + 9(48) = 1092$ Btu per lb. anhydrous ammonia

The work input to the aqua pump, AW (from pump computation) $= 11.7$ Btu per lb. anhydrous ammonia

$M'_A h'_A + M''_A h''_A = 1092 + 11.7 = 1103.7$ Btu per lb. anhydrous ammonia. $h'_B = 155.2$; $h''_B = 68$.

At generator temperature, 220°F., $h'_C = 313$; $h''_C = 188.1$

$M'_D h'_D + M''_D h''_D = 4(313) + 9(188.1) + 1103.7 - 4(155.2) - 9(68) = 2816$ Btu per lb. anhydrous ammonia, or 1149 Btu per min. per ton, or 114,890 Btu per min. (This is determined solely for use in generator calculations.) The heat transferred through the exchanger surface from weak to strong aqua: $Q = 4(313 - 155.2) + 9(188.1 - 68) = 1712$ Btu per lb. anhydrous ammonia, or 698 Btu per min. per ton, or 69,800 Btu per min.

Analyzer.—The analyzer is a direct contact heat exchanger which serves to further preheat the strong aqua before entrance to the generator by cooling the vapors leaving the generator and thus dehydrating them to a certain extent. The analyzer may be integral with the generator, *i.e.*, built into the generator structure, or it may be external to or separate from the generator. Irrespective of type, the analyzer consists of a series of trays over which the strong aqua and the rectifier drip, introduced at the top, flow by gravity counter to the flow of vapors. In this manner, by exposing a large solution surface to the vapors, a good transfer of heat is effected. After passing through the analyzer, the vapors go to the rectifier for more complete dehydration while the strong aqua is introduced to the generator for further heating.

Because the weight of strong aqua is several times that of the vapors and because the specific heat of the solution is more than double that of the vapors, the cooling effect on the latter is considerably greater, measured in temperature, than is the heating effect on the solution. Depending upon the efficiency of the analyzer, a temperature difference between incoming solution and outgoing vapors of from 10 to 20° may be had or, in cases where the exchanger is functioning very effectively, less than 10°. The vapors leaving will closely approximate equilibrium conditions for the pressure and temperature since there is continuous contact with the solution at nearly the same temperature. The effect of the analyzer on the vapors is to progressively increase the ammonia content and reduce the proportion of water vapor, while the concentration of the strong aqua is, of course, at the same time also somewhat reduced.

In the solution of problems, it is convenient and satisfactory to regard the generator and analyzer as a single unit. Viewed in this way, the analyzer affects the calculations for the generator simply by reducing the quantity of energy leaving in the vapors, decreasing by an equivalent amount the heat to be supplied.

That part of the solution to the illustrative problem which concerns the analyzer alone is confined to the determination of the properties of the vapors leaving.

Solution (For the analyzer).—The temperature of the strong aqua leaving the exchanger and entering the analyzer may be estimated as 180–190°. The temperature of the vapors at analyzer exit may therefore be taken as 200°F.

Properties of vapors:

Pressure = 175 lb. per sq. in. abs.
Partial pressure of water vapor = 7 lb. abs.
Partial pressure of ammonia vapor = 168 lb. abs.
Temperature of both = 200°F.
For the water vapor, $h = 1147.9$, $v = 55.69$.
For the ammonia vapor, $h = 706.7$, $v = 2.334$.

Ammonia vapor per lb. water vapor $= \dfrac{55.69}{2.334} = 23.9$ lb.

Rectifier.—The generator-analyzer division of the problem cannot be considered until the quantity of the vapors leaving the analyzer and the quantity and concentration of the drip returning to it are determined. These quantities are found by analysis of the rectifier which must therefore be discussed next.

The essential function of the rectifier is to cool the vapors from the analyzer by circulating water until only a very small fraction of water vapor remains.   The double pipe design is very effective for cooling, but shell and coil or shell and tube types may also be used.   The vapors are progressively water-cooled until a solution begins to form.   This solution is carried along with the vapors and by gravity while further cooling takes place, and the solution grows in quantity as water vapor and ammonia vapor are condensed to form it.   The states of the vapors going to the condenser and of the drip returning to the analyzer depend, for any given pressure, upon the ultimate temperature to which the vapors are reduced in the rectifier.   Since the final cooling is carried on with vapors and liquid in contact, both will leave in an equilibrium state for the existing pressure and temperature. At the usual rectifier pressures, which are slightly higher than

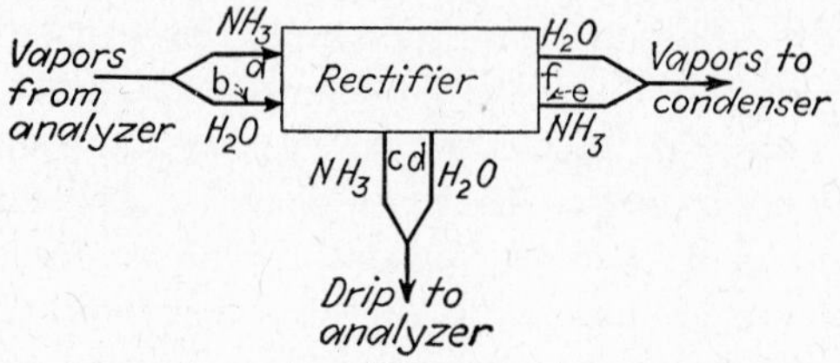

Fig. 45.

those in the condenser owing to flow resistance, temperatures of 100 to 120°F. will produce sufficiently dry ammonia for most cases.   If the cooling be carried too far, an excessive amount of ammonia will be returned in the drip, and while the dehydration will be more complete, there will not be sufficient practical improvement to warrant the additional heat consumption.   The rectifier is usually followed by a mechanical separator or trap whose function is to remove the last traces of entrained moisture from the vapors.   In some rectifier designs the drip is removed at several points so as to prevent excessive accumulation of liquid at the exit.   This also results in a lower drip concentration.

The rectifier flow diagram is shown in Fig. 45.   Three combined quantities are involved, the vapors from the analyzer, the drip to the analyzer, and the vapors to the condenser.   In the diagram, these quantities are shown as divided into their respective components.   Thus in the vapors entering, a represents ammonia and b water vapor; in the drip leaving, c is ammonia and d is water; and, at the vapor exit, ammonia vapor is at e and water vapor at f. The weights at each of these points will be determined first.

From analyzer data, the weight ratio of ammonia to water vapor in the mixture entering the rectifier M_a/M_b is known. The exit pressure and temperature, assuming all of the drip to leave at this point, determine the concentration x_m and x_w of the solution, and the weight concentration may be expressed as $M_c/(M_c + M_d)$. From this, the weight ratio of ammonia to water, M_c/M_d, may be found by

$$\frac{M_c}{M_d} = \frac{x_w}{1 - x_w}$$

Similarly, from exit pressure and temperature, the partial pressures of ammonia and water vapor in the vapors leaving may be determined. These permit the properties to be found and, from the specific volumes, the weight ratio M_e/M_f. Now the quantity of ammonia M_e passing to the condenser must be the same as that passing through the evaporator and returning to the absorber and is therefore known. This permits M_f to be immediately solved for. The weight relationships for the respective fluids are

$$M_a = M_c + M_e \tag{85}$$

for the ammonia, and

$$M_b = M_d + M_f \tag{86}$$

for the water and water vapor, in which both M_e and M_f are known for any particular case. With the ratios M_a/M_b and M_c/M_d also known, either of the foregoing equations can be written in the terms of the other, and by solving simultaneously, any one of the four unknown quantities may be found and the remaining three then easily determined. In the example which follows, the method of solving first for M_d is thus only one of four possible procedures in the solution of the problem, but for the sake of accuracy when a slide rule is used, it may be preferable to solve for the smallest quantity first.

The energy quantities for the rectifier may be handled in the customary manner, treating the various components individually. The heat of absorption associated with the formation of the solution must in this instance be used in its entirety because the solution is entirely formed within the rectifier. The error involved in taking the average concentration over a wide range, as in this case, has before been mentioned, but for the rectifier, the quantity is relatively small and the average may be so taken for simplicity without vitally affecting the results. When aqua ammonia concentrations exceed 0.594, the ammonia absorbed above this concentration supposedly produces no heat of absorption. Therefore, in dealing with the formation of a solution from the pure constituents, the average concentration as used in Mollier's equation cannot exceed 0.594/2 or 0.297 for that portion of the ammonia which produces heat of absorption, and for the remainder of the ammonia, with the solution above a weight concentration of 0.594, there will be no heat of absorption. It thus becomes necessary, in calculating the heat of absorption for a strong solution, to apply the heat of absorption for an average concentration of 0.297 to that quantity of ammonia M_x which will give a solution strength of 0.594 and to ignore the heat of absorption for any additional ammonia which may go into solution above this concentration. This will be demonstrated in the example which follows shortly. The rectifier energy equation is

$$M_a h_a + M_b h_b + M_x q = M_c h_c + M_d h_d + M_e h_e + M_f h_f + Q_R$$

or

$$Q_R = M_a h_a + M_b h_b + M_x q - M_c h_c - M_d h_d - M_e h_e -$$
$$M_f h_f \quad (87)$$

Solution (For the rectifier):

The known data are: at rectifier exit, $p = 171$ lb. per sq. in. abs., $t = 110°F.$, x_m (drip) $= 0.68$, partial pressure of water vapor $= 0.36$ lb. abs., $M_e = 40.8$ lb. per min.; and $M_a/M_b = 23.9$, or $M_a = 23.9 M_b$.

Weight concentration of drip, $x_w = \dfrac{0.68(17)}{0.68(17) + 0.32(18)} = 0.666$

$\dfrac{M_c}{M_d} = \dfrac{0.666}{0.334} = 2.0$, or $M_c = 2M_d$

Partial pressure of ammonia vapor at exit $= 170.64$ lb. abs

Specific volume of ammonia vapor at exit, $v_e = 1.88$

Specific volume of water vapor at exit $= 944$

$\dfrac{M_e}{M_f} = \dfrac{944}{1.88} = 501$ $\qquad M_f = \dfrac{40.8}{501} = 0.0813$ lb. per min.

Expressing Eq. (85) in terms of M_b and M_d,

$$23.9M_b = 2M_d + 40.8$$

From Eq. (86),

$$M_b = M_d + 0.0813$$

Solving simultaneously,

$M_d = 1.774$ lb. per min.
$M_b = 1.774 + 0.0813 = 1.855$ lb. per min.; $M_a = 1.855(23.9) =$
44.335 lb. per min.; $M_c = 44.335 - 40.8 = 3.535$ lb. per min.
For the energy quantities: $h_a = 706.7$; $h_b = 1147.9$; $h_c = 167$;
$h_d = 77.94$; $h_e = 648.9$; $h_f = 1111$. $q = 345(1 - 0.297) - 400(0.297)^2$
$= 207$ Btu per lb. ammonia absorbed up to a concentration of 0.594.

Ammonia absorbed to bring concentration to $0.594 = 0.594(1.774)/$
$0.406 = 2.594$ lb. per min. $= M_x$. Remaining ammonia has no heat of
absorption.

$Q_R = 44.335(706.7) + 1.855(1147.9) + 2.594(207) - 3.535(167) -$
$1.774(77.9) - 40.8(648.9) - 0.0813(1111) = 6704$ Btu per min., or
67 Btu per min. per ton, or 164.2 Btu per lb. of anhydrous ammonia
circulated.

It may be argued that, insofar as both weight and energy are
concerned, the water vapor leaving the rectifier may be neglected.
Considering the present uncertainty of data on aqua ammonia
solutions and vapors, it is undoubtedly true that the inclusion
of this small quantity in the calculations appears to be an
attempt at accuracy well beyond both the limits attained in the
determination of experimental data and the accuracy of computation.   Nevertheless, the exposition of underlying theory may be
undertaken with but meager information, and the application of
that theory will later be improved in accuracy as the data become
available.   Inconsistencies of this character should therefore be
overlooked in the numerical example presented in this chapter.

Generator.—The generator is the still or boiler for the system.
It consists of a shell with suitable connections for the introduction
and withdrawal of fluids and, when in operation, is partially
filled with aqua ammonia solution.   Heat is usually supplied by
low pressure steam which is passed into coils or tubes built
into the generator beneath the liquid level.   At the outlet, the
steam coil is provided with a trap which permits the passage of
condensate only.

As stated earlier, the analyzer will be considered in calculations as a part of the generator and the two treated as an integral unit. The strong aqua and the drip enter the generator by way of the analyzer from the exchanger and the rectifier, respectively, and the vapors depart for the rectifier by way of the analyzer. The weak aqua is taken from the bottom of the generator usually as far as possible from the point where the strong aqua is introduced. The generator action, like that in the absorber but in the reverse direction, is simply a process for the restoration of equilibrium in the solution. The aqua ammonia from the exchanger, being too strong for the generator conditions, is rapidly reduced in ammonia content until an equilibrium concentration

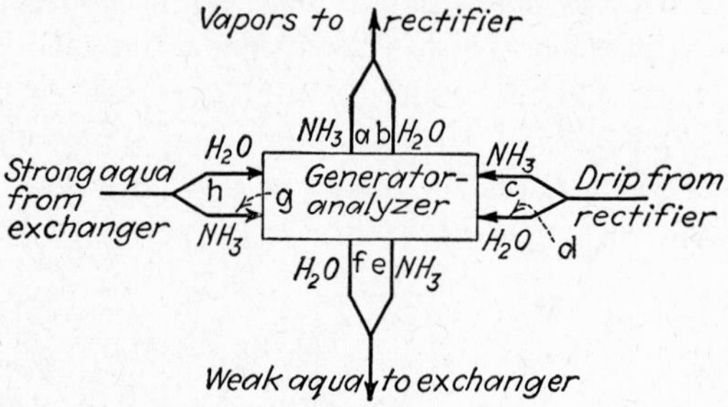

Fig. 46.

is established. This is as far as the process may be carried, and the solution is then removed to be subjected to the reverse action in the absorber.

In the flow diagram of Fig. 46, the fluids entering and leaving the generator-analyzer system are clearly indicated. As usual, the constituents will be separately treated, and in the diagram, a, c, e, and g represent ammonia while b, d, f, and h are water or water vapor. It will be noted that all of the quantities are known, by the time the generator calculations are made, because of their having previously been found when considering other parts of the system. It will therefore not be necessary to compute weights. All enthalpies are likewise known from previous work. The evaluation of the differential heat of absorption involved in the distillation of ammonia in the generator is complicated by the incoming solutions, strong aqua and drip, being of different concentrations, but the computations can be simplified by treating each quantity separately in the following manner. The entire quantity of drip may be regarded as being vaporized in the generator, and the heat of absorption will be the same for the distillation as it was in the rectifier for the formation of the solution. This will have already been calculated for the rectifier and can be used in the generator energy equation to represent this portion of the generator heat of absorption. The remainder concerns only the separation of ammonia from the strong aqua for which the differential heat of absorption will be calculated for an average concentration between the strong solution entering and the weak aqua leaving. The quantity considered as being taken from the strong aqua is, of course, equivalent to the anhydrous ammonia circulated in the system. The heat of absorption to be supplied in the generator is thus the heat of absorption for the rectifier solution $M_x q_{rect}$ plus the differential heat of solution for the ammonia quantity taken from the strong aqua $(M_a - M_c)q_{gen}$, where q_{gen} is derived from the average concentration of the strong and weak aqua. The total quantity will be represented in the energy equation by Mq, so that

$$Mq = M_x q_{rect} + (M_a - M_c)q_{gen}$$

It will be remembered that, in the exchanger calculations, the sum of the enthalpies of the strong aqua components was found for direct application to the generator. This value may be substituted for the expression $(M_g h_g + M_h h_h)$ in the energy equation.

The combined generator-analyzer energy equation is

$$(M_g h_g + M_h h_h) + M_c h_c + M_d h_d + Q_s = M_a h_a + M_b h_b + M_e h_e + M_f h_f + Mq$$

or

$$Q_s = M_a h_a + M_b h_b + M_e h_e + M_f h_f + Mq - (M_g h_g + M_h h_h) - M_c h_c - M_d h_d \qquad (88)$$

in which the energy quantity $(M_g h_g + M_h h_h)$ is found from exchanger data.

Solution (For the generator):

From exchanger data:

$M_g h_g + M_h h_h = 114,890$ Btu per min.; $M_e h_e = 40.8(4)(313) =$ 51,080 Btu per min.; $M_f h_f = 40.8(9)(188.1) = 69,070$ Btu per min.

From rectifier data:

$M_a h_a = 44.335(706.7) = 31,330$ Btu per min.; $M_b h_b = 1.855(1147.9)$
$= 2,130$ Btu per min.; $M_c h_c = 3.535(167) = 590$ Btu per min.; $M_d h_d =$
$1.774(77.9) = 138$ Btu per min.; $M_x q_{\text{rect}} = 537$ Btu per min.

Average generator concentration, $x_w = \dfrac{0.357 + 0.308}{2} = 0.3325$

$q_{\text{gen}} = 345(0.6675) - 400(0.3325)^2 = 185.7$ Btu per lb. anhydrous
ammonia circulated

$Mq = 537 + 40.8(185.7) = 8114$ Btu per min.

$Q_s = 31,330 + 2130 + 51,080 + 69,070 + 8114 - 114,890 - 590 -$
$138 = 46,106$ Btu per min., or 461 Btu per min. per ton, or 1130 Btu
per lb. anhydrous ammonia.

Steam consumption:

Assuming the condensate to leave at 220°F.; h at 20 lb. abs., dry,
$= 1156.3$; h_f at 220°F. $= 188.1$.

Steam consumption $= \dfrac{46,106}{1156.3 - 188.1} = 47.62$ lb. per min., or 0.476

lb. per min. per ton

In completing the example, an energy balance is to be made
for the system. The condenser is the only part which has not
been computed. This is done in the usual way except that, the
evaporation of the water vapor having been accounted for in
the generator, the condensation of the water vapor should be
considered in the condenser. This same quantity of water
passes through the evaporator and the absorber but is neglected
in those cases because the individual computations are insensitive
to the small amount involved.

The energy balance then consists simply of a balance between
the summation of the energies into and out of the system from or
to an outside source. The balance may be made on any basis
desired. In the present case, the basis is to be Btu per minute
per ton capacity.

Solution (Condenser, and system energy balance):

Condenser:

For the ammonia entering, h (from rectifier) $= 648.9$
For the ammonia leaving, h_f at 76°F. $= 127.4$
For the water vapor entering, h (from rectifier) $= 1111$
For the water leaving, h_f at 76°F. $= 44$

$$Q_R = 40.8(648.9 - 127.4) + 0.0813(1111 - 44) = 21,364 \text{ Btu per}$$
$$\text{min., or } 213.6 \text{ Btu per min. per ton}$$

Energy balance:

Part of system	Energy into system, Btu per min. per ton	Energy out of system, Btu per min. per ton
Absorber...............		385.3
Aqua Pump............	4.8	
Rectifier...............		67
Generator.............	461	
Condenser.............		213.6
Evaporator...........	200.0	
Total...............	665.8	665.9

Reviewing the ammonia absorption system in the light of the numerical example, it may be seen that this type of machine requires approximately seven times the energy input for a given refrigerating capacity that the compression machine needs. The quantity of energy alone, however, is hardly a reasonable criterion for comparison because the compression machine consumes high grade energy while the absorption system may utilize almost entirely relatively low grade energy. It would obviously be uneconomical to operate an absorption machine on an input of electrical energy, but it might prove the more economical system when the energy is obtainable from a low cost source such as low pressure exhaust or process steam, or cheap fuel.

The cooling water load, measured in heat units to be disposed of, is about $2\frac{1}{2}$ times as heavy in the absorption as in the compression machine. But because of the possibility of using the water through a considerably greater temperature range in the absorption system, there is not such a disparity in actual cooling water consumption, although this will always be heavier than for a compression system under comparable conditions.

Concerning the actual operation, the absorption machine undoubtedly demands more careful attention than the compression system. This applies to the regulation of load and to the general care required in more frequent purging, in the prevention of corrosion, and in checking solution strength and vapor rectification.

For reasons given earlier, the discussion in this chapter centers mainly about the ammonia absorption machine.   While it is true that the ammonia-water system is at present of the greatest importance in industrial units, there are many substances which might be used in combination in a system operating on the continuous absorption principle.[1]   While few of these substances have ever been in practical use, machines using other than ammonia and water have been and are being developed.[2]   In general, the principles outlined in the foregoing discussion will apply to the various possible solvent-refrigerant combinations.

49. Three-fluid Absorption System.—The elimination of the aqua pump from the absorption machine would produce a system with a complete absence of moving parts and work input.   This is the purpose of the three-fluid absorption system which employs a refrigerant, a solvent, and an inert gas.   The inert gas is confined to the low side of the system, *i.e.*, to the evaporator and absorber and, by its presence, makes possible a uniform total pressure throughout the system while, at the same time, permitting the refrigerant to evaporate at a low temperature corresponding to its partial pressure.   In the high side there exists only the refrigerant, with the usual trace of solvent, which is thereby subjected to the total pressure in the system and made to condense at normal cooling water or air temperatures in the usual manner.

The absence of noticeable pressure differences in the system permits the design of a unit in which the solution is circulated through absorber, exchanger, and generator by thermal action alone and the mechanical pump is dispensed with.   The parts are so arranged that the liquid refrigerant flows to the evaporator by gravity.   Care must be taken to keep the inert substance isolated in the proper parts of the system, or the pressures will become unbalanced and the machine will eventually be rendered inoperative.

---

[1] For a discussion of small absorption units and the possible substances for use as solvents and refrigerants, see TAYLOR, ROBERT S., *Refrigerating Engineering*, vol. 17, no. 5, May 1929.

[2] ZELLHOEFER, G. F., *Refrigerating Engineering*, vol. 33, no. 5, May 1937.

Probably the best known unit of this type is the Platen-Munters system using ammonia as the refrigerant. water as the solvent, and hydrogen as the inert third fluid.

Although the three-fluid principle abolishes the pump, the layout is complicated and there is some sacrifice of efficiency. It has not, therefore, been applied to industrial machines, where the pump is not particularly objectionable, but has found a field in domestic units where the necessity for automatic operation and the desirability of no moving parts render it especially adaptable.

PROBLEMS

21. Data for an absorber in an ammonia absorption system: Evaporator pressure = 37 lb. per sq. in. abs. Temperature of ammonia leaving evaporator and entering absorber = 15°F. Absorber pressure = 35 lb. abs. Weak aqua enters the absorber at 115°F. with a molal concentration of 0.28. Strong aqua leaves at 90°F., $x_w = 0.35$. Neglect water vapor returning from evaporator.

If 20 lb. of anhydrous ammonia are circulated in the system per minute, calculate the heat to be removed from the absorber in Btu per minute.

22. An aqua ammonia pump is to handle 640 lb. of solution per minute. Solution weight concentration $x_w = 0.32$. Solution temperature at suction = 95°F. Suction pressure = 25 lb. per sq. in. abs. Discharge pressure = 190 lb. abs. The combined hydraulic and mechanical efficiency is 60 per cent.

Calculate: (*a*) The necessary horsepower output of a motor to drive this pump; (*b*) the gallons per minute pumped.

23. For a certain case, the rectifier cooling water undergoes a 20° rise in temperature. How many pounds and gallons must be circulated per minute under the following conditions?

Pressure of vapors leaving analyzer and entering rectifier = 200 lb. per sq. in. abs.; temperature = 212°F. Temperature of vapors and drip leaving rectifier = 115°F. Pressure at exit = 197 lb. abs. Ammonia vapor passing to condenser = 50 lb. per minute.

24. In an absorption system where the temperature of condensation in the condenser is 94°F., the generator operates at a pressure which is 7.3 lb. per sq. in. higher than that of the condenser. The strong aqua enters the analyzer with a weight concentration of 0.38 at a temperature of 190°F. A weak aqua weight concentration of 0.30 is desired. Vapors leave the analyzer at 212°F. Drip returns to the analyzer at 115°F. Anhydrous ammonia circulated in the system = 50 lb. per minute. (See Prob. 23 for weights and drip concentration.) Allowing a 10° difference between steam temperature and generator temperature and assuming steam to be dry saturated and condensate to leave at generator temperature, calculate the steam consumption in pounds per hour.

25. The following data apply to an ammonia absorption system. Capacity = 150 tons. Pressures: condenser = 195 lb. abs.; evaporator = 25 lb. abs.; absorber = 23 lb. abs.; pump suction = 20 lb. abs.; pump discharge = 220 lb. abs.; generator = 205 lb. abs.; rectifier exit = 198 lb. abs. Temperatures: liquid leaving condenser and entering expansion valve = 82°F.; ammonia vapor at evaporator exit = 0°F.; strong aqua leaving absorber and entering pump = 88°F.; weak aqua leaving exchanger and entering absorber = 110°F.; weak aqua leaving generator and entering exchanger = 245°F.; vapors leaving analyzer and entering rectifier = 225°F.; vapors and drip leaving rectifier and entering condenser = 120°F.

The aqua pump handles 16 lb. of solution per pound of anhydrous ammonia absorbed. Combined pump efficiencies = 0.65.

Calculate for full capacity: (a) The heat to be supplied to or taken from each part of the system in Btu per minute; (b) the horsepower input to the pump; (c) the pump capacity in gallons per minute; (d) the steam required, pounds per hour, assuming dry saturated steam 10° higher than generator temperature and condensate leaving at generator temperature; (e) a complete energy balance for the system.

26. Calculate Prob. 25 without an analyzer in the system in order to show the saving effected by its use in Btu supplied per minute and pounds of steam per hour.

27. Calculate the rectifier of Prob. 25 for exit temperatures of 150, 135, 110, 100, and 90°F. Note the effect upon weights of vapor entering, water vapor leaving, and drip for the required amount of anhydrous ammonia circulated.

28. For generator temperatures of 250, 230, and 220°F., Prob. 25, calculate the weight of aqua to be circulated, and the pump horsepower.

CHAPTER X

REFRIGERATION IN AIR CONDITIONING

Atmospheric air is normally composed principally of nitrogen, oxygen, and water vapor in the order of their respective weight proportions. The remaining constituents, argon, carbon dioxide, helium, etc., together comprise approximately 1 per cent of the whole by weight and have but little influence upon the behavior or properties of air, dominated as they are by the presence of the diatomic gases. In addition to the aforementioned substances, which may be called the pure constituents, there exist in the natural atmosphere various and varying quantities of solid impurities such as dust, carbon, and organisms which are important in certain phases of air conditioning but do not affect the properties insofar as we are at present concerned.

For air conditioning, it is unnecessary to deal with each of the various individual constituents separately. Instead, air may be considered to consist of **dry air,** *i.e.,* air devoid of aqueous constituents, and **water vapor.** Dry air never occurs naturally but is always accompanied by water vapor which is present in varying quantities dependent largely upon the temperature and other conditions under which the air may have been exposed to moisture. The term "dry air" is also, as will be seen later, used for reference, and a mixture of dry air and water vapor may hereinafter be designated simply as "air." Although the amount of water vapor which may be present in a given sample of air will not ordinarily exceed 5 per cent of the weight of the sample, it exerts such a profound influence upon the physical and physiological characteristics of the air that the science of air conditioning, which deals with the control of temperature and moisture content and the purification of air, has developed to one of prime importance within the last twenty-five years. Refrigeration is closely associated with air conditioning because of the frequent necessity for either simple cooling or for cooling and dehumidification, both of which processes require the with-

drawal of heat from the air.   The accurate solution of problems
requires a knowledge of the thermal properties of air-vapor
mixtures which will now be discussed.

50. Dry-air–water-vapor Mixture.—A gaseous mixture is as
closely conformable to Dalton's law as are its principal constituents to the laws governing the perfect gas.   If the air-
vapor mixture will follow this law, calculations in air conditioning
and humidity may be rendered comparatively simple.   Dry air,
composed almost entirely of permanent gases, obeys very closely
the perfect gas laws within the range included in air conditioning.
The degree to which water vapor may be depended upon to
approximate perfect gas behavior is readily ascertainable by
examination of a steam diagram, such as the *T-s* or the *h-s*
chart, on which are plotted lines of constant temperature and
lines of constant enthalpy.   In the high pressure region these
lines will be seen to intersect at relatively large angles, but at
low pressures in the superheat region the temperature and
enthalpy lines will be found to be more nearly parallel, and in
restricted areas, they will appear quite parallel over considerable
ranges and will together intersect successive lines of constant
pressure.   This condition indicates that a throttling expansion
at constant enthalpy would also be isothermal, *i.e.*, the Joule-
Thomson coefficient $(dt/dp)_h$ would be zero or very nearly zero.
Since this is one criterion of a perfect gas, steam in these particular
areas may be expected to closely approximate perfect gas
behavior.   In air it fortunately happens that vapor pressures
are well within the range just mentioned, and Dalton's law
applies closely.   This permits the application of rational methods
for the determination of properties from observed data, and also
permits the individual treatment of each constituent, dry air
and water vapor, as though it alone were present at its particular partial pressure.   Inasmuch as the properties of both dry
air and steam are well known, the latter with great accuracy,
for the range concerned, the reliability of psychrometric calculations is assured.

**51. Observable Properties of Air and the Calculation of Vapor
Pressure.**—The determination of air properties is dependent
upon a knowledge of the vapor pressure which may be found
indirectly from physical observations of a given sample of air.
The observable data consist usually of the barometric pressure,

and the gage pressure if the air be confined, the **dry bulb temperature,** and the **wet bulb temperature.** For the last-named may
occasionally be substituted the direct observation of the dew
point temperature by means of some form of dew point apparatus, but the use of the wet bulb thermometer is far more
general and considerably less complicated in manipulation.
The barometric pressure in combination with gage pressure
gives total pressure of the mixture which is the sum of the
partial pressures of water vapor and dry air. The dry bulb
temperature is the true temperature of the mixture. The wet
bulb temperature, taken with a thermometer whose bulb is kept
moistened, is the only indication, among the observations, of the
humidity of the air.   It may readily be understood that evaporation of moisture from the wet bulb, in passing a current of air
over it, will produce a thermometer reading lower than that of
the dry bulb temperature and that the difference in temperatures
indicated by the two thermometers, called the **wet bulb depression,** will in general be a measure of the dryness of the air to
which they are exposed. Dry air, for which the wet bulb
depression is a maximum, and saturated air, in which the dry
and wet bulb temperatures are the same, constitute the two
extremes for any given dry bulb temperature.

The true wet bulb thermometer is assumed to give very closely
the temperature of **adiabatic saturation**[1] from which the vapor
properties in the air sample may be calculated.   Actually the
temperature of the wet bulb may deviate considerably from
that of adiabatic saturation, but if care is taken the error appears
to be negligible at air velocities past the unshielded bulb of about
1000 ft. per min. From this point on, wet bulb temperature
and the temperature of adiabatic saturation will be considered
as synonymous insofar as the air-steam mixture is concerned.

For calculating vapor pressure from observed data, Carrier
evolved the equation[2]

---

[1] If air be passed through a chamber and exposed to moisture wholly
contained therein in such a manner that the air becomes saturated by auto-
evaporation without transfer of heat to or from the exterior, and if the
process be continued until an equilibrium temperature is established, such
temperature is known as the temperature of adiabatic saturation.

[2] CARRIER, W. H., Rational Psychrometric Formulae, *Trans. A. S. M. E.*,
vol. 33, 1911.

$$p_s = p'_s - \frac{(p_t - p'_s)(t - t')}{2800 - 1.3t'} \qquad (89)$$

where t = dry bulb temperature, degrees Fahrenheit; t' = true wet bulb temperature (adiabatic saturation), degrees Fahrenheit; p_s = vapor pressure in the mixture; p'_s = vapor pressure corresponding to a saturation temperature of t'; p_t = barometric or total pressure. All pressures are in pounds per square inch absolute. This equation gives results which are in close agreement with experimental determinations.

52. Properties of Air.—The air properties, in addition to the vapor pressure, which are important for air-conditioning use are dew point temperature, absolute humidity, relative humidity, specific humidity, enthalpy, and specific volume or density.

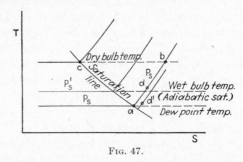

Fig. 47.

Of these, the first four may be called psychrometric properties, and the others thermal properties. Since, in a given sample or quantity of air, the dry air remains the fixed weight while water vapor may be removed by condensation or added by evaporation, air properties involving quantities of energy or matter are judiciously based upon unit quantity of dry air instead of mixture, as Btu of the mixture per pound of dry air, grains of vapor per pound of dry air, etc.

From what has been said in preceding sections, it may be seen that the properties of air can be determined by correctly combining the properties of its constituents, dry air and steam. Inasmuch as Dalton's law applies, each constituent may be treated independently after the partial pressures have been established, and the individual properties become readily determinable. The state of the water vapor in any dry-air–water-vapor mixture may be shown on a diagram such as the *T-s* diagram in Fig. 47. The dry bulb temperature and the vapor pressure line are indicated on the diagram. The wet bulb temperature is also shown, but since this is of importance simply as a physical observation from which the vapor pressure may be derived, it will not be further discussed. The state of the water vapor, existing at the temperature of the mixture and at the pressure P_s, is seen to be superheated and is represented by the point *b*. The degree of superheat is the difference between dry bulb and dew point temperatures. Were the air to be increased in moisture content without change in dry bulb temperature, the vapor pressure would increase, with decreasing superheat, until the state of the vapor would be that shown by the point *c*. This represents the highest vapor pressure possible for the temperature indicated; dry bulb, wet bulb, and dew point temperatures would be the same; and the air would be said to be **saturated**—really the state of the *water vapor* in the air is saturated. Conversely, for drier air at the same dry bulb temperature, the vapor pressure would be lower than that shown, with a consequent increase in superheat for the vapor remaining.

The **dew point temperature** may be seen from the diagram to be the temperature corresponding to the vapor pressure. It may also be defined as the lowest temperature to which air may be cooled at constant pressure, in thermal equilibrium, without condensation of moisture.

Absolute humidity expresses the weight of water vapor present in 1 cu. ft. of mixture. Since a cubic foot of mixture is also a cubic foot of each individual constituent, absolute humidity is no more than the specific weight, or density, of the vapor. This is usually expressed in grains per cubic foot in order to avoid small fractions, and

$$\text{Absolute humidity} = d_s = \frac{7000P_s}{R_sT} \qquad (90)$$

The gas constant R_s for steam in the humidity range is 85.7.

Relative humidity is the ratio of the actual absolute humidity, at point *b* of Fig. 47, to the saturated absolute humidity at the same dry bulb temperature, at point *c*. The saturated absolute humidity may be taken from steam tables if desired, or it may be calculated by the characteristic perfect gas equation from which it becomes obvious that relative humidity is also the ratio of the existing vapor pressure to the vapor pressure corresponding to the dry bulb temperature, *i.e.*,

Relative humidity

$$= \frac{\text{existing absolute humidity}}{\text{absolute humidity for saturated air at the dry bulb temperature}}$$

$$= \frac{\text{existing vapor pressure}}{\text{vapor pressure corresponding to dry bulb temperature}}$$

It is customary to express this ratio as a percentage.

Specific humidity is the weight of water vapor accompanying 1 lb. of dry air. It is usually expressed as grains of vapor per pound of dry air. Now since the specific volume of dry air is $v_a = R_a T/P_a$, or the density of dry air is $d_a = P_a/R_a T$, where P_a is the dry air partial pressure, specific humidity can be expressed in terms of absolute humidity as

Specific humidity = absolute humidity $\times v_a$

$$= \frac{\text{absolute humidity}}{d_a} \quad (91)$$

from which

$$\text{Specific humidity} = \frac{7000 P_s R_a}{P_a R_s} \quad (92)$$

Enthalpy of air is expressed as the enthalpy of the mixture per pound of dry air. This amounts to the sum of the enthalpies of 1 lb. of dry air and of that quantity of vapor which accompanies it. The enthalpy of dry air is $c_p T$, from Eq. (14). For convenience, the zero of enthalpy for dry air will be taken at 0°F., and with the specific heat of dry air in the range desired equal to 0.24 Btu per lb. per deg., the enthalpy is arbitrarily $0.24t$. The enthalpy of superheated steam at pressures lower than 1 lb. per sq. in. abs. may be calculated by adding to the enthalpy of the saturated vapor, taken from steam tables at the vapor pressure, the heat of superheat using a mean specific heat of 0.45 Btu per lb. per deg. thus

$$h_s = h_g + 0.45(t - t_{sat})$$

The enthalpy of the mixture in Btu per lb. dry air is then

$$h_m = 0.24t + \frac{M_s}{M_a}[h_g + 0.45(t - t_{sat})] \quad (93)$$

in which M_s/M_a is the ratio by weight of water vapor to dry air, or the specific humidity expressed in pounds. From the previous reference to adiabatic saturation it may be seen that the enthalpy of the mixture leaving an adiabatic saturator must be the same as the entering per pound of dry air, so that for Eq. (93) may be substituted

$$h_m = 0.24t' + \frac{M'_s}{M_a}(h'_g) - \frac{M'_s - M_s}{M_a}(h'_f) \qquad (94)$$

where the primed symbols represent properties for adiabatic saturation.

There is, both in the literature and in practice, wide use made of a property which has been termed by Carrier the "sigma function,"[1] but is also frequently and erroneously called "total heat." The sigma function is defined as the enthalpy of the mixture less the enthalpy of the liquid at the temperature of adiabatic saturation, or in Btu per pound dry air:

$$\Sigma = h_m - \frac{M_s}{M_a}h'_f = 0.24t' + \frac{M'_s}{M_a}h'_{fg} \qquad (95)$$

This property has the advantage over enthalpy of being dependent only upon the temperature of adiabatic saturation and the disadvantage of not including all of the energy in a process involving condensation or evaporation. On psychrometric charts, the designation "total heat" usually refers to the sigma function[2] and should be treated as such and not as enthalpy.

The volume of the mixture per pound of dry air is obviously either the volume of 1 lb. of dry air at its partial pressure or the volume of the corresponding weight of vapor at the vapor pressure, i.e., as previously expressed,

$$v_m = \frac{R_a T}{P_a} = \frac{M_s}{M_a} \times \frac{R_s T}{P_s} \qquad (96)$$

It may occasionally be desirable, in order to find the total weight of material, to determine the density of the mixture in

---

[1] CARRIER, W. H., and C. O. MACKEY, A review of existing psychrometric data in relation to practical engineering problems, *Trans. A. S. M. E.*, 1936.

[2] An exception to this, however, is the psychrometric chart by F. O. Urban for the General Electric Company, on which "total heat" refers to enthalpy. See *Refrigerating Engineering*, vol. 30, November, 1935.

pounds per cubic foot. Since the densities of the constituents have been previously discussed, the combined density is clearly $d_m = d_a + d_s$.

The specific heat of air is increased by the addition of vapor owing to the fact that the heat capacity of the vapor is larger than that of the air it displaces. If the specific heat of the mixture is required, it may be determined by combining the specific heats of the two components in proportion to the weight of each present, thus

$$c_m = \frac{M_a c_a + M_s c_s}{M_a + M_s} \tag{97}$$

The use of the psychrometric chart in determining air properties is satisfactory for engineering applications to which the chart will apply. The same is true of psychrometric tables. However, since the present purpose is the development of principles, no further reference will be made to chart or tables, and data will be computed from fundamentals.

Example.—The following data were observed for air within a duct. Barometer = 30.2 in.; gage pressure of air = 0.5 in. of water; dry bulb temperature = 76°F.; true wet bulb temperature = 70°F.

Calculate for this air: (a) Vapor pressure and the dew point temperature; (b) absolute humidity, grains per cubic foot; (c) relative humidity; (d) specific humidity, grains of vapor per pound dry air; (e) enthalpy, Btu per pound dry air; (f) specific volume, cubic feet per pound dry air; (g) density of the mixture, pounds per cubic foot; (h) specific heat of the mixture at constant pressure, Btu per degree per pound mixture.

Solution:

Total pressure $p_t = 30.2(0.491) + \dfrac{0.5}{2.31(12)} = 14.846$ lb. per sq. in. abs.

(a) Vapor pressure $p_s = 0.363 - \dfrac{14.483(6)}{2800 - 1.3(70)} = 0.332$ lb. abs.

Dew point temperature = 67.4°F.

Partial pressure of dry air $p_a = 14.846 - 0.332 = 14.514$ lb. abs.

(b) Absolute humidity $= \dfrac{7000(0.332)(144)}{85.7(536)} = 7.28$ grains per cu. ft.

(c) Relative humidity $= \dfrac{0.332}{0.444} = 0.748$ or 74.8 per cent

(d) $v_a = \dfrac{53.35(536)}{14.514(144)} = 13.68$ cu. ft. per lb.

Specific humidity $= 13.68(7.28) = 99.6$ grains per lb. dry air

(e) $h_m = 0.24(76) + \dfrac{99.6}{7000}[1091.2 + 0.45(8.6)] = 33.79$ Btu per lb. dry air

(f) Specific volume $= 13.68$ cu. ft. per lb. dry air

(g) $d_a = \dfrac{1}{13.68} = 0.0731$ lb. per cu. ft.

$d_s = \dfrac{7.28}{7000} = 0.00104$ lb. per cu. ft.

$d_m = 0.0731 + 0.00104 = 0.07414$ lb. of mixture per cu. ft.

(h) $c_{pm} = \dfrac{0.24 + \dfrac{99.6(0.45)}{7000}}{1 + \dfrac{99.6}{7000}} = 0.243$ Btu per deg. per lb. mixture,

also $c_{pm} = \dfrac{0.0731(0.24) + 0.00104(0.45)}{0.07414} = 0.243$ Btu per deg. per lb. mixture.

Specific heat may also be expressed in Btu for the mixture per degree per pound dry air if desired. For this case it would be 0.2464.

53. Cooling and Dehumidification of Air.—Air cooling is almost always carried out under flow conditions and, therefore, at practically constant total pressure. The cooling is effected in a chamber either by **surface cooling** or by **spray cooling.** In the former, air is passed over surfaces which are kept cool by the internal circulation of water, brine, or the refrigerant itself. Owing to the fact that the air is not all exposed to the cold surfaces in the same degree, some portions may be cooled to a considerably lower temperature than others. But uniformity of temperature will be restored by mixing before the air leaves the apparatus, and the effect of poor distribution among the cooling coils is the production of lower localized temperatures than would be indicated if homogeneous cooling were assumed. In determining the heat withdrawn, only the terminal conditions need be considered. In spray cooling, cold water or brine is sprayed directly into the air in order to produce the desired temperature by contact, and a certain amount of air washing is secured at the same time.

Under certain conditions, dictated by the initial state of the air and by the final requirements, it may be necessary to cool the air only to some temperature in excess of the dew point without precipitation of moisture. This may be termed **simple** or **dry cooling** accomplished by the use of a surface cooler. For a process of this kind, the water vapor in the air would be cooled at constant vapor pressure and the final state point would be indicated as *d* in Fig. 47. However, in view of what was said in the preceding paragraph regarding nonuniform exposure to the cooling coils, an attempt to dry cool air to a temperature near the dew point will usually result in the removal of moisture from that portion of the air which comes into most intimate contact with the surfaces. In mixing with the remainder of the air, this portion will be raised in temperature and the whole may leave the apparatus at a temperature above the initial dew point but with less vapor than it originally possessed. The state point would then be *d'* of Fig. 47. In a case of this sort, any dehumidification which has occurred may be considered as incidental but must nevertheless be taken into account in calculations. Dry cooling calculations may perhaps be most easily carried out by the use of the specific heat of the mixture, but other than this, they involve no principles which are not included in dehumidifying. Also since dehumidification may take place accidentally when only dry cooling is required, we may pass on at once to the problem of the deliberate removal of moisture from air.

Consideration of the various uses of conditioned air, or of systems for recirculating or by-passing the air, is a part of the science of air conditioning and has no place in this work which can only discuss the calculation of the refrigerating load required in actually cooling the air in accordance with the demands of some air-conditioning system.

The greatest amount of refrigeration in air conditioning will occur in the production of relatively dry air for any desired purpose from either the warm humid outside air, which is naturally prevalent in warm seasons, or from recirculated air to which moisture has been added in fulfilling its function.

Irrespective of the purpose to which the conditioned air is to be put, dehumidification is accomplished by sufficiently cooling the mixture below the dew point to remove the necessary quantity of moisture. The spray dehumidifier is widely used for large sizes, but the surface cooler may also be used. In the first, the spray water or brine is cooled by refrigeration before entering the spray chamber, and the water leaving the apparatus is the quantity entering augmented by the condensate from the air. In the surface type of cooler, condensation takes place upon the coils and is removed as it collects.   For the complete conditioning of a given quantity of air, the dehumidifier will have to be followed by a heater, and the rudimentary apparatus must thus consist of both cooler and heater as shown in Fig. 48.   Air enters at 1, is cooled and dehumidified in the cooler, and is finally delivered from the heater at 3 in the required condition of temperature and humidity.   Since, with constant total pressure, the dew point and vapor pressure do not change if moisture is neither added to nor taken from the air, these must be the same at 2 as at 3.   Further, when air is dehumidified by uniform cooling below the original dew point, it must be saturated upon

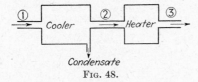

FIG. 48.

leaving the dehumidifier.   It may thus be seen that the temperature to which air must be cooled in a drying process is the final dew point temperature.   This will be the condition at 2.

In order to understand the action of the vapor in the mixture during partial condensation, the *T-s* diagram for the process is shown in Fig. 49 with the same notation as Fig. 48.   Starting at point 1, the first part of the cooling process results in desuperheating the vapor.   If a surface cooler is used, the process will proceed from 1 to *A* at constant vapor pressure, but in a spray cooler, some moisture will be evaporated from the spray during the initial cooling and the process will follow the path indicated from 1 to *A'*.   Cooling below *A* or *A'* immediately produces condensation which continues progressively as the temperature is carried lower.   The constitution of air is such that water is not considered as part of the inherent moisture, so that the condensate becomes simply a separate quantity of water and the vapor remaining in the air is in the dry saturated state at a vapor pressure which is constantly diminishing as the cooling continues. The process for the vapor thus proceeds along the saturation line passing successively lower vapor pressure lines until the desired vapor pressure, and dew point, is reached.   At the same time, the vapor quantity is continually decreasing so that the representation of the process on the diagram does not picture the change for all of the original vapor but rather traces the state point for 1 lb. of residual vapor after each decrement of temperature.   The liquid may be considered, in proportionately increasing quantity, as undergoing a like cooling on the liquid line until it is removed from the apparatus.   The remainder of the conditioning process consists of dry heating at constant vapor pressure to the desired state at 3.

The quantity of air to be treated will usually be expressed in cubic feet per unit time at either 1 or 3, Fig. 48.   Since the

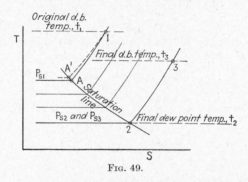

Fig. 49.

volumes at 1, 2, and 3 are all different, it is well to deal entirely with dry air weight which does not change, and the wisdom of expressing mixture properties in terms of 1 lb. of dry air becomes apparent.   The specific humidity remains constant under any conditions so long as neither air nor moisture is added to or taken from the mixture.   This property, with vapor pressure and dew point, is thus the same at 2 as at 3.   Furthermore, the difference between the specific humidities at 1 and at 2 is the weight of moisture condensed per pound of dry air passing through the dehumidifier.

The energy equation for the cooler, referring to Fig. 48, is

$$M_a h_{m1} = M_a h_{m2} + M_c h_{fc} + Q_R$$

or

$$Q_R = M_a h_{m1} - M_a h_{m2} - M_c h_{fc} = M_a(h_{m1} - h_{m2}) - M_c h_{fc} \quad (98)$$

where M_c is the weight of condensate removed in the time that M_a lb. of dry air are passing, and h_{fc} is the enthalpy of the liquid at the temperature of condensate removal. This will give the heat units to be withdrawn in the unit of time adopted for the weights flowing, from which the tons of refrigeration may be readily calculated.

It appears from what has been said that the important properties in a problem of this type are specific humidity and enthalpy. If these be determined for the air at entrance to, and at exit from, the cooler, and the weight of dry air flowing be known, then the problem of cooling and dehumidifying, insofar as the refrigerating load is concerned, becomes exceedingly simple.

Example.—An air-conditioned space is to be supplied with 10,000 cu. ft. of air per minute at 65°F., 40 per cent relative humidity. Air is supplied to the dehumidifier at 90°F., wet bulb temperature of 84°F. The condensate leaves the dehumidifier at the same temperature as the outgoing air. Assume the air to be at standard atmospheric pressure throughout.

Calculate the refrigerating load required in tons.

Solution (Refer to Fig. 48 for notation):

$p_{s3} = p_{s2} = 0.4(0.3056) = 0.1222$ lb. abs.

Dew point temperature at $3 = t_2 = 40.1°F.$

$p_{a3} = 14.696 - 0.1222 = 14.5738$ lb. abs.

$$v_{a3} = \frac{53.35(525)}{14.57(144)} = 13.35 \text{ cu. ft. per lb. dry air}$$

$$M_a = \frac{10,000}{13.35} = 749 \text{ lb. per min.}$$

Specific humidity at 3 and $2 = \dfrac{7000(0.122)(53.35)}{14.57(85.7)} = 36.5$ grains per lb. dry air

$$h_{m2} = 0.24(40.1) + \frac{36.5}{7000}(1079.3) = 15.23 \text{ Btu per lb. dry air}$$

$$p_{s1} = 0.577 - \frac{(14.119)(6)}{2691} = 0.545 \text{ lb. abs.}$$

Initial dew point $= 82.2°F.$

$p_{a1} = 14.696 - 0.545 = 14.151$ lb. abs.

Specific humidity at $1 = \dfrac{7000(0.545)(53.35)}{14.151(85.7)} = 167.8$ grains per lb. dry air

$$h_{m1} = 0.24(90) + \frac{167.8}{7000}[1097.6 + 0.45(7.8)] = 48 \text{ Btu per lb. dry air}$$

Moisture condensed $= 749\left(\dfrac{167.8 - 36.5}{7000}\right) = 14.07$ lb. per min.

$Q_R = 749(48 - 15.23) - 14.07(8.1) = 24,430$ Btu per min.
Refrigerating capacity required $= 122.15$ tons.

The total pressure in the foregoing example is placed at the standard atmosphere in order that the values may be checked by a standard psychrometric chart if desired. It will be noted that consideration of the enthalpy of the condensate decreases the estimated refrigeration load by about $\frac{1}{2}$ ton, which in this case is insignificant. This quantity will always be small when the final dew point is low and in such cases may usually be neglected. The use of the sigma function instead of enthalpy in the example would result in an estimated load of approximately 118 tons which is about 3 per cent lower than the true value.

The choice of refrigerants desirable for use in refrigerating machines which are applied to air cooling is considerably more restricted than for those in general industrial use because of the possibility of the refrigerant being released into the air-conditioned space by leakage or mechanical failure. For comfort cooling, the use of a nontoxic and nonirritating refrigerant is preferable, but the terms "nontoxic" and "nonirritating" must be used in the comparative sense since no refrigerant, with the exception of water vapor, is harmless if the concentration be permitted to become sufficiently high. Under ordinary circumstances in air conditioning where considerable ventilation is required, the concentration is unlikely to approach the danger point with carbon dioxide, methylene chloride (CH_2Cl_2, Carrene), or dichlorodifluoromethane (CCl_2F_2, Freon 12). Carrene, Freon, and water are probably the favorite refrigerants for comfort cooling, but others may be, and are, used extensively. For air which is conditioned for other than human consumption, the possibility of leakage would also influence the choice of refrigerant, but this would be governed more by physical and chemical effects than by physiological reactions. The type of system also has a bearing upon the dangers involved. A surface cooler utilizing indirect cooling by brine introduces less risk, for instance, than would a surface cooler with direct expansion, or a spray cooler. Ammonia might be used in the first with a considerable degree of safety but in the last two types would be considered hazardous.

In any air-conditioning system, refrigeration simply fulfills the single function of cooling the air as required by the particular type of system in use, and from the standpoint of the refrigerating machine, it is immaterial what disposition is ultimately made of the air so cooled. Similarly, although economy of refrigerating load may result from the by-passing and recirculation of air and from heat exchangers within the system, various layouts so involve the principles of air conditioning and ventilation as to belong entirely in that field.

With these facts in mind, the present chapter has been planned with the sole purpose of discussing the fundamentals which control the processes at that point in the air-conditioning system where refrigeration directly applies, *i.e.*, in the cooler or dehumidifier.

PROBLEMS

29. A fan handles 75,000 cu. ft. of atmospheric air per hour. Barometer = 29.5 in.; dry bulb temperature = 87°F.; wet bulb temperature = 78°F.

Calculate: (*a*) The absolute, relative, and specific humidities; (*b*) the weight of dry air per hour; (*c*) the weight of water vapor per hour; (*d*) the enthalpy of the mixture per pound dry air; (*e*) the density of the mixture; (*f*) the specific heat of the mixture at constant pressure.

30. In a certain location, 6,000 cu. ft. of outside air per minute at 105°F. and a wet bulb temperature of 72°F. are to be cooled to 70°F. The barometer is 28.0 in.

Calculate: (*a*) The relative humidity of the air leaving the cooler; (*b*) the refrigerating effect required in tons.

31. A dehumidifier removes 650 lb. of moisture per hour from the air which it cools to 45°F. The entering air is at 87°F. and a relative humidity of 70 per cent. The gage pressure in the cooler is 5 in. of water. Barometer = 30.4 in. Hg.

Compute the cooling load in tons.

32. A drying room requires air at 80°F., 20 per cent relative humidity. This air must come from outside where the temperature is 82°F. and the dew point is 75°F.

If the total pressure of the air is 14.5 lb. abs. and 900,000 cu. ft. of outside air per hour are required, calculate the refrigerating capacity necessary.

33. The storage of some insulating materials requires very dry air, say 2 per cent relative humidity at 100°F. This air will largely be recirculated, but some make-up is required from outside.

Calculate the tons of refrigeration required per 1000 cu. ft. per min. of conditioned make-up air if the outside air is at (*a*) 90°F., 75 per cent relative humidity; (*b*) 50°F., 80 per cent relative humidity; and (*c*) 20°F., 60 per cent relative humidity.

34. A refrigerating machine using Freon 12 as the refrigerant is used to dehumidify air in a surface cooler by direct expansion.   The air is to be conditioned to 68°F., 40 per cent relative humidity.

If the refrigerant temperature must be 10° lower than the temperature of air leaving the cooler, what will be the evaporator pressure?

CHAPTER XI

WATER VAPOR REFRIGERATING SYSTEM

In the earlier attempts to produce refrigeration by mechanical means, the use of water as the refrigerant, either alone or in conjunction with other substances, occupied a prominent place. The inherent disadvantages of water as a refrigerant are the high evaporating vacuum required, the enormous volume of vapor to be compressed, and the comparatively high freezing point. These drawbacks proved for many years obstacles too great to be overcome, and the water vapor system became one of purely academic interest until the advent of air conditioning when the notable superiorities of water provided a stimulus which has resulted in the recent rapid development of this type of machine. Air cooling is one industrial application of refrigeration which does not, in the refrigerating sense, ordinarily require low temperatures. This circumstance eliminates one of the principal objections to the use of water as the working medium. Add to this the obvious advantage of cheapness and the fact that it is the only truly safe modern refrigerant, and it will be seen that water vapor systems may be well worth consideration for practical application. Of the two remaining outstanding objections mentioned earlier, the first, that of high vacuums, has been largely overcome by progress in design and construction, and the second has been rendered nonobjectionable by the development of those types of compressor which will handle the large volumes, *i.e.*, the centrifugal compressor and the steam ejector.

54. Operation of Water Vapor System.—The water vapor system does not differ in fundamental principle from other vapor compression cycles previously discussed, but the characteristics of water and water vapor necessitate some and make desirable other changes in the basic layout of the system.

Exclusive of the mode of compression, which will be more fully discussed later, the schematic layout of the fundamentals of a water vapor system is shown in Fig. 50. Unlike machines using other substances, the nature of the refrigerant in this case renders its close confinement to the system unnecessary, and the refrigeration in the evaporator is applied to the water itself which is then circulated in order to perform the cooling function desired. The comparatively warm supply water is thus introduced into the evaporator at 1 and, being subjected therein to a very low pressure, is cooled to the corresponding temperature by the vaporization of a very small proportion. The vapor so formed, together with air released from the supply water by the low pressure, is removed by the compressor at 3, boosted in pressure, and discharged into the condenser at 4, while the chilled water remaining is pumped from the evaporator at 2. In order to expose a large surface of liquid for flash cooling, the supply water is usually introduced into the evaporator in a spray. If

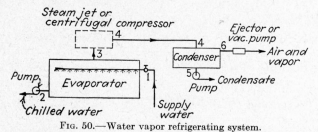

Fig. 50.—Water vapor refrigerating system.

the process in which it is used does not consume the chilled water, it may be returned to the evaporator for recirculation; otherwise the supply water, or that portion of it which is make-up, is taken from the main.

The action in the evaporator is essentially adiabatic, and the energy equation is

$$M_1 h_1 = M_2 h_2 + M_3 h_3 \qquad (99)$$

Since $M_1 = M_2 + M_3$, and the refrigerating effect is produced by flash cooling, Eq. (99) may be written to express that effect as

$$\text{Refrigerating effect} = M_2(h_1 - h_2) = M_3(h_3 - h_1) \quad (100)$$

The temperatures of supply water and chilled water provide the means for finding h_1 and h_2, and for h_3 the vapor may be considered to leave the evaporator in the saturated state with a quality ranging from 0.95 to dry.

The volume of vapor to be removed from the evaporator by the compressor is simply $M_3 v_3$. By comparison, the quantity of air released from the supply water, which also passes through the compressor, is very small and has an entirely negligible effect upon evaporator and compressor calculations because in these organs there is no opportunity for accumulation.

Example.—A water vapor refrigerating machine is to produce 250 gal. per minute of chilled water at 45°F. The supply water is at 60°F., and the quality of the vapor leaving the evaporator and entering the compressor is 0.97.

Calculate: (*a*) The capacity of the machine, tons; (*b*) the pounds of vapor to be removed from the evaporator per min.; (*c*) the volume of vapor to be removed from the evaporator, cubic feet per minute, and cubic feet per minute per ton.

Solution (Refer to Fig. 50):

$h_1 = 28.06$; $h_2 = 13.06$; $h_3 = 1049.4$; $v_3 = 1975$ cu. ft. per lb.
$M_2 = 250(8.35) = 2087.5$ lb. per min.

(*a*) Refrigerating effect $= 2087.5(15) = 31,312$ Btu per min. $= 156.6$ tons

(*b*) Vapor removed, $M_3 = \dfrac{2087.5(15)}{1021.3} = 30.66$ lb. per min.

Supply water, $M_1 = 2087.5 + 30.66 = 2118.2$ lb. per min.

(*c*) Vapor volume at compressor suction $= 30.66(1975) = 60,550$ cu. ft. per min., or 387 cu. ft. per min. per ton

The vapor volume, equivalent to what has been previously called the theoretical piston displacement, increases as the cold water temperature is lowered and becomes less for higher evaporator temperatures. In all cases, the volume is so large as to practically prohibit the use of a reciprocating compressor. Temperatures at or below 32°F. may be obtained by the use of brine or of some other antifreeze in the evaporator. Owing to the difficulties introduced, however, it is not usual to employ this type of machine for the lower temperatures.

The condenser operates at a pressure which conforms to the temperature necessary to produce condensation. With the cooling water ordinarily available, the temperature will be from 90 to 100°F. and the pressure slightly less than 1 lb. per sq. in. abs. It is important that this pressure be held as low as possible so as to reduce the pressure ratio through which the compressor operates, and in order to do so, provision must be made for the efficient removal of air which would otherwise rapidly collect in sufficient quantity to raise the pressure to that of the atmosphere. The air removal is effected by an auxiliary pump or by a steam ejector at 6 in Fig. 50, while most of the vapor from the compressor which enters the condenser at 4 is removed as condensate by a liquid pump at 5. Exclusive of circulating water pumps, the power, or the steam, required to operate the water vapor system includes, in addition to the main compressor, the consumption by condensate and air pumps.

When the condenser vacuum pump is of the steam ejector type, the air removal is usually carried out in two stages in order to conserve steam and water. The first ejector discharges into an **intercondenser** operating at a pressure intermediate between that of the main, or **primary,** condenser and the atmosphere. The second ejector takes air and uncondensed vapor from the intercondenser and discharges into the **after** condenser which is at atmospheric pressure. Here the water vapor is very largely condensed, and the air is vented to the atmosphere.

55. Centrifugal Water Vapor System.—The centrifugal compressor, capable of handling large volumes of fluid, is well suited for use in the water vapor machine with either electric motor or steam turbine drive. The usual pressure ratios of compression are from 4 to 10, the latter figure representing conditions which may be regarded as extreme. On the same basis, the differential pressures against which the vapor must be pumped are from 0.5 lb. per sq. in. to 0.9 lb. per sq. in. Because of the rarefied state of the vapor within the operating range (densities of from 0.00035 to 0.003 lb. per cu. ft.), stage compression becomes a practical necessity.

The compression takes place adiabatically but not isentropically. The actual increase in enthalpy thus exceeds the isentropic increase, and the ratio of the latter to the former is termed, as stated in Sec. 34, the compressor efficiency. For adiabatic compression, the energy equation is

$$AW + Mh_3 = Mh_4$$

or

$$AW = M(h_4 - h_3) \tag{101}$$

Given the compressor efficiency, the actual enthalpy increase is the isentropic increase divided by this efficiency, and the final enthalpy is the sum of the initial enthalpy and the actual enthalpy rise. Thus, for any given initial condition, both the shaft work per pound of vapor and the condition of the vapor at compressor discharge may be readily calculated.

Example.—Consider the machine in the example of the previous section as equipped with a centrifugal compressor and mechanical vacuum pumps. The condenser pressure is 2 in. Hg abs. Compressor efficiency = 0.65. The condensate leaves the condenser at 90°F. The power to drive condensate and air pumps may be considered as 6 per cent of the total.

Calculate: (*a*) The compressor horsepower and the horsepower per ton; (*b*) the total horsepower required and the total horsepower per ton; (*c*) the heat rejected in the condenser, Btu per minute; (*d*) the coefficient of performance.

Solution (Refer to Fig. 50):

$h_3 = 1049.4$; $s_3 = 2.0794$; $h_5 = 58$.
After isentropic compression to 2 in. Hg, $h = 1168$
Isentropic $\Delta h = 1168 - 1049.4 = 118.6$ Btu per lb.

Actual $\Delta h = \dfrac{118.6}{0.65} = 182.5$ Btu per lb.

$h_4 = 1049.4 + 182.5 = 1231.9$ (2 in. Hg and 380°F.)
(*a*) $AW = 30.66(182.5) = 5595$ Btu per min.

Compressor hp. $= \dfrac{5595}{42.4} = 132$, or 0.843 hp. per ton

(*b*) Total hp. $= \dfrac{132}{0.94} = 140.4$, or 0.897 hp. per ton

(*c*) $Q = 30.66(1231.9 - 58) = 35,992$ Btu per min. or 230 Btu per min. per ton

(*d*) Coefficient of performance $= \dfrac{200}{0.897(42.4)} = 5.26$ (based on total hp.)

The apparently high coefficient of performance in the foregoing example is due to the comparatively favorable temperature range through which the machine operates rather than to any inherent superiority of water vapor over other commonly used refrigerants. For the same conditions, the ideal Carnot coefficient of performance would be slightly greater than 9.

56. Steam Ejector Water Vapor System.—If so desired, a steam jet aspirator may be substituted for the centrifugal compressor in the water vapor system in order to remove the refrigerating vapor from the evaporator, compress it, and deliver it to the condenser.   This exchanges a mechanical for a thermal compressor which may be preferred for certain service conditions where steam is more plentiful and less expensive than power and where there is at the same time no dearth of cooling water.

The steam ejector is essentially a kinetic device which utilizes the momentum of a high velocity jet of steam to entrain and accelerate a slower moving medium into which it is directed. The resulting kinetic energy of the mixture is subsequently used for self-compression of the substance to a higher pressure in the device which thus fulfills the function of a compressor.

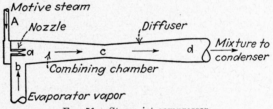

Fig. 51.—Steam jet compressor.

Reference to the schematic representation of the steam jet compressor shown in Fig. 51 will serve to illustrate the operation. The device is wholly actuated by relatively high pressure steam at A expanding through a nozzle and issuing therefrom at high velocity at a.   This steam will be termed the **motive vapor** in order to distinguish it from the **evaporator vapor** produced in the flash chamber and entering the ejector at b.   In the **combining chamber** the high velocity motive vapor mixes with the evaporator vapor in such a manner as to utilize almost all of the initial momentum of each fluid.   This results in a considerable velocity of the mixture at c where it enters the **diffuser,** or **booster,** so shaped as to reduce the velocity in the most efficient method in order to produce an increase in pressure.   It is thus in the diffuser that the actual compression takes place. The combined fluid finally leaves the apparatus at d at, or slightly above, condenser pressure.

Considering the entire process as adiabatic and the weight of the evaporator vapor as unity, the energy equation for the device as a whole is

$$M_A h_A + h_b = (M_A + 1)h_d \tag{102}$$

with the kinetic energies at A, b, and d small enough to be neglected. Since the usual problem consists of the determination of M_A and h_d, with the conditions at A and b known, it may be seen that Eq. (102) is insufficient for the purpose, and it becomes necessary to consider the various energy transformations individually.

In the nozzle the motive steam undergoes an adiabatic expansion during which a portion of the available energy is transformed into kinetic energy. Neglecting the initial kinetic energy, which is small, the energy equation for this expansion is

$$h_A = h_a + \frac{V_a^2}{2gJ} \tag{103}$$

or

$$V_a = 224\sqrt{h_A - h_a} \tag{104}$$

Here the expression $h_A - h_a$ may be termed the actual enthalpy drop which is always smaller than the available energy, or isentropic enthalpy drop, because of losses. It is customary to express the ratio of the actual to the isentropic drop as the **nozzle efficiency,** which will be designated as e_n. This efficiency will ordinarily range from 0.87 to 0.95 in properly designed nozzles, depending upon initial conditions and the degree of expansion. Thus

$$h_A - h_a = (h_A - h_a')e_n \tag{105}$$

in which h_a' is the enthalpy following isentropic expansion and is readily determinable for any particular case from steam tables or diagrams. The actual velocity and enthalpy of steam issuing from a nozzle may thus be determined, and other properties found as desired.[1]

In the combining chamber, the motive and evaporator vapors mix for the purpose of transmitting a sufficient amount of kinetic energy from the former to the latter in order to carry out the subsequent compression. However, the direct entrainment of the low velocity vapor by the jet results in an unavoidable loss of

[1] For a more complete discussion of the flow of steam in nozzles, consult any standard work on engineering thermodynamics.

kinetic energy owing to impact and turbulence so that the surviving kinetic energy of the mixture is but a fraction of that originally possessed by the jet. This fraction which is successfully transmitted to the mixture is called the **entrainment efficiency** e_e. That proportion $1 - e_e$ of the jet energy which is lost is transformed into heat and is absorbed by the mixture, producing therein a corresponding increase in enthalpy. For the combining process, the momentum of the mixture is nearly equal to the sum of the momenta of the original constituents. According to Kalustian,[1] the momentum loss is less than 10 per cent, while the entrainment efficiency is about 65 per cent. Again denoting the ratio of motive vapor to evaporator vapor as M_a, the energy equation for entrainment is

$$M_a h_a + \frac{M_a V_a^2}{2gJ} + h_b = (M_a + 1)\left[h_c + \frac{V_c^2}{2gJ}\right] \tag{106}$$

which may also be expressed

$$h_c = \frac{M_a\left(h_a + \dfrac{V_a^2}{2gJ}\right) + h_b - \dfrac{(M_a + 1)V_c^2}{2gJ}}{M_a + 1}$$

or, using the substitution indicated by Eq. (103),

$$h_c = \frac{M_a h_A + h_b - \dfrac{(M_a + 1)V_c^2}{2gJ}}{M_a + 1} \tag{107}$$

The kinetic energy relationship is

$$e_e M_a V_a^2 = (M_a + 1)V_c^2 \tag{108}$$

or

$$V_c^2 = \frac{e_e M_a V_a^2}{M_a + 1} \tag{109}$$

or

$$M_a = \frac{V_c^2}{e_e V_a^2 - V_c^2} \tag{110}$$

The function of the diffuser is to cause the kinetic energy of the vapor at c to be utilized for self-compression from evapo-

---

[1] *Refrigerating Engineering*, vol. 28, no. 4, October, 1934.

rator pressure to that existing in the condenser.   This compression is adiabatic but, like entrainment, cannot be effected without loss and is therefore not isentropic.   The action is analogous to the final energy transformation in centrifugal compression, the kinetic energy being here acquired by a different means.   The actual enthalpy increase for the process thus exceeds the isentropic rise, the ratio of the latter to the former being termed the **diffuser efficiency** e_d.   In ordinary cases this is about 75 per cent. The diffuser energy equation is

$$\frac{V_c^2}{2gJ} = h_d - h_c = \frac{h_d' - h_c}{e_d} \tag{111}$$

where h_d' is the enthalpy which would result from isentropic compression.

Now, inasmuch as the energy of compression $h_d - h_c$, between given terminal pressures, with a constant diffuser efficiency, depends upon the state of the substance at c which, in turn, is a function of the relative quantities of motive and evaporator vapors, it is evident that the problem becomes one of trial and error with the correct values indicated when the energy equations balance.   Since the conditions at a and at b will ordinarily be known, an approximation of the state of the mixture at c may be assumed and a trial value of V_c^2 determined from Eq. (111). This, in turn, will permit the approximate evaluation of M_a from Eq. (110).   Substitution of this value in the energy equation for the combining chamber [Eq. (107)] will indicate the correctness of the original assumption regarding the state at c. The trial and error process will be repeated until the correct and corresponding values of M_a and h_c are determined.   The true state of the vapor leaving the device at d may then be found and the whole checked by Eq. (102).

It should be noted that the critical condition for the operation of the ejector is expressed by Eq. (111).   The lower the jet velocity, the more motive steam will be required to impart to the mixture the required velocity V_c for compression.   It is evident that decreasing jet velocity would result first in excessive steam consumption and finally in failure of the device to function. Inasmuch as the jet energy is largely dependent upon the condition of the steam supplied to the nozzle, the approximate limiting condition may be easily determined for any specific case by the application of Eq. (108) in which, for large quantities of motive steam, M_a may be considered equal to $M_a + 1$. The minimum available energy for the motive steam thus may be expressed as

$$h_A - h_a' = \frac{V_c^2}{2gJe_ee_n} = \frac{h_d - h_c}{e_ee_n} \tag{112}$$

in which V_c is the velocity required for compression of, practically, the motive vapor only from the state at c to the required condenser pressure.

The extreme sensitivity of the specific steam consumption to the jet velocity, when nearing the critical minimum, results in an inherent inflexibility in load carrying ability which is characteristic of the ejector type of compressor. In this respect the ejector is similar in action to the injector for which the rate of discharge of water is limited to a very small range, *i.e.*, it will either deliver a fairly fixed quantity or none at all. This characteristic has led to the incorporation in some cases of several ejectors in a single machine in order to make possible the economical variation in load by cutting out entire units as desired.

Inspection of the energy equations set forth in the preceding paragraphs will demonstrate that as V_c is increased, due to an increase in the required work of compression, the specific steam consumption will also rise. The increase in steam consumption becomes more marked as the limit of the ejector is approached, so that it is particularly important in this type of system to operate with as high an evaporator pressure and as low a condenser pressure as possible.

In practice, for the purpose of securing better entrainment, manufacturers frequently use a nozzle assembly with several small nozzles in place of the single larger one shown for simplicity in Fig. 51.

Example.—A steam jet water vapor machine is to produce 250 gal. per min. of chilled water at 45°F. The supply water is at 60°F., and the quality of the vapor leaving the evaporator and entering the ejector is 0.97. The condenser pressure is 2 in. Hg abs. Condensate leaves the condenser at 90°F. (These data correspond to a previous example.) The motive steam is supplied at 140 lb. abs., 370°F. Nozzle efficiency = 90 per cent. Entrainment efficiency = 65 per cent. Diffuser efficiency = 75 per cent. The steam consumption of the auxiliary ejectors may be considered as 6 per cent of the total. Neglect the power demands of water pumps.

Calculate: (*a*) The steam consumption of the main ejector, pounds per hour and pounds per hour per ton; (*b*) the total steam consumption, pounds per hour and pounds per hour per ton; (*c*) the heat rejected in the primary condenser, Btu per minute and Btu per minute per ton.

Solution (Refer to Fig. 51):

$h_A = 1203.5$ at 140 lb. abs., 370°F.

$h_a' = 803$ (after isentropic expansion to 0.3 in. Hg)

$h_A - h_a' = 400.5$ Btu per lb. motive steam

$h_A - h_a = 0.9(400.5) = 360.5$ Btu per lb. $V_a = 224\sqrt{360.5} =$
4250 ft. per sec.

$h_a = 1203.5 - 360.5 = 843; x_a = 0.778; x_b = 0.97; h_b = 1049.4$

First trial:

Assume $x_c = 0.87$, for which $h_c = 943$

Then $h_d' = 1043$ (after isentropic compression to 2 in. Hg);

$h_d' - h_c = 100$ Btu; $h_d - h_c = \dfrac{100}{0.75} = 133.3$ Btu

From Eq. (111),

$$V_c^2 = 133.3(2)gJ = 6,680,000$$

From Eq. (110),

$$M_a = \frac{6,680,000}{0.65(4250)^2 - 6,680,000} = 1.31 \text{ lb. per lb. of evaporator vapor}$$

Using this value for M_a in Eq. (107),

$$h_c = \frac{1.31(1203.5) + 1049.4 - 2.31(6,680,000/50,100)}{2.31} = 1004$$

Second trial:

$h_c = 1004; h_d' = 1113; h_d' - h_c = 109; h_d - h_c = \dfrac{109}{0.75} = 145.$

$V_c^2 = 145(50,100) = 7,270,000$

$$M_a = \frac{7,270,000}{0.65(4250)^2 - 7,270,000} = 1.61 \text{ lb. per lb. evaporator vapor}$$

$$h_c = \frac{1.61(1203.5) + 1049.4 - \dfrac{2.61(7,270,000)}{50,100}}{2.61} = 1000; x_c = 0.925.$$

Third trial:

$h_c = 1000; \; h_d' = 1108; \; h_d' - h_c = 108; \; h_d - h_c = \dfrac{108}{0.75} = 144.$

$h_d = 1000 + 144 = 1144; \; V_c^2 = 144(50,100) = 7,215,000.$

$M_a = \dfrac{7,215,000}{11,770,000 - 7,215,000} = 1.58$ lb. per lb. evaporator vapor

Checking by Eq. (102):

$\qquad 1.58(1203.5) + 1049.4 = 2.58(1144)$

The result of this is 2951 = 2951.5.

(*a*) (Data as necessary taken from previous examples):
   Evaporator vapor = 30.66 lb. per min.
   Ejector steam consumption = 1.58(30.66) = 48.5 lb. per min., or
   $\qquad\qquad\qquad\qquad\qquad\qquad\qquad\qquad\qquad\qquad$ 2910 lb. per hr.

   Steam rate = $\dfrac{48.5}{156.6} = 0.31$ lb. per min. per ton, or 18.6 lb. per hr.

   $\hfill$ per ton

(*b*) Total steam consumption = $\dfrac{2910}{0.94} = 3100$ lb. per hr. or 19.8 lb. per

   $\hfill$ hr. per ton

(*c*) Steam to primary condenser = 30.66 + 48.5 = 79.16 lb. per min.
   $Q = 79.16(1144 - 58) = 85,970$ Btu per min., or 549 Btu per min.

   $\hfill$ per ton

The heat required for the generation of the motive steam will be $h_A - h_5$ (see Figs. 50, 51), or, in this instance, $1203.5 - 58 = 1145.5$ Btu per lb. The ratio of the refrigerating effect to the heat supplied to produce that effect is therefore $= 12,000/19.8(1145.5) = 0.529$.

Like the absorption system, the steam jet water vapor cycle requires but a very small proportion of mechanical energy for its operation. A coefficient of performance may not, therefore, be truly expressed for this type of machine, but a pseudocoefficient can be arbitrarily devised for the purpose of comparison with other types of systems. There is no standard procedure for this, but, if the motive steam were used in, say a turbine to drive a compressor, about 50 per cent of the energy available in expanding to *condenser* pressure might be considered as the turbine work output and the compressor input. For the last example, the energy available per pound of motive steam between 140 lb. abs., 370°F., and 2 in. Hg abs. is 317.5 Btu per lb. The coefficient of performance would thus be, according to this standard, 12,000/[19.8(0.5)(317.5)] = 3.82, based upon total steam consumption. The corresponding horsepower per ton would be 1.23.

As a practical problem, the determination of the minimum available energy of the motive steam at which the ejector will operate is not of particular importance since excessive steam consumption will have rendered the operation unsatisfactory long before this point is reached. However, the condition of the motive steam to be supplied to an ejector for any given maximum allowable steam consumption, as dictated, for example, by cooling water considerations, may frequently be of interest. This may be closely approximated by the application of the principles presented in the preceding paragraphs.

PROBLEMS

35. A water vapor refrigerating system with centrifugal compression is to have 250 tons capacity with chilled water at 45°F. Condenser pressure is 1 lb. per sq. in. abs. Condensate leaves the condenser at 90°F. Water is supplied to the evaporator at 70°F. Vapor leaving the evaporator has a quality of 95 per cent. Compressor efficiency is 65 per cent. Power for auxiliaries is not to be considered.

Calculate: (a) The quantity of chilled water, pounds per minute and gallons per minute; (b) the volume of evaporator vapor handled by the compressor, cubic feet per minute; (c) the volume of vapor discharged by the compressor, cubic feet per minute; (d) the compressor horsepower and horsepower per ton; (e) the heat rejected to the condenser water, Btu per minute, and the condenser water required with a 12° rise, pounds per minute and gallons per minute; (f) the coefficient of performance.

36. For the machine of Prob. 35, the chilled water temperature is to be changed to (i) 50°F.; (ii) 40°F.; (iii) 35°F. Assume the volume of suction vapor handled by the compressor to remain constant at the value determined in Prob. 35.

Calculate for each case: (a) The chilled water quantity, pounds per minute and gallons per minute; (b) the capacity of the machine in tons; (c) the compressor horsepower and horsepower per ton; (d) the coefficient of performance.

37. Dry saturated steam at 25 lb. per sq. in. gage pressure is to be used to operate a steam jet refrigerating system. Calculate the steam consumption of the main jet in pounds per hour per ton for the following conditions: condenser pressure, 1 lb. abs.; supply water at 70°F.; chilled water at 50°F.; nozzle efficiency, 94 per cent; entrainment efficiency, 65 per cent; diffuser efficiency, 75 per cent; evaporator vapor enters the ejector with 3 per cent moisture.

38. Other conditions given in the preceding problem remaining the same, determine the main ejector steam consumption in pounds per hour per ton for chilled water temperatures of (a) 45°F.; (b) 40°F.; (c) 35°F. Conversely, for a fixed quantity of motive steam, find the percentage capacity for each of the above chilled water temperatures based upon the capacity at 50°F. as 100 per cent.

39. It is desired, in a steam jet system, to produce 500 gal. per min. of chilled water at 45°F. from supply water at 67°F. The steam consumption is not to exceed 15,000 lb. per hour, of which the main jets may be assumed to use 94 per cent. Condenser saturation temperature is 95°F. $e_n = 0.92$; $e_e = 0.65$; and $e_d = 0.75$. Quality leaving the evaporator is 96 per cent.

Determine the minimum absolute pressure for dry saturated motive steam.

CHAPTER XII

OTHER APPLICATIONS

ADSORPTION SYSTEM

Some solids exhibit the peculiar characteristic of attracting gases or vapors and holding them in a state of considerable density comparable to that of the liquid phase for the gases involved. The process is known as **adsorption;** the solid adsorbing material is called the **adsorbent,** and the fluid adsorbed is the **adsorbate.** Adsorption appears to be, in some cases, a phenomenon of surface attraction for which there exists no definitely proved theory. For adsorbents of this class it follows that the quantity of adsorbate held will be proportional to the extent of the surface exposed, and substances which exist with a naturally large ratio of surface to actual substance volume are therefore the best surface adsorbents. In other cases, capillary condensation is apparently more important than surface attraction. For this there is a well-founded theory by which it may be shown that a capillary is capable, under certain conditions, of so acting upon a vapor as to cause its condensation and retention within the capillary. Adsorbents of this class are porous in structure with pores of a variety of sizes but all capillary in nature. Most practical adsorbents probably utilize both principles in their action. The extent of the interior surfaces of these substances may be judged from the fact that some adsorbents are capable of adsorbing up to 20 per cent or more of their weight in adsorbate.

For any adsorbent there exists an equilibrium concentration of adsorbate which is dependent upon the temperature and the vapor pressure. In general, the amount of adsorbate which may be held increases as the vapor pressure is increased and as the temperature is decreased, the characteristics in this respect being roughly comparable to those of liquid absorbents (Chap. IX). This permits the alternate adsorption and recovery of a vapor by the simple manipulation of temperatures. Since adsorption is affected in an inverse manner by pressure, the necessary temperature range will depend somewhat upon the respective pressures existing during adsorption and recovery.

The process of adsorption is accompanied by an evolution of heat. Conversely, the liberation of a vapor from the adsorbent requires heat. These energy quantities include the latent heat of vaporization as well as an additional amount, termed **heat of adsorption,** which probably results from compression of the adsorbate to a higher density than that of the normal liquid. Some authorities include both heat quantities in the heat of adsorption. The heat of adsorption, like the heat of absorption, may be expressed as the **differential** heat of adsorption or as the **integral** heat of adsorption depending upon whether or not the adsorbate is added to a gas-free adsorbent or to an adsorbent on which some adsorbate is already present. Also like the heat of solution, the magnitude of the heat of adsorption varies with the concentration, being largest at lower concentrations. There are but few data extant concerning the heats of adsorption of even relatively widely used substances, and authorities disagree regarding its importance in engineering calculations. It appears, however, that the heat of adsorption, as used here, may be neglected in cases which do not involve low adsorbate concentrations without vitally affecting the results.

From the foregoing it may readily be seen that adsorption can be used for the thermal compression of a refrigerant in a manner somewhat similar to that used in the absorption system. In the adsorption system, however, the combined adsorbent and refrigerant may not readily be circulated, as is the solution in an absorption machine, between "adsorber" and "generator," and the one device will evidently have to serve both purposes. The adsorber must thus be alternately heated and cooled with the result that the system will be intermittent in operation. The cycle as a whole may be divided into two general processes, the *refrigerating* process during which adsorption of the refrigerant takes place, and the *restoration* or *regeneration* process during which the refrigerant is distilled from the adsorbent.

The simplest adsorption machine is composed of but two units, each of which must, however, fulfill a dual function. The units are an adsorber, which also acts as a still, and an evaporator, which is alternately used as a condenser. These two parts must be connected together, a single pipe sufficing for this purpose.

During the restoration process, heat is supplied to the adsorber and vapor is driven off. At the same time, the evaporator is kept relatively cool by the application of cooling air or water. Now the evaporation of refrigerant from the adsorbent into the fixed volume of the apparatus causes the pressure to rise until condensation occurs. Thereafter, vapor is simply transferred by evaporation in the adsorber and condensation in the evaporator. When the concentration on the adsorbent has diminished to about as low a value as it will for the pressure and temperature existing, the process is terminated by the removal of the heat source from the adsorber. This leaves the active refrigerant very largely collected as a liquid in the evaporator. The refrigerating process is now commenced by transferring the source of natural cooling medium, air or water, from the evaporator to the adsorber, while the evaporator is exposed to the substance from which heat is to be removed. The pressure within the apparatus is diminished by adsorption to the point where vaporization takes place in the evaporator at low temperature. This will be accompanied by a refrigerating effect in the usual manner. The action ceases when the adsorbate attains the equilibrium concentration, at which point the proper changes are made for a repetition of the cycle.

The principal disadvantage in the simple system just described lies in the necessity for placing the evaporator alternately in a position to reject heat to a natural receiver and then in a position to absorb heat from the refrigerated substance. This involves practical difficulties which are prohibitive in any but the smallest units. A more practicable system would provide both evaporator and condenser instead of having one device serve in the dual capacity. The schematic arrangement for a system of this type is shown in Fig. 52.

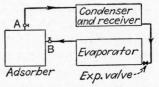

Fig. 52.—Elementary adsorption system.

Because the adsorbent must be heated and cooled yet may not readily be transferred, both adsorption and distillation have to be accomplished within the single apparatus in any system. This, however, does not constitute a major difficulty in practice. In the system illustrated in Fig. 52, the condenser is permanently connected to a supply of cooling water or air, and the evaporator is continually in contact with the refrigerated substance. Arrangements must be made to provide the adsorber with either heat or cooling water as required. The restoration process takes place with valve *A* open, valve *B* closed, and heat supplied to the adsorber. The refrigerant is condensed and stored in the condenser. After the termination of this action, the refrigerating process is carried out with valve *A* closed, *B* open, and heat removed from the adsorber. The refrigeration is intermittent but might conceivably be rendered continuous by the employment of two adsorbers which would act alternately.

The energy quantities for the adsorption system may be easily calculated by the application of methods frequently discussed heretofore if dependable data on the heat of adsorption and on equilibrium conditions are available. In the absence of such data, approximate results may be obtained, neglecting the heat of adsorption, insofar as heat quantities are concerned, although no estimate may be made of the quantity of adsorbent required for a given capacity. In practical energy computations it should not be forgotten that the heat capacities of the adsorber and the adsorbent themselves must be considered in the heating and cooling processes which accompany the periodic recovery and adsorption of the refrigerant. This imposes an additional and unproductive heating and cooling load upon the system. In the absorption system, this loss was minimized by operating the absorber and generator as separate units and by the use of the heat exchanger. In the adsorption machine the loss may be reduced by decreasing the frequency of heating and cooling through the use of larger amounts of adsorbent. If carried very far, however, this method has disadvantages, such as increased space requirements, which overcome the saving in heat so effected. The quantity of adsorbent used in any specific case is therefore a compromise between these two considerations.

Characteristics desired in adsorbents for use in refrigerating systems are large adsorbate capacity relative to total adsorbent volume, good thermal conductivity, low thermal capacity, durability, and no tendency for chemical reaction with the refrigerant. No actual adsorbent can, of course, satisfy all of these specifications. Of the many substances which will act as adsorbents, the most widely used for refrigeration is **silica gel**

(SiO_2). This glasslike substance is highly porous with resulting good capacity, but its thermal conductivity is poor and there is apparently an unfavorable reaction with ammonia. Activated charcoal from many sources is another adsorbent with good capacity. Other solids, such as activated alumina, are frequently used for the adsorption of water vapor from the atmosphere.

HEAT PUMP AS HEATING DEVICE

The removal of heat at relatively low temperature in order to produce a refrigerating effect has so far been considered the prime function of the heat pump, but it is evident that the heat rejected from the device might be used to supply heat, as to a building, at relatively high temperature. The application of this principle was proposed by Lord Kelvin in 1852—he called the unit a "warming engine"—and the idea is therefore almost as old as the refrigerating machine itself. Such a **heating cycle** may not properly be termed a refrigerating system since cooling is not the object, but essentially it does not differ from the refrigerating cycle, the only difference being that the heat rejected from the system is utilized in the heating cycle while the heat supplied is used in the refrigerating machine.

From the standpoint of pure economy of energy, the heating cycle is unsurpassed since it takes a large proportion of the heat which it supplies to a building from the low temperature outside air, or other natural source, and requires only the relatively small amount of motive energy to be supplied at cost to the consumer. But the energy input to operate a compression machine is high grade and costly, while heat for a building may be satisfactorily derived directly from the combustion of fuel which provides a much cheaper form of energy, unit for unit. While the *energy* economy may thus be good, the first cost of the heating cycle is high, and it cannot ordinarily compete with more conventional heating systems on the cost basis which is usually the ultimate criterion of practicability. The heat pump, however, possesses the undoubted advantage over the combustion heating system of the ability to also cool a building in summer by simply reversing the flow of energy in order to remove heat from inside and reject it to the outside air. When there is not too great a discrepancy between the summer and winter loads, the warming engine may conceivably become feasible. It would thus be expected to apply to best advantage in moderate climates without extreme winter temperatures. The natural resources of the locality would also be an important factor in determining the desirability of using, for instance, the electrically driven heating cycle—the most favorable location from this standpoint being one in which the price of fuels is high and in which there is an abundance of hydroelectric power.

In order to illustrate the general scheme with a simple system, consider a building (Fig. 53) to which 100,000 Btu per hr. must

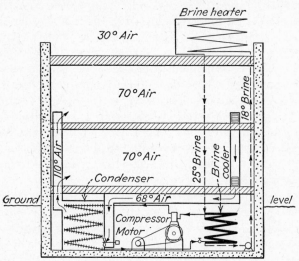

Fig. 53.—The heating cycle.

be supplied with the outside air at 30°F. in order to maintain an indoor temperature of 70°F. A variety of arrangements is possible, but a simple vapor compression system is here used with electric motor drive. Heat is received by the refrigerant from brine in a brine cooler, the brine in turn receiving heat from the atmosphere through coils located on the roof. Heat is rejected from the machine in an air-cooled condenser, the air so heated being then circulated through the building. Air and brine temperatures have been selected to indicate the sacrifices which must be made in order to secure adequate heat transfer. For this case, the machine would have to operate between pressures corresponding to about 13°F. in the evaporator and to 115 to 120°F. in the condenser. These conditions are considerably more severe than the outdoor and indoor temperatures alone would appear to indicate. It may thus be seen that the heat transfer losses in a system of this sort would be relatively very large but might be somewhat reduced by such modifications as direct expansion without the medium of brine, either by use of an outside evaporator or by passing outdoor air through an indoor evaporator by means of ducts; abstraction of heat from comparatively warm sea, river, lake, or well water instead of from the outside air; and multiple condensers so arranged in series that each contributes a small temperature rise to the air and operates at a pressure adapted to the temperature of the air to which it is exposed. The last scheme renders compression of all the refrigerant to the highest pressure unnecessary and thereby effects a saving but complicates the compressor and the general operation of the unit. The second mentioned modification has attractive possibilities due to the fact that, in addition to the advantage of better heat transfer, the water could be used for heating in the winter and cooling in the summer which, because of a more even temperature than that of the atmosphere, would materially reduce the temperature range through which the machine would have to operate.

Because of the nature of the heating process, a considerable portion of the mechanical and thermal losses of the heating cycle may be utilized, either deliberately or incidentally, for direct heating of the building in which the unit operates. The heat supplied by a machine is thus the heat withdrawn from the natural source plus the heat equivalent of the work input plus such motor or engine losses as occur in the production of the work and may be utilized for heating. The effective over-all coefficient of performance for a heating cycle may be considered as the ratio of the total amount of heat supplied by the unit to the corresponding purchased energy required. The latter would be, for an electric motor-driven unit, the electrical energy input; for an engine driven unit, the energy input in the fuel.

Example.—For the system shown in Fig. 53 in which the building requires 100,000 Btu per hr., calculate: (*a*) The capacity of the unit, tons (as a refrigerating machine); (*b*) the motor horsepower; (*c*) the hourly energy input to the motor, Btu and kilowatt-hours; (*d*) The over-all coefficient of performance; (*e*) the heat received from the outside air, Btu per hour; (*f*) the electrical energy consumption per hour for direct heating, kilowatt-hours; (g) the coal consumption for direct heating (50 per cent furnace efficiency), pounds per hour; (h) the oil consumption for direct heating (65 per cent furnace efficiency), pounds per hour and gallons per hour; (i) the natural gas consumption for direct heating (70 per cent furnace efficiency), cubic feet per hour; (j) the manufactured gas consumption for direct heating (70 per cent furnace efficiency), cubic feet per hour.

For this case, the power consumption (motor output) for the unit, considered as a refrigerating machine, may be taken as 1.7 hp. per ton. Motor efficiency, 0.87.   Heats of combustion: coal, 14,000 Btu per lb.; oil, 19,000 Btu per lb.; natural gas, 1100 Btu per cu. ft.; manufactured gas, 600 Btu per cu. ft.   Specific gravity of fuel oil, 0.88.

Solution:

1.7 hp. = 1.7(2544) = 4325 Btu per hr.

Motor input = $\dfrac{4325}{0.87}$ = 4970 Btu per hr. per ton

The motor loss is therefore 4970 − 4325 = 645 Btu per hr. per ton which may be considered as applied to direct heating.

Heat output of condenser (and cylinder jacket) per ton = 12,000 + 4325 = 16,325 Btu per hr.

Total heat output of machine per ton = 16,325 + 645 = 16,970 Btu per hr.

In this instance this is, of course, equivalent to 12,000 + 4970.

(a) Capacity of unit, considered as a refrigerating machine = $\dfrac{100,000}{16,970}$
= 5.89 tons

(b) Motor hp. = 5.89(1.7) = 10.0

(c) Motor input = $\dfrac{10(2544)}{0.87}$ = 29,240 Btu per hr. or 8.58 kw.

(d) Coefficient of performance = $\dfrac{100,000}{29,240}$ = 3.42

(e) Heat received from outside air = 5.89(12,000) = 70,680 Btu per hr.

(f) Electric energy for direct heating = $\dfrac{100,000}{3412}$ = 29.3 kw.

(g) Coal for direct heating = $\dfrac{100,000}{0.5(14,000)}$ = 14.3 lb. per hr.

(h) Oil for direct heating = $\dfrac{100,000}{0.65(19,000)}$ = 8.1 lb. per hr. or $\dfrac{8.1}{0.88(8.33)}$
= 1.1 gal. per hr.

(*i*) Natural gas for direct heating $= \dfrac{100,000}{0.7(1100)} = 130$ cu. ft. per hr.

(*j*) Manufactured gas for direct heating $= \dfrac{100,000}{0.7(600)} = 238$ cu. ft. per hr.

It is interesting to note the possibilities in Diesel engine drive for this unit. Taking the specific fuel consumption of the engine as 0.45 lb. per bhp.-hr., the fuel required per ton (refrigerating) capacity will be $1.7(0.45) = 0.765$ lb. per hr. representing $0.765(19,000) = 14,535$ Btu per hr. Of this, 4325 Btu per hr. per ton leave the engine in the form of work and the remainder, 10,210 Btu per hr. per ton, are rejected by the engine in cooling water, exhaust, and by radiation. Much of this loss may be recovered and applied to direct heating. Assuming 80 per cent of the waste heat recovered, the heat supplied to the building per ton capacity is $16,325 + 0.8(10,210) = 24,495$ Btu per hr.

$$\text{Capacity required} = \frac{100,000}{24,495} = 4.08 \text{ tons}$$
$$\text{Power required} = 4.08(1.7) = 6.94 \text{ hp.}$$
$$\text{Fuel required} = 6.94(0.45) = 3.12 \text{ lb. per hr. or}$$
$$0.425 \text{ gal. per hr.}$$
$$\text{Coefficient of performance} = \frac{100,000}{3.12(19,000)} = 1.7$$

Relative fuel and electrical energy costs may be readily approximated for any given locality from such data as were obtained in the foregoing example. Cost calculations will indicate that, on the basis of fuel consumption alone, the Diesel driven heating unit would be more economical than any of the other heating systems, including direct heating with bituminous coal, in many localities. As a heating unit alone, however, the initial cost of the heating cycle is greater than that of any of the other systems; but when a substantial proportion of the capacity of the system may be applied to cooling in the summer, the combined heating and air-conditioning first cost should compare favorably with that of a conventional heating plant plus air-conditioning equipment. For this reason, air conditioning would preferably be incorporated with the heating cycle.

For winter operation a humidifier would be used and provision would be made for ventilation by the admission of the required amount of fresh air to be conditioned and mixed with that which is recirculated.   For summer use, the condenser and evaporator, as shown in Fig. 53, would be so connected that they would exchange functions, the summer evaporator acting as an air cooler and dehumidifier.   The heat removed from the inside air would be rejected, along with the heat equivalent of the compressor work, to the atmosphere or to the water which acts as the source of heat for cold weather operation and as the cooling medium in warm weather.

PROBLEMS

40. Assuming the heat loss from a building to be 4000 Btu per hr. per deg. temperature difference between outside and inside, calculate the local energy cost per day of 24 hr. of maintaining a uniform indoor temperature of 70°F., using such of the following direct heating methods as are applicable: (*a*) anthracite coal; (*b*) bituminous coal; (*c*) oil; (*d*) natural gas; (*e*) manufactured gas; (*f*) electrical; for an outdoor temperature either corresponding to the local winter mean or of 30°F. Take furnace efficiencies conforming to good practice for the type of system considered.

41. Consider the installation of a heating cycle for the building in Prob. 40 with the same outdoor and indoor temperatures.   Direct expansion is to be used with an outdoor evaporator operating at a saturation temperature 15° lower than the outdoor temperature.   The inside air will be heated to a temperature such that the condenser will operate at 125°F. saturation.   The power consumption (compressor input) may be assumed as 1.65 times the Carnot cycle power based upon high and low saturation temperatures.

a. Determine for electric drive, using a reasonable motor efficiency: (i) the required refrigeration capacity of the machine in tons; (ii) the horsepower output of the driving motor; (iii) the kilowatt input to the motor; (iv) the local cost of energy per day.

b. Determine for Diesel engine drive, using a reasonable specific fuel consumption and considering 75 per cent of the waste heat as recoverable: (i) the refrigeration capacity required; (ii) the engine horsepower; (iii) the fuel consumption per hour and per day; (iv) the local cost of fuel per day.

TABLE I.—SATURATED AMMONIA: TEMPERATURE TABLE

Temperature, degrees Fahrenheit	Pressure		Volume vapor, ft.³/lb.	Density vapor, lb./ft.³	Enthalpy		Latent heat, Btu/lb.	Entropy		Temperature, degrees Fahrenheit
	Absolute, lb./in.²	Gage, lb./in.²			Liquid, Btu/lb.	Vapor, Btu/lb.		Liquid, Btu/lb. degrees Fahrenheit	Vapor, Btu/lb. degrees Fahrenheit	
t	p	$g.\ p.$	v_g	$1/v_g$	h_f	h_g	h_{fg}	s_f	s_g	t
−60	5.55	*18.6	44.73	0.02235	−21.2	589.6	610.8	−0.0517	1.4769	−60
−59	5.74	*18.2	43.37	0.02306	−20.1	590.0	610.1	−0.0490	1.4741	−59
−58	5.93	*17.8	42.05	0.02378	−19.1	590.4	609.5	−0.0464	1.4713	−58
−57	6.13	*17.4	40.79	0.02452	−18.0	590.8	608.8	−0.0438	1.4686	−57
−56	6.33	*17.0	39.56	0.02528	−17.0	591.2	608.2	−0.0412	1.4658	−56
−55	6.54	*16.6	38.38	0.02605	−15.9	591.6	607.5	−0.0386	1.4631	−55
−54	6.75	*16.2	37.24	0.02685	−14.8	592.1	606.9	−0.0360	1.4604	−54
−53	6.97	*15.7	36.15	0.02766	−13.8	592.4	606.2	−0.0334	1.4577	−53
−52	7.20	*15.3	35.09	0.02850	−12.7	592.9	605.6	−0.0307	1.4551	−52
−51	7.43	*14.8	34.06	0.02936	−11.7	593.2	604.9	−0.0281	1.4524	−51
−50	7.67	*14.3	33.08	0.03023	−10.6	593.7	604.3	−0.0256	1.4497	−50
−49	7.91	*13.8	32.12	0.03113	− 9.6	594.0	603.6	−0.0230	1.4471	−49
−48	8.16	*13.3	31.20	0.03205	− 8.5	594.4	602.9	−0.0204	1.4445	−48
−47	8.42	*12.8	30.31	0.03299	− 7.4	594.9	602.3	−0.0179	1.4419	−47
−46	8.68	*12.2	29.45	0.03395	− 6.4	595.2	601.6	−0.0153	1.4393	−46
−45	8.95	*11.7	28.62	0.03494	− 5.3	595.6	600.9	−0.0127	1.4368	−45
−44	9.23	*11.1	27.82	0.03595	− 4.3	596.0	600.3	−0.0102	1.4342	−44
−43	9.51	*10.6	27.04	0.03698	− 3.2	596.4	599.6	−0.0076	1.4317	−43
−42	9.81	*10.0	26.29	0.03804	− 2.1	596.8	598.9	−0.0051	1.4292	−42
−41	10.10	*9.3	25.56	0.03912	− 1.1	597.2	598.3	−0.0025	1.4267	−41
−40	10.41	*8.7	24.86	0.04022	0.0	597.6	597.6	0.0000	1.4242	−40
−39	10.72	*8.1	24.18	0.04135	1.1	598.0	596.9	0.0025	1.4217	−39
−38	11.04	*7.4	23.53	0.04251	2.1	598.3	596.2	0.0051	1.4193	−38
−37	11.37	*6.8	22.89	0.04369	3.2	598.7	595.5	0.0076	1.4169	−37
−36	11.71	*6.1	22.27	0.04489	4.3	599.1	594.8	0.0101	1.4144	−36
−35	12.05	*5.4	21.68	0.04613	5.3	599.5	594.2	0.0126	1.4120	−35
−34	12.41	*4.7	21.10	0.04739	6.4	599.9	593.5	0.0151	1.4096	−34
−33	12.77	*3.9	20.54	0.04868	7.4	600.2	592.8	0.0176	1.4072	−33
−32	13.14	*3.2	20.00	0.04999	8.5	600.6	592.1	0.0201	1.4048	−32
−31	13.52	*2.4	19.48	0.05134	9.6	601.0	591.4	0.0226	1.4025	−31
−30	13.90	*1.6	18.97	0.05271	10.7	601.4	590.7	0.0250	1.4001	−30
−29	14.30	*0.8	18.48	0.05411	11.7	601.7	590.0	0.0275	1.3978	−29
−28	14.71	0.0	18.00	0.05555	12.8	602.1	589.3	0.0300	1.3955	−28
−27	15.12	0.4	17.54	0.05701	13.9	602.5	588.6	0.0325	1.3932	−27
−26	15.55	0.8	17.09	0.05850	14.9	602.8	587.9	0.0350	1.3909	−26
−25	15.98	1.3	16.66	0.06003	16.0	603.2	587.2	0.0374	1.3886	−25
−24	16.42	1.7	16.24	0.06158	17.1	603.6	586.5	0.0399	1.3863	−24
−23	16.88	2.2	15.83	0.06317	18.1	603.9	585.8	0.0423	1.3840	−23
−22	17.34	2.6	15.43	0.06479	19.2	604.3	585.1	0.0448	1.3818	−22
−21	17.81	3.1	15.05	0.06644	20.3	604.6	584.3	0.0472	1.3796	−21
−20	18.30	3.6	14.68	0.06813	21.4	605.0	583.6	0.0497	1.3774	−20
−19	18.79	4.1	14.32	0.06985	22.4	605.3	582.9	0.0521	1.3752	−19
−18	19.30	4.6	13.97	0.07161	23.5	605.7	582.2	0.0545	1.3729	−18
−17	19.81	5.1	13.62	0.07340	24.6	606.1	581.5	0.0570	1.3708	−17
−16	20.34	5.6	13.29	0.07522	25.6	606.4	580.8	0.0594	1.3686	−16
−15	20.88	6.2	12.97	0.07709	26.7	606.7	580.0	0.0618	1.3664	−15
−14	21.43	6.7	12.66	0.07898	27.8	607.1	579.3	0.0642	1.3643	−14
−13	21.99	7.3	12.36	0.08092	28.9	607.5	578.6	0.0666	1.3621	−13
−12	22.56	7.9	12.06	0.08289	30.0	607.8	577.8	0.0690	1.3600	−12
−11	23.15	8.5	11.78	0.08490	31.0	608.1	577.1	0.0714	1.3579	−11

* Inches of mercury below 1 standard atmosphere (29.92 in.).

SOURCE.—"Tables of Thermodynamic Properties of Ammonia," *Circ. Bur. Standards* 142.

TABLE I.—SATURATED AMMONIA: TEMPERATURE TABLE (*Continued*)

Temperature, degrees Fahrenheit	Pressure		Volume vapor, ft.³/lb.	Density vapor, lb./ft.³	Enthalpy		Latent heat, Btu./lb.	Entropy		Temperature, degrees Fahrenheit
	Absolute, lb./in.²	Gage, lb./in.²			Liquid, Btu./lb.	Vapor, Btu./lb.		Liquid, Btu./lb. degrees Fahrenheit	Vapor, Btu./lb. degrees Fahrenheit	
t	p	$g.\ p.$	v_g	$1/v_g$	h_f	h_g	h_{fg}	s_f	s_g	t
−10	23.74	9.0	11.50	0.08695	32.1	608.5	576.4	0.0738	1.3558	−10
− 9	24.35	9.7	11.23	0.08904	33.2	608.8	575.6	0.0762	1.3537	− 9
− 8	24.97	10.3	10.97	0.09117	34.3	609.2	574.9	0.0786	1.3516	− 8
− 7	25.61	10.9	10.71	0.09334	35.4	609.5	574.1	0.0809	1.3495	− 7
− 6	26.26	11.6	10.47	0.09555	36.4	609.8	573.4	0.0833	1.3474	− 6
− 5	26.92	12.2	10.23	0.09780	37.5	610.1	572.6	0.0857	1.3454	− 5
− 4	27.59	12.9	9.991	0.1001	38.6	610.5	571.9	0.0880	1.3433	− 4
− 3	28.28	13.6	9.763	0.1024	39.7	610.8	571.1	0.0904	1.3413	− 3
− 2	28.98	14.3	9.541	0.1048	40.7	611.1	570.4	0.0928	1.3393	− 2
− 1	29.69	15.0	9.326	0.1072	41.8	611.4	569.6	0.0951	1.3372	− 1
0	30.42	15.7	9.116	0.1097	42.9	611.8	568.9	0.0975	1.3352	0
1	31.16	16.5	8.912	0.1122	44.0	612.1	508.1	0.0998	1.3332	1
2	31.92	17.2	8.714	0.1148	45.1	612.4	567.3	0.1022	1.3312	2
3	32.69	18.0	8.521	0.1174	46.2	612.7	566.5	0.1045	1.3292	3
4	33.47	18.8	8.333	0.1200	47.2	613.0	565.8	0.1069	1.3273	4
5	34.27	19.6	8.150	0.1227	48.3	613.3	565.0	0.1092	1.3253	5
6	35.09	20.4	7.971	0.1254	49.4	613.6	564.2	0.1115	1.3234	6
7	35.92	21.2	7.798	0.1282	50.5	613.9	563.4	0.1138	1.3214	7
8	36.77	22.1	7.629	0.1311	51.6	614.3	562.7	0.1162	1.3195	8
9	37.63	22.9	7.464	0.1340	52.7	614.6	561.9	0.1185	1.3176	9
10	38.51	23.8	7.304	0.1369	53.8	614.9	561.1	0.1208	1.3157	10
11	39.40	24.7	7.148	0.1399	54.9	615.2	560.3	0.1231	1.3137	11
12	40.31	25.6	6.996	0.1429	56.0	615.5	559.5	0.1254	1.3118	12
13	41.24	26.5	6.847	0.1460	57.1	615.8	558.7	0.1277	1.3099	13
14	42.18	27.5	6.703	0.1492	58.2	616.1	557.9	0.1300	1.3081	14
15	43.14	28.4	6.562	0.1524	59.2	616.3	557.1	0.1323	1.3062	15
16	44.12	29.4	6.425	0.1556	60.3	616.6	556.3	0.1346	1.3043	16
17	45.12	30.4	6.291	0.1590	61.4	616.9	555.5	0.1369	1.3025	17
18	46.13	31.4	6.161	0.1623	62.5	617.2	554.7	0.1392	1.3006	18
19	47.16	32.5	6.034	0.1657	63.6	617.5	553.9	0.1415	1.2988	19
20	48.21	33.5	5.910	0.1692	64.7	617.8	553.1	0.1437	1.2969	20
21	49.28	34.6	5.789	0.1728	65.8	618.0	552.2	0.1460	1.2951	21
22	50.36	35.7	5.671	0.1763	66.9	618.3	551.4	0.1483	1.2933	22
23	51.47	36.8	5.556	0.1800	68.0	618.6	550.6	0.1505	1.2915	23
24	52.59	37.9	5.443	0.1837	69.1	618.9	549.8	0.1528	1.2897	24
25	53.73	39.0	5.334	0.1875	70.2	619.1	548.9	0.1551	1.2879	25
26	54.90	40.2	5.227	0.1913	71.3	619.4	548.1	0.1573	1.2861	26
27	56.08	41.4	5.123	0.1952	72.4	619.7	547.3	0.1596	1.2843	27
28	57.28	42.6	5.021	0.1992	73.5	619.9	546.4	0.1618	1.2825	28
29	58.50	43.8	4.922	0.2032	74.6	620.2	545.6	0.1641	1.2808	29
30	59.74	45.0	4.825	0.2073	75.7	620.5	544.8	0.1663	1.2790	30
31	61.00	46.3	4.730	0.2114	76.8	620.7	543.9	0.1686	1.2773	31
32	62.29	47.6	4.637	0.2156	77.9	621.0	543.1	0.1708	1.2755	32
33	63.59	48.9	4.547	0.2199	79.0	621.2	542.2	0.1730	1.2738	33
34	64.91	50.2	4.459	0.2243	80.1	621.5	541.4	0.1753	1.2721	34
35	66.26	51.6	4.373	0.2287	81.2	621.7	540.5	0.1775	1.2704	35
36	67.63	52.9	4.289	0.2332	82.3	622.0	539.7	0.1797	1.2686	36
37	69.02	54.3	4.207	0.2377	83.4	622.2	538.8	0.1819	1.2669	37
38	70.43	55.7	4.126	0.2423	84.6	622.5	537.9	0.1841	1.2652	38
39	71.87	57.2	4.048	0.2470	85.7	622.7	537.0	0.1863	1.2635	39
40	73.32	58.6	3.971	0.2518	86.8	623.0	536.2	0.1885	1.2618	40
41	74.80	60.1	3.897	0.2566	87.9	623.2	535.3	0.1908	1.2602	41
42	76.31	61.6	3.823	0.2616	89.0	623.4	534.4	0.1930	1.2585	42
43	77.83	63.1	3.752	0.2665	90.1	623.7	533.6	0.1952	1.2568	43
44	79.38	64.7	3.682	0.2716	91.2	623.9	532.7	0.1974	1.2552	44

TABLE I.—Saturated Ammonia: Temperature Table (*Continued*)

Temperature, degrees Fahrenheit	Pressure		Volume vapor, ft.³/lb.	Density vapor, lb./ft.³	Enthalpy			Entropy		Temperature, degrees Fahrenheit
	Absolute, lb./in.²	Gage, lb./in.²			Liquid, Btu/lb.	Vapor, Btu/lb.	Latent heat, Btu/lb.	Liquid, Btu/lb. degrees Fahrenheit	Vapor, Btu/lb. degrees Fahrenheit	
t	p	g. p.	v_g	$1/v_g$	h_f	h_g	h_{fg}	s_f	s_g	t
45	80.96	66.3	3.614	0.2767	92.3	624.1	531.8	0.1996	1.2535	**45**
46	82.55	67.9	3.547	0.2819	93.5	624.4	530.9	0.2018	1.2519	46
47	84.18	69.5	3.481	0.2872	94.6	624.6	530.0	0.2040	1.2502	47
48	85.82	71.1	3.418	0.2926	95.7	624.8	529.1	0.2062	1.2486	48
49	87.49	72.8	3.355	0.2981	96.8	625.0	528.2	0.2083	1.2469	49
50	89.19	74.5	3.294	0.3036	97.9	625.2	527.3	0.2105	1.2453	**50**
51	90.91	76.2	3.234	0.3092	99.1	625.5	526.4	0.2127	1.2437	51
52	92.66	78.0	3.176	0.3149	100.2	625.7	525.5	0.2149	1.2421	52
53	94.43	79.7	3.119	0.3207	101.3	625.9	524.6	0.2171	1.2405	53
54	96.23	81.5	3.063	0.3265	102.4	626.1	523.7	0.2192	1.2389	54
55	98.06	83.4	3.008	0.3325	103.5	626.3	522.8	0.2214	1.2373	**55**
56	99.91	85.2	2.954	0.3385	104.7	626.5	521.8	0.2236	1.2357	56
57	101.8	87.1	2.902	0.3446	105.8	626.7	520.9	0.2257	1.2341	57
58	103.7	89.0	2.851	0.3508	106.9	626.9	520.0	0.2279	1.2325	58
59	105.6	90.9	2.800	0.3571	108.1	627.1	519.0	0.2301	1.2310	59
60	107.6	92.9	2.751	0.3635	109.2	627.3	518.1	0.2322	1.2294	**60**
61	109.6	94.9	2.703	0.3700	110.3	627.5	517.2	0.2344	1.2278	61
62	111.6	96.9	2.656	0.3765	111.5	627.7	516.2	0.2365	1.2262	62
63	113.6	98.9	2.610	0.3832	112.6	627.9	515.3	0.2387	1.2247	63
64	115.7	101.0	2.565	0.3899	113.7	628.0	514.3	0.2408	1.2231	64
65	117.8	103.1	2.520	0.3968	114.8	628.2	513.4	0.2430	1.2216	**65**
66	120.0	105.3	2.477	0.4037	116.0	628.4	512.4	0.2451	1.2201	66
67	122.1	107.4	2.435	0.4108	117.1	628.6	511.5	0.2473	1.2186	67
68	124.3	109.6	2.393	0.4179	118.3	628.8	510.5	0.2494	1.2170	68
69	126.5	111.8	2.352	0.4251	119.4	628.9	509.5	0.2515	1.2155	69
70	128.8	114.1	2.312	0.4325	120.5	629.1	508.6	0.2537	1.2140	**70**
71	131.1	116.4	2.273	0.4399	121.7	629.3	507.6	0.2558	1.2125	71
72	133.4	118.7	2.235	0.4474	122.8	629.4	506.6	0.2579	1.2110	72
73	135.7	121.0	2.197	0.4551	124.0	629.6	505.6	0.2601	1.2095	73
74	138.1	123.4	2.161	0.4628	125.1	629.8	504.7	0.2622	1.2080	74
75	140.5	125.8	2.125	0.4707	126.2	629.9	503.7	0.2643	1.2065	**75**
76	143.0	128.3	2.089	0.4786	127.4	630.1	502.7	0.2664	1.2050	76
77	145.4	130.7	2.055	0.4867	128.5	630.2	501.7	0.2685	1.2035	77
78	147.9	133.2	2.021	0.4949	129.7	630.4	500.7	0.2706	1.2020	78
79	150.5	135.8	1.988	0.5031	130.8	630.5	499.7	0.2728	1.2006	79
80	153.0	138.3	1.955	0.5115	132.0	630.7	498.7	0.2749	1.1991	**80**
81	155.6	140.9	1.923	0.5200	133.1	630.8	497.7	0.2769	1.1976	81
82	158.3	143.6	1.892	0.5287	134.3	631.0	496.7	0.2791	1.1962	82
83	161.0	146.3	1.861	0.5374	135.4	631.1	495.7	0.2812	1.1947	83
84	163.7	149.0	1.831	0.5462	136.6	631.3	494.7	0.2833	1.1933	84
85	166.4	151.7	1.801	0.5552	137.8	631.4	493.6	0.2854	1.1918	**85**
86	169.2	154.5	1.772	0.5643	138.9	631.5	492.6	0.2875	1.1904	86
87	172.0	157.3	1.744	0.5735	140.1	631.7	491.6	0.2895	1.1889	87
88	174.8	160.1	1.716	0.5828	141.2	631.8	490.6	0.2917	1.1875	88
89	177.7	163.0	1.688	0.5923	142.4	631.9	489.5	0.2937	1.1860	89
90	180.6	165.9	1.661	0.6019	143.5	632.0	488.5	0.2958	1.1846	**90**
91	183.6	168.9	1.635	0.6116	144.7	632.1	487.4	0.2979	1.1832	91
92	186.6	171.9	1.609	0.6214	145.8	632.2	486.4	0.3000	1.1818	92
93	189.6	174.9	1.584	0.6314	147.0	632.3	485.3	0.3021	1.1804	93
94	192.7	178.0	1.559	0.6415	148.2	632.5	484.3	0.3041	1.1789	94
95	195.8	181.1	1.534	0.6517	149.4	632.6	483.2	0.3062	1.1775	**95**
96	198.9	184.2	1.510	0.6620	150.5	632.6	482.1	0.3083	1.1761	96
97	202.1	187.4	1.487	0.6725	151.7	632.8	481.1	0.3104	1.1747	97
98	205.3	190.6	1.464	0.6832	152.9	632.9	480.0	0.3125	1.1733	98
99	208.6	193.9	1.441	0.6939	154.0	632.9	478.9	0.3145	1.1719	99

TABLE I.—SATURATED AMMONIA: TEMPERATURE TABLE (*Continued*)

Temperature, degrees Fahrenheit	Pressure		Volume vapor, ft.³/lb.	Density vapor, lb./ft.³	Enthalpy		Latent heat, Btu./lb.	Entropy		Temperature, degrees Fahrenheit
	Absolute, lb./in.²	Gage, lb./in.²			Liquid, Btu./lb.	Vapor, Btu./lb.		Liquid, Btu./lb. degrees Fahrenheit	Vapor, Btu./lb. degrees Fahrenheit	
t	p	$g.\,p.$	v_g	$1/v_g$	h_f	h_g	h_{fg}	s_f	s_g	t
100	211.9	197.2	1.419	0.7048	155.2	633.0	477.8	0.3166	1.1705	**100**
101	215.2	200.5	1.397	0.7159	156.4	633.1	476.7	0.3187	1.1691	101
102	218.6	203.9	1.375	0.7270	157.6	633.2	475.6	0.3207	1.1677	102
103	222.0	207.3	1.354	0.7384	158.7	633.3	474.6	0.3228	1.1663	103
104	225.4	210.7	1.334	0.7498	159.9	633.4	473.5	0.3248	1.1649	104
105	228.9	214.2	1.313	0.7615	161.1	633.4	472.3	0.3269	1.1635	**105**
106	232.5	217.8	1.293	0.7732	162.3	633.5	471.2	0.3289	1.1621	106
107	236.0	221.3	1.274	0.7852	163.5	633.6	470.1	0.3310	1.1607	107
108	239.7	225.0	1.254	0.7972	164.6	633.6	469.0	0.3330	1.1593	108
109	243.3	228.6	1.235	0.8095	165.8	633.7	467.9	0.3351	1.1580	109
110	247.0	232.3	1.217	0.8219	167.0	633.7	466.7	0.3372	1.1566	**110**
111	250.8	236.1	1.198	0.8344	168.2	633.8	465.6	0.3392	1.1552	111
112	254.5	239.8	1.180	0.8471	169.4	633.8	464.4	0.3413	1.1538	112
113	258.4	243.7	1.163	0.8600	170.6	633.9	463.3	0.3433	1.1524	113
114	262.2	247.5	1.145	0.8730	171.8	633.9	462.1	0.3453	1.1510	114
115	266.2	251.5	1.128	0.8862	173.0	633.9	460.9	0.3474	1.1497	**115**
116	270.1	255.4	1.112	0.8996	174.2	634.0	459.8	0.3495	1.1483	116
117	274.1	259.4	1.095	0.9132	175.4	634.0	458.6	0.3515	1.1469	117
118	278.2	263.5	1.079	0.9269	176.6	634.0	457.4	0.3535	1.1455	118
119	282.3	267.6	1.063	0.9408	177.8	634.0	456.2	0.3556	1.1441	119
120	286.4	271.7	1.047	0.9549	179.0	634.0	455.0	0.3576	1.1427	**120**
121	290.6	275.9	1.032	0.9692	180.2	634.0	453.8	0.3597	1.1414	121
122	294.8	280.1	1.017	0.9837	181.4	634.0	452.6	0.3618	1.1400	122
123	299.1	284.4	1.002	0.9983	182.6	634.0	451.4	0.3638	1.1386	123
124	303.4	288.7	0.987	1.0132	183.9	634.0	450.1	0.3659	1.1372	124
125	307.8	293.1	0.973	1.028	185.1	634.0	448.9	0.3679	1.1358	**125**

TABLE II.—SATURATED AMMONIA: ABSOLUTE-PRESSURE TABLE

Pressure (abs.), lb./in.²	Temperature, degrees Fahrenheit	Volume vapor, ft.³/lb.	Density vapor, lb./ft.³	Enthalpy		Latent heat, Btu./lb.	Entropy			Pressure (abs.), lb./in.²
				Liquid, Btu./lb.	Vapor, Btu./lb.		Liquid, Btu./lb. degrees Fahrenheit	Evaporation, Btu./lb. degrees Fahrenheit	Vapor, Btu./lb. degrees Fahrenheit	
p	t	v_g	$1/v_g$	h_f	h_g	h_{fg}	s_f	s_{fg}	s_g	p
5.0	−63.11	49.31	0.02029	−24.5	588.3	612.8	−0.0599	1.5456	1.4857	**5.0**
5.5	−60.27	45.11	0.02217	−21.5	589.5	611.0	−0.0524	1.5301	1.4777	5.5
6.0	−57.64	41.59	0.02405	−18.7	590.6	609.3	−0.0455	1.5158	1.4703	6.0
6.5	−55.18	38.59	0.02591	−16.1	591.6	607.7	−0.0390	1.5026	1.4636	6.5
7.0	−52.88	36.01	0.02777	−13.7	592.5	606.2	−0.0330	1.4904	1.4574	7.0
7.5	−50.70	33.77	0.02962	−11.3	593.4	604.7	−0.0274	1.4790	1.4516	**7.5**
8.0	−48.64	31.79	0.03146	− 9.2	594.2	603.4	−0.0221	1.4683	1.4462	8.0
8.5	−46.69	30.04	0.03329	− 7.1	595.0	602.1	−0.0171	1.4582	1.4411	8.5
9.0	−44.83	28.48	0.03511	− 5.1	595.7	600.8	−0.0123	1.4486	1.4363	9.0
9.5	−43.05	27.08	0.03693	− 3.2	596.4	599.6	−0.0077	1.4396	1.4319	9.5
10.0	−41.34	25.81	0.03874	− 1.4	597.1	598.5	−0.0034	1.4310	1.4276	**10.0**
10.5	−39.71	24.66	0.04055	+ 0.3	597.7	597.4	+0.0007	1.4228	1.4235	10.5
11.0	−38.14	23.61	0.04235	2.0	598.3	596.3	0.0047	1.4149	1.4196	11.0
11.5	−36.62	22.65	0.04414	3.6	598.9	595.3	0.0085	1.4074	1.4159	11.5
12.0	−35.16	21.77	0.04593	5.1	599.4	594.3	0.0122	1.4002	1.4124	12.0
12.5	−33.74	20.96	0.04772	6.7	600.0	593.3	0.0157	1.3933	1.4090	**12.5**
13.0	−32.37	20.20	0.04950	8.1	600.5	592.4	0.0191	1.3866	1.4057	13.0
13.5	−31.05	19.50	0.05128	9.6	601.0	591.4	0.0225	1.3801	1.4026	13.5
14.0	−29.76	18.85	0.05305	10.9	601.4	590.5	0.0257	1.3739	1.3996	14.0
14.5	−28.51	18.24	0.05482	12.2	601.9	589.7	0.0288	1.3679	1.3967	14.5
15.0	−27.29	17.67	0.05658	13.6	602.4	588.8	0.0318	1.3620	1.3938	**15.0**
15.5	−26.11	17.14	0.05834	14.8	602.8	588.0	0.0347	1.3564	1.3911	15.5
16.0	−24.95	16.64	0.06010	16.0	603.2	587.2	0.0375	1.3510	1.3885	16.0
16.5	−23.83	16.17	0.06186	17.2	603.6	586.4	0.0403	1.3456	1.3859	16.5
17.0	−22.73	15.72	0.06361	18.4	604.0	585.6	0.0430	1.3405	1.3835	17.0
17.5	−21.66	15.30	0.06535	19.6	604.4	584.8	0.0456	1.3354	1.3810	**17.5**
18.0	−20.61	14.90	0.06710	20.7	604.8	584.1	0.0482	1.3305	1.3787	18.0
18.5	−19.59	14.53	0.06884	21.8	605.1	583.3	0.0507	1.3258	1.3765	18.5
19.0	−18.58	14.17	0.07058	22.9	605.5	582.6	0.0531	1.3211	1.3742	19.0
19.5	−17.60	13.83	0.07232	23.9	605.8	581.9	0.0555	1.3166	1.3721	19.5
20.0	−16.64	13.50	0.07405	25.0	606.2	581.2	0.0578	1.3122	1.3700	**20.0**
20.5	−15.70	13.20	0.07578	26.0	606.5	580.5	0.0601	1.3078	1.3679	20.5
21.0	−14.78	12.90	0.07751	27.0	606.8	579.8	0.0623	1.3036	1.3659	21.0
21.5	−13.87	12.62	0.07924	27.9	607.1	579.2	0.0645	1.2995	1.3640	21.5
22.0	−12.98	12.35	0.08096	28.9	607.4	578.5	0.0666	1.2955	1.3621	22.0
22.5	−12.11	12.09	0.08268	29.8	607.7	577.9	0.0687	1.2915	1.3602	**22.5**
23.0	−11.25	11.85	0.08440	30.8	608.1	577.3	0.0708	1.2876	1.3584	23.0
23.5	−10.41	11.61	0.08612	31.7	608.3	576.6	0.0728	1.2838	1.3566	23.5
24.0	− 9.58	11.39	0.08783	32.6	608.6	576.0	0.0748	1.2801	1.3549	24.0
24.5	− 8.76	11.17	0.08955	33.5	608.9	575.4	0.0768	1.2764	1.3532	24.5
25.0	− 7.96	10.96	0.09126	34.3	609.1	574.8	0.0787	1.2728	1.3515	**25.0**
25.5	− 7.17	10.76	0.09297	35.2	609.4	574.2	0.0805	1.2693	1.3498	25.5
26.0	− 6.39	10.56	0.09468	36.0	609.7	573.7	0.0824	1.2658	1.3482	26.0
26.5	− 5.63	10.38	0.09638	36.8	609.9	573.1	0.0842	1.2625	1.3467	26.5
27.0	− 4.87	10.20	0.09809	37.7	610.2	572.5	0.0860	1.2591	1.3451	27.0
27.5	− 4.13	10.02	0.09979	38.4	610.4	572.0	0.0878	1.2558	1.3436	**27.5**
28.0	− 3.40	9.853	0.1015	39.3	610.7	571.4	0.0895	1.2526	1.3421	28.0
28.5	− 2.68	9.691	0.1032	40.0	610.9	570.9	0.0912	1.2494	1.3406	28.5
29.0	− 1.97	9.534	0.1049	40.8	611.1	570.3	0.0929	1.2463	1.3392	29.0
29.5	− 1.27	9.383	0.1066	41.6	611.4	569.8	0.0945	1.2433	1.3378	29.5
30	− 0.57	9.236	0.1083	42.3	611.6	569.3	0.0962	1.2402	1.3364	**30**
31	+ 0.79	8.955	0.1117	43.8	612.0	568.2	0.0993	1.2343	1.3336	31
32	2.11	8.693	0.1150	45.2	612.4	567.2	0.1024	1.2286	1.3310	32
33	3.40	8.445	0.1184	46.6	612.8	566.2	0 1055	1.2230	1.3285	33
34	4.66	8.211	0.1218	48.0	613.2	565.2	0.1084	1.2176	1.3260	34

SOURCE.—"Tables of Thermodynamic Properties of Ammonia," *Circ. Bur. Standards* 142.

TABLE II.—SATURATED AMMONIA: ABSOLUTE-PRESSURE TABLE (*Continued*)

Pressure (abs.), lb./in.²	Temperature, degrees Fahrenheit	Volume vapor, ft.³/lb.	Density vapor, lb./ft.³	Enthalpy		Latent heat, Btu/lb.	Entropy			Pressure (abs.), lb./in.²
				Liquid, Btu/lb.	Vapor, Btu/lb.		Liquid, Btu/lb. degrees Fahrenheit	Evaporation, Btu/lb. degrees Fahrenheit	Vapor, Btu/lb. degrees Fahrenheit	
p	t	v_g	$1/v_g$	h_f	h_g	h_{fg}	s_f	s_{fg}	s_g	p
35	5.89	7.991	0.1251	49.3	613.6	564.3	0.1113	1.2123	1.3236	**35**
36	7.09	7.782	0.1285	50.6	614.0	563.4	0.1141	1.2072	1.3213	36
37	8.27	7.584	0.1319	51.9	614.3	562.4	0.1168	1.2022	1.3190	37
38	9.42	7.396	0.1352	53.2	614.7	561.5	0.1195	1.1973	1.3168	38
39	10.55	7.217	0.1386	54.4	615.0	560.6	0.1221	1.1925	1.3146	39
40	11.66	7.047	0.1419	55.6	615.4	559.8	0.1246	1.1879	1.3125	**40**
41	12.74	6.885	0.1452	56.8	615.7	558.9	0.1271	1.1833	1.3104	41
42	13.81	6.731	0.1486	57.9	616.0	558.1	0.1296	1.1788	1.3084	42
43	14.85	6.583	0.1519	59.1	616.3	557.2	0.1320	1.1745	1.3065	43
44	15.88	6.442	0.1552	60.2	616.6	556.4	0.1343	1.1703	1.3046	44
45	16.88	6.307	0.1586	61.3	616.9	555.6	0.1366	1.1661	1.3027	**45**
46	17.87	6.177	0.1619	62.4	617.2	554.8	0.1389	1.1620	1.3009	46
47	18.84	6.053	0.1652	63.4	617.4	554.0	0.1411	1.1580	1.2991	47
48	19.80	5.934	0.1685	64.5	617.7	553.2	0.1433	1.1540	1.2973	48
49	20.74	5.820	0.1718	65.5	618.0	552.5	0.1454	1.1502	1.2956	49
50	21.67	5.710	0.1751	66.5	618.2	551.7	0.1475	1.1464	1.2939	**50**
51	22.58	5.604	0.1785	67.5	618.5	551.0	0.1496	1.1427	1.2923	51
52	23.48	5.502	0.1818	68.5	618.7	550.2	0.1516	1.1390	1.2906	52
53	24.36	5.404	0.1851	69.5	619.0	549.5	0.1536	1.1354	1.2890	53
54	25.23	5.309	0.1884	70.4	619.2	548.8	0.1556	1.1319	1.2875	54
55	26.09	5.218	0.1917	71.4	619.4	548.0	0.1575	1.1284	1.2859	**55**
56	26.94	5.129	0.1950	72.3	619.7	547.4	0.1594	1.1250	1.2844	56
57	27.77	5.044	0.1983	73.3	619.9	546.6	0.1613	1.1217	1.2830	57
58	28.59	4.962	0.2015	74.2	620.1	545.9	0.1631	1.1184	1.2815	58
59	29.41	4.882	0.2048	75.0	620.3	545.3	0.1650	1.1151	1.2801	59
60	30.21	4.805	0.2081	75.9	620.5	544.6	0.1668	1.1119	1.2787	**60**
61	31.00	4.730	0.2114	76.8	620.7	543.9	0.1685	1.1088	1.2773	61
62	31.78	4.658	0.2147	77.7	620.9	543.2	0.1703	1.1056	1.2759	62
63	32.55	4.588	0.2180	78.5	621.1	542.6	0.1720	1.1026	1.2746	63
64	33.31	4.519	0.2213	79.4	621.3	541.9	0.1737	1.0996	1.2733	64
65	34.06	4.453	0.2245	80.2	621.5	541.3	0.1754	1.0966	1.2720	**65**
66	34.81	4.389	0.2278	81.0	621.7	540.7	0.1770	1.0937	1.2707	66
67	35.54	4.327	0.2311	81.8	621.9	540.1	0.1787	1.0907	1.2694	67
68	36.27	4.267	0.2344	82.6	622.0	539.4	0.1803	1.0879	1.2682	68
69	36.99	4.208	0.2377	83.4	622.2	538.8	0.1819	1.0851	1.2670	69
70	37.70	4.151	0.2409	84.2	622.4	538.2	0.1835	1.0823	1.2658	**70**
71	38.40	4.095	0.2442	85.0	622.6	537.6	0.1850	1.0795	1.2645	71
72	39.09	4.041	0.2475	85.8	622.8	537.0	0.1866	1.0768	1.2634	72
73	39.78	3.988	0.2507	86.5	622.9	536.4	0.1881	1.0741	1.2622	73
74	40.46	3.937	0.2540	87.3	623.1	535.8	0.1896	1.0715	1.2611	74
75	41.13	3.887	0.2573	88.0	623.3	535.3	0.1910	1.0689	1.2599	**75**
76	41.80	3.838	0.2606	88.8	623.4	534.6	0.1925	1.0663	1.2588	76
77	42.46	3.790	0.2638	89.5	623.5	534.0	0.1940	1.0637	1.2577	77
78	43.11	3.744	0.2671	90.2	623.7	533.5	0.1954	1.0612	1.2566	78
79	43.76	3.699	0.2704	90.9	623.8	532.9	0.1968	1.0587	1.2555	79
80	44.40	3.655	0.2736	91.7	624.0	532.3	0.1982	1.0563	1.2545	**80**
81	45.03	3.612	0.2769	92.4	624.1	531.7	0.1996	1.0538	1.2534	81
82	45.66	3.570	0.2801	93.1	624.3	531.2	0.2010	1.0514	1.2524	82
83	46.28	3.528	0.2834	93.8	624.4	530.6	0.2024	1.0490	1.2514	83
84	46.89	3.488	0.2867	94.5	624.6	530.1	0.2037	1.0467	1.2504	84
85	47.50	3.449	0.2899	95.1	624.7	529.6	0.2051	1.0443	1.2494	**85**
86	48.11	3.411	0.2932	95.8	624.8	529.0	0.2064	1.0420	1.2484	86
87	48.71	3.373	0.2964	96.5	625.0	528.5	0.2077	1.0397	1.2474	87
88	49.30	3.337	0.2997	97.2	625.1	527.9	0.2090	1.0375	1.2465	88
89	49.89	3.301	0.3030	97.8	625.2	527.4	0.2103	1.0352	1.2455	89

TABLE II.—SATURATED AMMONIA: ABSOLUTE-PRESSURE TABLE (*Continued*)

Pressure (abs.), lb./in.²	Temperature, degrees Fahrenheit	Volume vapor, ft.³/lb.	Density vapor, lb./ft.³	Enthalpy		Latent heat, Btu/lb.	Entropy			Pressure (abs.), lb./in.²
				Liquid, Btu/lb.	Vapor, Btu/lb.		Liquid, Btu/lb. degrees Fahrenheit	Evaporation, Btu/lb. degrees Fahrenheit	Vapor, Btu/lb. degrees Fahrenheit	
p	t	v_g	$1/v_g$	h_f	h_g	h_{fg}	s_f	s_{fg}	s_g	p
90	50.47	3.266	0.3062	98.4	625.3	526.9	0.2115	1.0330	1.2445	**90**
91	51.05	3.231	0.3095	99.1	625.5	526.4	0.2128	1.0308	1.2436	91
92	51.62	3.198	0.3127	99.8	625.6	525.8	0.2141	1.0286	1.2427	92
93	52.19	3.165	0.3160	100.4	625.7	525.3	0.2153	1.0265	1.2418	93
94	52.76	3.132	0.3192	101.0	625.8	524.8	0.2165	1.0243	1.2408	94
95	53.32	3.101	0.3225	101.6	625.9	524.3	0.2177	1.0222	1.2399	**95**
96	53.87	3.070	0.3258	102.3	626.1	523.8	0.2190	1.0201	1.2391	96
97	54.42	3.039	0.3290	102.9	626.2	523.2	0.2201	1.0181	1.2382	97
98	54.97	3.010	0.3323	103.5	626.3	522.8	0.2213	1.0160	1.2373	98
99	55.51	2.980	0.3355	104.1	626.4	522.3	0.2225	1.0140	1.2365	99
100	56.05	2.952	0.3388	104.7	626.5	521.8	0.2237	1.0119	1.2356	**100**
102	57.11	2.896	0.3453	105.9	626.7	520.8	0.2260	1.0079	1.2339	102
104	58.16	2.843	0.3518	107.1	626.9	519.8	0.2282	1.0041	1.2323	104
106	59.19	2.791	0.3583	108.3	627.1	518.8	0.2305	1.0002	1.2307	106
108	60.21	2.741	0.3648	109.4	627.3	517.9	0.2327	0.9964	1.2291	108
110	61.21	2.693	0.3713	110.5	627.5	517.0	0.2348	0.9927	1.2275	**110**
112	62.20	2.647	0.3778	111.7	627.7	516.0	0.2369	0.9890	1.2259	112
114	63.17	2.602	0.3843	112.8	627.9	515.1	0.2390	0.9854	1.2244	114
116	64.13	2.559	0.3909	113.9	628.1	514.2	0.2411	0.9819	1.2230	116
118	65.08	2.517	0.3974	114.9	628.2	513.2	0.2431	0.9784	1.2215	118
120	66.02	2.476	0.4039	116.0	628.4	512.4	0.2452	0.9749	1.2201	**120**
122	66.94	2.437	0.4104	117.1	628.6	511.5	0.2471	0.9715	1.2186	122
124	67.86	2.399	0.4169	118.1	628.7	510.6	0.2491	0.9682	1.2173	124
126	68.76	2.362	0.4234	119.1	628.9	509.8	0.2510	0.9649	1.2159	126
128	69.65	2.326	0.4299	120.1	629.0	508.9	0.2529	0.9616	1.2145	128
130	70.53	2.291	0.4364	121.1	629.2	508.1	0.2548	0.9584	1.2132	**130**
132	71.40	2.258	0.4429	122.1	629.3	507.2	0.2567	0.9552	1.2119	132
134	72.26	2.225	0.4494	123.1	629.5	506.4	0.2585	0.9521	1.2106	134
136	73.11	2.193	0.4559	124.1	629.6	505.5	0.2603	0.9490	1.2093	136
138	73.95	2.162	0.4624	125.1	629.8	504.7	0.2621	0.9460	1.2081	138
140	74.79	2.132	0.4690	126.0	629.9	503.9	0.2638	0.9430	1.2068	**140**
142	75.61	2.103	0.4755	126.9	630.0	503.1	0.2656	0.9400	1.2056	142
144	76.42	2.075	0.4820	127.9	630.2	502.3	0.2673	0.9371	1.2044	144
146	77.23	2.047	0.4885	128.8	630.3	501.5	0.2690	0.9342	1.2032	146
148	78.03	2.020	0.4951	129.7	630.4	500.7	0.2707	0.9313	1.2020	148
150	78.81	1.994	0.5016	130.6	630.5	499.9	0.2724	0.9285	1.2009	**150**
152	79.60	1.968	0.5081	131.5	630.6	499.1	0.2740	0.9257	1.1997	152
154	80.37	1.943	0.5147	132.4	630.7	498.3	0.2756	0.9229	1.1985	154
156	81.13	1.919	0.5212	133.3	630.9	497.6	0.2772	0.9202	1.1974	156
158	81.89	1.895	0.5277	134.2	631.0	496.8	0.2788	0.9175	1.1963	158
160	82.64	1.872	0.5343	135.0	631.1	496.1	0.2804	0.9148	1.1952	**160**
162	83.39	1.849	0.5408	135.9	631.2	495.3	0.2820	0.9122	1.1942	162
164	84.12	1.827	0.5473	136.8	631.3	494.5	0.2835	0.9096	1.1931	164
166	84.85	1.805	0.5539	137.6	631.4	493.8	0.2850	0.9070	1.1920	166
168	85.57	1.784	0.5604	138.4	631.5	493.1	0.2866	0.9044	1.1910	168
170	86.29	1.764	0.5670	139.3	631.6	492.3	0.2881	0.9019	1.1900	**170**
172	87.00	1.744	0.5735	140.1	631.7	491.6	0.2895	0.8994	1.1889	172
174	87.71	1.724	0.5801	140.9	631.7	490.8	0.2910	0.8969	1.1879	174
176	88.40	1.705	0.5866	141.7	631.8	490.1	0.2925	0.8944	1.1869	176
178	89.10	1.686	0.5932	142.5	631.9	489.4	0.2939	0.8920	1.1859	178
180	89.78	1.667	0.5998	143.3	632.0	488.7	0.2954	0.8896	1.1850	**180**
182	90.46	1.649	0.6063	144.1	632.1	488.0	0.2968	0.8872	1.1840	182
184	91.14	1.632	0.6129	144.8	632.1	487.3	0.2982	0.8848	1.1830	184
186	91.80	1.614	0.6195	145.6	632.2	486.6	0.2996	0.8825	1.1821	186
188	92.47	1.597	0.6261	146.4	632.3	485.9	0.3010	0.8801	1.1811	188

TABLE II.—SATURATED AMMONIA: ABSOLUTE-PRESSURE TABLE (*Continued*)

Pressure (abs.), lb./in.²	Temperature, degrees Fahrenheit	Volume vapor, ft.³/lb.	Density vapor, lb./ft.³	Enthalpy		Latent heat, Btu/lb.	Entropy			Pressure (abs.), lb./in.²
				Liquid, Btu/lb.	Vapor, Btu/lb.		Liquid, Btu/lb. degrees Fahrenheit	Evaporation, Btu/lb. degrees Fahrenheit	Vapor, Btu/lb. degrees Fahrenheit	
p	t	v_g	$1/v_g$	h_f	h_g	h_{fg}	s_f	s_{fg}	s_g	p
190	93.13	1.581	0.6326	147.2	632.4	485.2	0.3024	0.8778	1.1802	**190**
192	93.78	1.564	0.6392	147.9	632.4	484.5	0.3037	0.8755	1.1792	192
194	94.43	1.548	0.6458	148.7	632.5	483.8	0.3050	0.8733	1.1783	194
196	95.07	1.533	0.6524	149.5	632.6	483.1	0.3064	0.8710	1.1774	196
198	95.71	1.517	0.6590	150.2	632.6	482.4	0.3077	0.8688	1.1765	198
200	96.34	1.502	0.6656	150.9	632.7	481.8	0.3090	0.8666	1.1756	**200**
205	97.90	1.466	0.6821	152.7	632.8	480.1	0.3122	0.8612	1.1734	205
210	99.43	1.431	0.6986	154.6	633.0	478.4	0.3154	0.8559	1.1713	210
215	100.94	1.398	0.7152	156.3	633.1	476.8	0.3185	0.8507	1.1692	215
220	102.42	1.367	0.7318	158.0	633.2	475.2	0.3216	0.8455	1.1671	220
225	103.87	1.336	0.7484	159.7	633.3	473.6	0.3246	0.8405	1.1651	**225**
230	105.30	1.307	0.7650	161.4	633.4	472.0	0.3275	0.8356	1.1631	230
235	106.71	1.279	0.7817	163.1	633.5	470.4	0.3304	0.8307	1.1611	235
240	108.09	1.253	0.7984	164.7	633.6	468.9	0.3332	0.8260	1.1592	240
245	109.46	1.227	0.8151	166.4	633.7	467.3	0.3360	0.8213	1.1573	245
250	110.80	1.202	0.8319	168.0	633.8	465.8	0.3388	0.8167	1.1555	**250**
255	112.12	1.178	0.8487	169.5	633.8	464.3	0.3415	0.8121	1.1536	255
260	113.42	1.155	0.8655	171.1	633.9	462.8	0.3441	0.8077	1.1518	260
265	114.71	1.133	0.8824	172.6	633.9	461.3	0.3468	0.8033	1.1501	265
270	115.97	1.112	0.8993	174.1	633.9	459.8	0.3494	0.7989	1.1483	270
275	117.22	1.091	0.9162	175.6	634.0	458.4	0.3519	0.7947	1.1466	**275**
280	118.45	1.072	0.9332	177.1	634.0	456.9	0.3545	0.7904	1.1449	280
285	119.66	1.052	0.9502	178.6	634.0	455.4	0.3569	0.7863	1.1432	285
290	120.86	1.034	0.9672	180.0	634.0	454.0	0.3594	0.7821	1.1415	290
295	122.05	1.016	0.9843	181.5	634.0	452.5	0.3618	0.7781	1.1399	295
300	123.21	0.999	1.0015	182.9	634.0	451.1	0.3642	0.7741	1.1383	**300**

TABLE III.—PROPERTIES OF LIQUID AMMONIA

Temperature, degrees Fahrenheit, t	Saturation						Latent heat of pressure variation, Btu/in.², l	Variation of h with p (t constant), Btu/lb. lb./in.² $\left(\dfrac{\partial h}{\partial p}\right)_t$	Compressibility, per lb./in.² × 10⁶ $-\dfrac{1}{v}\left(\dfrac{\partial v}{\partial p}\right)_t$	Temperature, degrees Fahrenheit, t
	Pressure (abs.), lb./in.², p	Volume, ft.³/lb., v_f	Density, lb./ft.³, $\dfrac{1}{v_f}$	Specific heat, Btu/lb. degrees Fahrenheit, c	Enthalpy, Btu/lb., h_f	Latent heat, Btu/lb., h_{fg}				
Triple point	0.88	0.01961*	51.00*	.....	.....	.....	.....	.....	.....	−107.86
−100	1.24	0.02182	45.83	(1.040)	(−63.0)	(633)	.....	.....	.....	−100
−95	1.52	0.02197	45.52	(1.042)	(−57.8)	(631)	.....	.....	.....	−95
−90	1.86	0.02207	45.32	(1.043)	(−52.6)	(628)	.....	.....	.....	−90
−85	2.27	0.02216	45.12	(1.045)	(−47.4)	(625)	.....	.....	.....	−85
−80	2.74	0.02226	44.92	(1.046)	(−42.2)	(622)	.....	.....	.....	−80
−75	3.29	0.02236	44.72	(1.048)	(−36.9)	(619)	.....	.....	.....	−75
−70	3.94	0.02246	44.52	(1.050)	(−31.7)	(616)	.....	.....	.....	−70
−65	4.69	0.02256	44.32	(1.052)	(−26.4)	(613)	.....	.....	.....	−65
−60	5.55	0.02267	44.11	1.054	(−21.18)	610.8	−0.0016	0.0026	4.4	−60
−55	6.54	0.02278	43.91	1.056	(−15.90)	607.5	−0.0016	0.0026	4.5	−55
−50	7.67	0.02288	43.70	1.058	−10.61	604.3	−0.0017	0.0026	4.6	−50
−45	8.95	0.02299	43.49	1.060	−5.31	600.9	−0.0017	0.0026	4.7	−45
−40	10.41	0.02310	43.28	1.062	0.00	597.6	−0.0018	0.0025	4.8	−40
−35	12.05	0.02322	43.08	1.064	+5.32	594.2	−0.0018	0.0025	5.0	−35
−30	13.90	0.02333	42.86	1.066	10.66	590.7	−0.0019	0.0025	5.1	−30
−25	15.98	0.02345	42.65	1.068	16.00	587.2	−0.0019	0.0024	5.2	−25
−20	18.30	0.02357	42.44	1.070	21.36	583.6	−0.0020	0.0024	5.4	−20
−15	20.88	0.02369	42.22	1.073	26.73	580.0	−0.0020	0.0024	5.5	−15
−10	23.74	0.02393	41.78	1.075	32.11	576.4	−0.0021	0.0023	5.7	−10
−5	26.92	0.02406	41.56	1.078	37.51	572.6	−0.0022	0.0023	5.8	−5
0	30.42	0.02419	41.34	1.080	42.92	568.9	−0.0022	0.0022	6.0	0
5	34.27	0.02432	41.11	1.083	48.35	565.0	−0.0023	0.0022	6.2	5
10	38.51	0.02446	40.89	1.085	53.79	561.1	−0.0024	0.0021	6.4	10
15	43.14	0.02460	40.66	1.088	59.24	557.1	−0.0025	0.0021	6.6	15
20	48.21	0.02474	40.43	1.091	64.71	553.1	−0.0025	0.0020	6.8	20
25	53.73	0.02488	40.20	1.094	70.20	548.9	−0.0026	0.0020	7.0	25
30	59.74	0.02503	39.96	1.097	75.71	544.8	−0.0027	0.0019	7.3	30
35	66.26	0.02518	39.72	1.100	81.23	540.5	−0.0028	0.0019	7.5	35
40	73.32	0.02533	39.49	1.104	86.77	536.2	−0.0029	0.0018	7.8	40
45	80.96	0.02548	39.24	1.108	92.34	531.8	−0.0030	0.0017	8.1	45
50	89.19	0.02564	39.00	1.112	97.93	527.3	−0.0031	0.0017	8.4	50
55	98.06	0.02581	38.75	1.116	103.54	522.8	−0.0032	0.0016	8.8	55
60	107.6	0.02597	38.50	1.120	109.18	518.1	−0.0033	0.0015	9.1	60
65	117.8	0.02614	38.25	1.125	114.85	513.4	−0.0034	0.0014	9.5	65
70	128.8	0.02632	38.00	1.129	120.54	508.6	−0.0035	0.0013	10.0	70

* Properties of solid ammonia at the triple point (−107.86° F.).

TABLE III.—PROPERTIES OF LIQUID AMMONIA (*Continued*)

Temperature, degrees Fahrenheit	Saturation						Latent heat of pressure variation, Btu/lb. $\dfrac{}{\text{lb./in.}^2}$	Variation of h with p (t constant), $\dfrac{\text{Btu/lb.}}{\text{lb./in.}^2}$	Compressibility, per lb./in.² $\times 10^6$	Temperature, degrees Fahrenheit
	Pressure (abs.), lb./in.²	Volume, ft.³/lb.	Density, lb./ft.³	Specific heat, Btu/lb. degrees Fahrenheit	Enthalpy, Btu/lb.	Latent heat, Btu/lb.				
t	p	v_f	$\dfrac{1}{v_f}$	c	h_f	h_{fg}	l	$\left(\dfrac{\partial h}{\partial p}\right)_t$	$-\dfrac{1}{v}\left(\dfrac{\partial v}{\partial p}\right)_t$	t
75	140.5	0.02650	37.74	1.133	126.25	503.7	−0.0037	0.0012	10.4	**75**
80	153.0	0.02668	37.48	1.138	131.99	498.7	−0.0038	0.0011	10.9	80
85	166.4	0.02687	37.21	1.142	137.75	493.6	−0.0040	0.0010	11.4	85
90	180.6	0.02707	36.95	1.147	143.54	488.5	−0.0041	0.0009	12.0	90
95	195.8	0.02727	36.67	1.151	149.36	483.2	−0.0043	0.0008	12.6	95
100	211.9	0.02747	36.40	1.156	155.21	477.8	−0.0045	0.0006	13.3	**100**
105	228.9	0.02769	36.12	1.162	161.09	472.3	−0.0047	0.0005	14.1	105
110	247.0	0.02790	35.84	1.168	167.01	466.7	−0.0049	0.0003	14.9	110
115	266.2	0.02813	35.55	1.176	172.97	460.9	−0.0051	0.0001	15.8	115
120	286.4	0.02836	35.26	1.183	178.98	455.0	−0.0053	0.0000	16.7	120
125	307.8	0.02860	34.96	(1.189)	(185)	(449)	.....	.....	.....	**125**
130	330.3	0.02885	34.66	(1.197)	(191)	(443)	.....	.....	.....	130
135	354.1	0.02911	34.35	(1.205)	(197)	(436)	.....	.....	.....	135
140	379.1	0.02938	34.04	(1.213)	(203)	(430)	.....	.....	.....	140
145	405.5	0.02966	33.72	(1.222)	(210)	(423)	.....	.....	.....	145
150	433.2	0.02995	33.39	(1.23)	(216)	(416)	.....	.....	.....	**150**
155	462.3	0.03025	33.06	(1.24)	(222)	(409)	.....	.....	.....	155
160	492.8	0.03056	32.72	(1.25)	(229)	(401)	.....	.....	.....	160
165	524.8	0.03089	32.37	(1.26)	(235)	(394)	.....	.....	.....	165
170	558.4	0.03124	32.01	(1.27)	(241)	(386)	.....	.....	.....	170
175	593.5	0.03160	31.65	(1.29)	(248)	(377)	.....	.....	.....	**175**
180	630.3	0.03198	31.27	(1.30)	(255)	(369)	.....	.....	.....	180
185	668.7	0.03238	30.88	(1.32)	(262)	(360)	.....	.....	.....	185
190	708.9	0.03281	30.48	(1.34)	(269)	(351)	.....	.....	.....	190
195	750.9	0.03326	30.06	(1.36)	(276)	(342)	.....	.....	.....	195
200	794.7	0.03375	29.63	(1.38)	(283)	(332)	.....	.....	.....	**200**
210	888.1	0.03482	28.72	(1.43)	(297)	(310)	.....	.....	.....	210
220	989.5	0.0361	27.7	(1.49)	(313)	(287)	.....	.....	.....	220
230	1,099.5	0.0376	26.6	(1.57)	(329)	(260)	.....	.....	.....	230
240	1,218.5	0.0395	25.3	(1.70)	(346)	(229)	.....	.....	.....	240
250	1,347	0.0422	23.7	(1.90)	(365)	(192)	.....	.....	.....	**250**
260	1,486	0.0463	21.6	(2.33)	(387)	(142)	.....	.....	.....	260
270	1,635	0.0577	17.3	(5.30)	(419)	(52)	.....	.....	.....	270
Critical.......	1,657	0.0686	14.6	∞	(433)	0	−∞	−∞	∞	271.4

NOTE.—The figures in parentheses were calculated from empirical equations given in *Bur. Standards Sci. Papers* 313 and 315 and represent values obtained by extrapolation beyond the range covered in the experimental work.

SOURCE.—"Tables of Thermodynamic Properties of Ammonia," *Circ. Bur. Standards* 142.

Table IV.—Properties of Superheated Ammonia Vapor

v = volume in cubic feet per pound; h = enthalpy in Btu per pound; s = entropy in Btu per pound degrees Fahrenheit

Temperature, degrees Fahrenheit	Absolute pressure in pounds per square inch (saturation temperature in italics)											
	7 −52.88°			8 −48.64°			9 −44.38°			10 −41.34°		
	v	h	s	v	h	s	v	h	s	v	h	s
Saturation	36.01	592.5	1.4574	31.79	594.2	1.4462	28.48	595.7	1.4363	25.81	597.1	1.4276
−50	36.29	594.0	1.4611									
−40	37.25	599.3	1.4739	32.52	598.8	1.4573	28.85	598.3	1.4426	25.90	597.8	1.4293
−30	38.19	604.5	1.4861	33.36	604.1	1.4697	29.59	603.6	1.4551	26.58	603.2	1.4420
−20	39.13	609.6	1.4979	34.19	609.3	1.4816	30.34	608.9	1.4672	27.26	608.5	1.4542
−10	40.07	614.7	1.5094	35.01	614.4	1.4932	31.07	614.0	1.4788	27.92	613.7	1.4659
0	41.00	619.8	1.5206	35.83	619.5	1.5044	31.80	619.2	1.4902	28.58	618.9	1.4773
10	41.93	624.9	1.5314	36.64	624.6	1.5154	32.53	624.3	1.5012	29.24	624.0	1.4884
20	42.85	629.9	1.5421	37.45	629.7	1.5261	33.26	629.4	1.5119	29.90	629.1	1.4992
30	43.77	635.0	1.5525	38.26	634.7	1.5365	33.98	634.5	1.5224	30.55	634.2	1.5097
40	44.69	640.0	1.5627	39.07	639.8	1.5467	34.70	639.5	1.5327	31.20	639.3	1.5200
50	45.61	645.0	1.5727	39.88	644.8	1.5568	35.42	644.6	1.5427	31.85	644.4	1.5301
60	46.53	650.1	1.5825	40.68	649.9	1.5666	36.13	649.7	1.5526	32.49	649.5	1.5400
70	47.44	655.2	1.5921	41.48	655.0	1.5763	36.85	654.8	1.5623	33.14	654.6	1.5497
80	48.36	660.2	1.6016	42.28	660.1	1.5858	37.56	659.9	1.5718	33.78	659.7	1.5593
90	49.27	665.3	1.6110	43.08	665.2	1.5952	38.27	665.0	1.5812	34.42	664.8	1.5687
100	50.18	670.4	1.6202	43.88	670.3	1.6044	38.98	670.1	1.5904	35.07	670.0	1.5779
110	51.09	675.5	1.6292	44.68	675.4	1.6135	39.70	675.3	1.5995	35.71	675.1	1.5870
120	52.00	680.7	1.6382	45.48	680.5	1.6224	40.40	680.4	1.6085	36.35	680.3	1.5960
130	52.91	685.8	1.6470	46.27	685.7	1.6312	41.11	685.6	1.6173	36.99	685.4	1.6049
140	53.82	691.0	1.6557	47.07	690.9	1.6399	41.82	690.7	1.6260	37.62	690.6	1.6136
150	54.73	696.2	1.6643	47.87	696.1	1.6485	42.53	695.9	1.6346	38.26	695.8	1.6222
160	55.63	701.4	1.6727	48.66	701.3	1.6570	43.24	701.2	1.6431	38.90	701.1	1.6307
170	56.54	706.6	1.6811	49.46	706.5	1.6654	43.95	706.4	1.6515	39.54	706.3	1.6391
180	57.45	711.9	1.6894	50.25	711.8	1.6737	44.65	711.7	1.6598	40.17	711.6	1.6474

Temperature, degrees Fahrenheit	11 −38.14°			12 −35.16°			13 −32.37°			14 −29.76°		
Saturation	23.61	598.3	1.4196	21.77	599.4	1.4124	20.20	600.5	1.4057	18.85	601.4	1.3996
−30	24.12	602.7	1.4300	22.07	602.3	1.4190	20.33	601.8	1.4088			
−20	24.74	608.1	1.4423	22.64	607.7	1.4314	20.86	607.2	1.4213	19.33	606.8	1.4119
−10	25.35	613.3	1.4542	23.20	613.0	1.4434	21.38	612.6	1.4334	19.82	612.2	1.4241
0	25.95	618.5	1.4656	23.75	618.2	1.4549	21.90	617.9	1.4450	20.30	617.6	1.4358
10	26.55	623.7	1.4768	24.31	623.4	1.4661	22.41	623.1	1.4563	20.78	622.8	1.4472
20	27.15	628.9	1.4876	24.86	628.6	1.4770	22.92	628.3	1.4672	21.26	628.0	1.4582
30	27.74	634.0	1.4982	25.41	633.7	1.4877	23.43	633.5	1.4779	21.73	633.2	1.4688
40	28.34	639.1	1.5085	25.95	638.9	1.4980	23.93	638.6	1.4883	22.20	638.4	1.4793
50	28.93	644.2	1.5187	26.49	644.0	1.5082	24.43	643.8	1.4985	22.67	643.6	1.4896
60	29.52	649.3	1.5286	27.03	649.1	1.5182	24.94	648.9	1.5085	23.14	648.7	1.4996
70	30.10	654.4	1.5383	27.57	654.3	1.5279	25.43	654.1	1.5183	23.60	653.9	1.5094
80	30.69	659.6	1.5479	28.11	659.4	1.5375	25.93	659.2	1.5279	24.06	659.0	1.5191
90	31.28	664.7	1.5573	28.65	664.5	1.5470	26.43	664.4	1.5374	24.53	664.2	1.5285
100	31.86	669.8	1.5666	29.19	669.7	1.5562	26.93	669.5	1.5467	24.99	669.4	1.5378
110	32.44	675.0	1.5757	29.72	674.8	1.5654	27.42	674.7	1.5558	25.45	674.5	1.5470
120	33.03	680.1	1.5847	30.26	680.0	1.5744	27.92	679.9	1.5649	25.91	679.7	1.5560
130	33.61	685.3	1.5936	30.79	685.2	1.5833	28.45	685.1	1.5737	26.37	684.9	1.5649
140	34.19	690.5	1.6023	31.33	690.4	1.5920	28.90	690.3	1.5825	26.83	690.1	1.5737
150	34.77	695.7	1.6109	31.86	695.6	1.6006	29.40	695.5	1.5911	27.29	695.4	1.5824
160	35.35	700.9	1.6194	32.39	700.8	1.6092	29.89	700.7	1.5997	27.74	700.6	1.5909
170	35.93	706.2	1.6278	32.92	706.1	1.6176	30.38	706.0	1.6081	28.20	705.9	1.5993
180	36.51	711.5	1.6362	33.46	711.4	1.6259	30.87	711.3	1.6164	28.66	711.2	1.6076
190	37.09	716.8	1.6444	33.99	716.7	1.6341	31.36	716.6	1.6246	29.11	716.5	1.6159
200	37.67	722.1	1.6525	34.52	722.0	1.6422	31.85	721.9	1.6328	29.57	721.8	1.6240

Source.—"Tables of Thermodynamic Properties of Ammonia," *Circ. Bur. Standards* 142.

TABLE IV.—PROPERTIES OF SUPERHEATED AMMONIA VAPOR (*Continued*)

Temperature, degrees Fahrenheit	Absolute pressure in pounds per square inch (saturation temperature in italics)											
	15 −27.29°			16 −24.95°			17 −22.73°			18 −20.61°		
	v	*h*	*s*	*v*	*h*	*s*	*v*	*h*	*s*	*v*	*h*	*s*
Saturation	*17.67*	*602.4*	*1.3938*	*16.64*	*603.2*	*1.3885*	*15.72*	*604.0*	*1.3835*	*14.90*	*604.8*	*1.3787*
−20	18.01	606.4	1.4031	16.86	606.0	1.3948	15.83	605.6	1.3870	14.93	605.1	1.3795
−10	18.47	611.9	1.4154	17.29	611.5	1.4072	16.24	611.1	1.3994	15.32	610.7	1.3921
0	18.92	617.2	1.4272	17.72	616.9	1.4191	16.65	616.6	1.4114	15.70	616.2	1.4042
10	19.37	622.5	1.4386	18.14	622.2	1.4306	17.05	621.9	1.4230	16.08	621.6	1.4158
20	19.82	627.8	1.4497	18.56	627.5	1.4417	17.45	627.2	1.4342	16.46	626.9	1.4270
30	20.26	633.0	1.4604	18.97	632.7	1.4525	17.84	632.5	1.4450	16.83	632.2	1.4380
40	20.70	638.2	1.4709	19.39	638.0	1.4630	18.23	637.7	1.4556	17.20	637.5	1.4486
50	21.14	643.4	1.4812	19.80	643.2	1.4733	18.62	642.9	1.4659	17.57	642.7	1.4590
60	21.58	648.5	1.4912	20.21	648.3	1.4834	19.01	648.1	1.4761	17.94	647.9	1.4691
70	22.01	653.7	1.5011	20.62	653.5	1.4933	19.39	653.3	1.4860	18.30	653.1	1.4790
80	22.44	658.9	1.5108	21.03	658.7	1.5030	19.78	658.5	1.4957	18.67	658.4	1.4887
90	22.88	664.0	1.5203	21.43	663.9	1.5125	20.16	663.7	1.5052	19.03	663.6	1.4983
100	23.31	669.2	1.5296	21.84	669.1	1.5218	20.54	668.9	1.5146	19.39	668.8	1.5077
110	23.74	674.4	1.5388	22.24	674.3	1.5310	20.92	674.1	1.5238	19.75	674.0	1.5169
120	24.17	679.6	1.5478	22.65	679.5	1.5401	21.30	679.3	1.5328	20.11	679.2	1.5260
130	24.60	684.8	1.5567	23.05	684.7	1.5490	21.68	684.5	1.5418	20.47	684.4	1.5349
140	25.03	690.0	1.5655	23.45	689.9	1.5578	22.06	689.8	1.5506	20.83	689.7	1.5438
150	25.46	695.3	1.5742	23.86	695.1	1.5665	22.44	695.0	1.5593	21.19	694.9	1.5525
160	25.88	700.5	1.5827	24.26	700.4	1.5750	22.82	700.3	1.5678	21.54	700.2	1.5610
170	26.31	705.8	1.5911	24.66	705.7	1.5835	23.20	705.6	1.5763	21.90	705.5	1.5695
180	26.74	711.1	1.5995	25.06	711.0	1.5918	23.58	710.9	1.5846	22.26	710.8	1.5778
190	27.16	716.4	1.6077	25.46	716.3	1.6001	23.95	716.2	1.5929	22.61	716.1	1.5861
200	27.59	721.7	1.6158	25.86	721.6	1.6082	24.33	721.5	1.6010	22.97	721.4	1.5943
220	28.44	732.4	1.6318	26.66	732.3	1.6242	25.08	732.2	1.6170	23.68	732.2	1.6103

Temperature	19 −18.58°			20 −16.64°			21 −14.78°			22 −12.98°		
	v	*h*	*s*	*v*	*h*	*s*	*v*	*h*	*s*	*v*	*h*	*s*
Saturation	*14.17*	*605.5*	*1.3742*	*13.50*	*606.2*	*1.3700*	*12.90*	*606.8*	*1.3659*	*12.35*	*607.4*	*1.3621*
−10	14.49	610.3	1.3851	13.74	610.0	1.3784	13.06	609.6	1.3720	12.45	609.2	1.3659
0	14.85	615.9	1.3973	14.09	615.5	1.3907	13.40	615.2	1.3844	12.77	614.8	1.3784
10	15.21	621.3	1.4090	14.44	621.0	1.4025	13.73	620.7	1.3962	13.09	620.4	1.3903
20	15.57	626.7	1.4203	14.78	626.4	1.4138	14.06	626.1	1.4077	13.40	625.8	1.4018
30	15.93	632.0	1.4312	15.11	631.7	1.4248	14.38	631.5	1.4187	13.71	631.2	1.4129
40	16.28	637.3	1.4419	15.45	637.0	1.4356	14.70	636.8	1.4295	14.02	636.6	1.4237
50	16.63	642.5	1.4523	15.78	642.3	1.4460	15.02	642.1	1.4400	14.32	641.9	1.4342
60	16.98	647.7	1.4625	16.12	647.5	1.4562	15.34	647.3	1.4502	14.63	647.1	1.4445
70	17.33	653.0	1.4724	16.45	652.8	1.4662	15.65	652.6	1.4602	14.93	652.4	1.4545
80	17.67	658.2	1.4822	16.78	658.0	1.4760	15.97	657.8	1.4700	15.23	657.7	1.4643
90	18.02	663.4	1.4918	17.10	663.2	1.4856	16.28	663.1	1.4796	15.53	662.9	1.4740
100	18.36	668.6	1.5012	17.43	668.5	1.4950	16.59	668.3	1.4891	15.83	668.1	1.4834
110	18.70	673.8	1.5104	17.76	673.7	1.5042	16.90	673.5	1.4983	16.12	673.4	1.4927
120	19.04	679.1	1.5195	18.08	678.9	1.5133	17.21	678.8	1.5075	16.42	678.6	1.5019
130	19.38	684.3	1.5285	18.41	684.2	1.5223	17.52	684.0	1.5165	16.72	683.9	1.5109
140	19.72	689.5	1.5373	18.73	689.4	1.5312	17.83	689.3	1.5253	17.01	689.2	1.5197
150	20.06	694.8	1.5460	19.05	694.7	1.5399	18.14	694.6	1.5340	17.31	694.4	1.5285
160	20.40	700.1	1.5546	19.37	700.0	1.5485	18.44	699.8	1.5426	17.60	699.7	1.5371
170	20.74	705.4	1.5631	19.70	705.3	1.5569	18.75	705.1	1.5510	17.89	705.0	1.5456
180	21.08	710.7	1.5714	20.02	710.6	1.5653	19.06	710.5	1.5595	18.19	710.4	1.5539
190	21.42	716.0	1.5797	20.34	715.9	1.5736	19.36	715.8	1.5678	18.48	715.7	1.5622
200	21.75	721.3	1.5878	20.66	721.2	1.5817	19.67	721.1	1.5759	18.77	721.1	1.5704
220	22.43	732.1	1.6039	21.30	732.0	1.5978	20.28	731.9	1.5920	19.35	731.8	1.5865

Table IV.—Properties of Superheated Ammonia Vapor (*Continued*)

Temperature, degrees Fahrenheit	Absolute pressure in pounds per square inch (saturation temperature in italics)											
	23 −11.25°			24 −9.58°			25 −7.96°			26 −6.39°		
	v	h	s	v	h	s	v	h	s	v	h	s
Saturation	11.85	608.1	1.3584	11.39	608.6	1.3549	10.96	609.1	1.3515	10.56	609.7	1.3482
−10	11.89	608.8	1.3600									
0	12.20	614.5	1.3726	11.67	614.1	1.3670	11.19	613.8	1.3616	10.74	613.4	1.3564
10	12.50	620.0	1.3846	11.96	619.7	1.3791	11.47	619.4	1.3738	11.01	619.1	1.3686
20	12.80	625.5	1.3961	12.25	625.2	1.3907	11.75	625.0	1.3855	11.28	624.7	1.3804
30	13.10	630.9	1.4073	12.54	630.7	1.4019	12.03	630.4	1.3967	11.55	630.2	1.3917
40	13.40	636.3	1.4181	12.82	636.1	1.4128	12.30	635.8	1.4077	11.81	635.6	1.4027
50	13.69	641.6	1.4287	13.11	641.4	1.4234	12.57	641.2	1.4183	12.08	641.0	1.4134
60	13.98	646.9	1.4390	13.39	646.7	1.4337	12.84	646.5	1.4287	12.34	646.3	1.4238
70	14.27	652.2	1.4491	13.66	652.0	1.4438	13.11	651.8	1.4388	12.59	651.6	1.4339
80	14.56	657.5	1.4589	13.94	657.3	1.4537	13.37	657.1	1.4487	12.85	656.9	1.4439
90	14.84	662.7	1.4686	14.22	662.6	1.4634	13.64	662.4	1.4584	13.11	662.2	1.4536
100	15.13	668.0	1.4780	14.49	667.8	1.4729	13.90	667.7	1.4679	13.36	667.5	1.4631
110	15.41	673.2	1.4873	14.76	673.1	1.4822	14.17	673.0	1.4772	13.61	672.8	1.4725
120	15.70	678.5	1.4965	15.04	678.4	1.4914	14.43	678.2	1.4864	13.87	678.1	1.4817
130	15.98	683.8	1.5055	15.31	683.6	1.5004	14.69	683.5	1.4954	14.12	683.4	1.4907
140	16.26	689.0	1.5144	15.58	688.9	1.5093	14.95	688.8	1.5043	14.37	688.7	1.4996
150	16.55	694.3	1.5231	15.85	694.2	1.5180	15.21	694.1	1.5131	14.62	694.0	1.5084
160	16.83	699.6	1.5317	16.12	699.5	1.5266	15.47	699.4	1.5217	14.87	699.3	1.5170
170	17.11	704.9	1.5402	16.39	704.8	1.5352	15.73	704.7	1.5303	15.12	704.6	1.5256
180	17.39	710.3	1.5486	16.66	710.2	1.5436	15.99	710.1	1.5387	15.37	710.0	1.5340
190	17.67	715.6	1.5569	16.93	715.5	1.5518	16.25	715.4	1.5470	15.62	715.3	1.5423
200	17.95	721.0	1.5651	17.20	720.9	1.5600	16.50	720.8	1.5552	15.86	720.7	1.5505
220	18.51	731.7	1.5812	17.73	731.7	1.5761	17.02	731.6	1.5713	16.36	731.5	1.5666
240	19.07	742.6	1.5969	18.27	742.6	1.5919	17.53	742.5	1.5870	16.85	742.4	1.5824

Temperature, degrees Fahrenheit	27 −4.87°			28 −3.40°			30 −0.57°			32 +2.11°		
	v	h	s	v	h	s	v	h	s	v	h	s
Saturation	10.20	610.2	1.3451	9.853	610.7	1.3421	9.236	611.6	1.3364	8.693	612.4	1.3310
0	10.33	613.0	1.3513	9.942	612.7	1.3465	9.250	611.9	1.3371			
10	10.59	618.8	1.3637	10.20	618.4	1.3589	9.492	617.8	1.3497	8.874	617.1	1.3411
20	10.85	624.4	1.3755	10.45	624.1	1.3708	9.731	623.5	1.3618	9.099	622.9	1.3532
30	11.11	629.9	1.3869	10.70	629.6	1.3822	9.966	629.1	1.3733	9.321	628.5	1.3649
40	11.37	635.4	1.3979	10.95	635.1	1.3933	10.20	634.6	1.3845	9.540	634.1	1.3762
50	11.62	640.8	1.4087	11.19	640.5	1.4041	10.43	640.1	1.3953	9.757	639.6	1.3871
60	11.87	646.1	1.4191	11.44	645.9	1.4145	10.65	645.5	1.4059	9.972	645.1	1.3977
70	12.12	651.5	1.4292	11.68	651.2	1.4247	10.88	650.9	1.4161	10.18	650.5	1.4080
80	12.37	656.8	1.4392	11.92	656.6	1.4347	11.10	656.2	1.4261	10.40	655.9	1.4181
90	12.61	662.1	1.4489	12.15	661.9	1.4445	11.33	661.6	1.4359	10.61	661.2	1.4280
100	12.86	667.4	1.4585	12.39	667.2	1.4540	11.55	666.9	1.4456	10.81	666.6	1.4376
110	13.10	672.7	1.4679	12.63	672.5	1.4634	11.77	672.2	1.4550	11.02	671.9	1.4470
120	13.34	678.0	1.4771	12.86	677.8	1.4726	11.99	677.5	1.4642	11.23	677.3	1.4563
130	13.59	683.3	1.4861	13.10	683.1	1.4817	12.21	682.9	1.4733	11.44	682.6	1.4655
140	13.83	688.6	1.4950	13.33	688.4	1.4906	12.43	688.2	1.4823	11.64	687.9	1.4744
150	14.07	693.9	1.5038	13.56	693.7	1.4994	12.65	693.5	1.4911	11.85	693.3	1.4833
160	14.31	699.2	1.5125	13.80	699.1	1.5081	12.87	698.8	1.4998	12.05	698.6	1.4920
170	14.55	704.5	1.5210	14.03	704.4	1.5167	13.08	704.2	1.5083	12.26	704.0	1.5006
180	14.79	709.9	1.5295	14.26	709.8	1.5251	13.30	709.6	1.5168	12.46	709.4	1.5090
190	15.03	715.2	1.5378	14.49	715.1	1.5334	13.52	714.9	1.5251	12.66	714.7	1.5174
200	15.27	720.6	1.5460	14.72	720.5	1.5416	13.73	720.3	1.5334	12.86	720.1	1.5256
220	15.75	731.4	1.5621	15.18	731.3	1.5578	14.16	731.1	1.5495	13.27	731.0	1.5418
240	16.23	742.3	1.5779	15.64	742.2	1.5736	14.59	742.0	1.5653	13.67	741.9	1.5576
260	16.70	753.2	1.5933	16.10	753.2	1.5890	15.02	753.0	1.5808	14.08	752.9	1.5731

TABLE IV.—PROPERTIES OF SUPERHEATED AMMONIA VAPOR (*Continued*)

Temperature, degrees Fahrenheit	Absolute pressure in pounds per square inch (saturation temperature in italics)											
	34 *4.66°*			36 *7.09°*			38 *9.42°*			40 *11.66°*		
	v	h	s	v	h	s	v	h	s	v	h	s
Saturation	*8.211*	*613.2*	*1.3260*	*7.782*	*614.0*	*1.3213*	*7.396*	*614.7*	*1.3168*	*7.047*	*615.4*	*1.3125*
10	8.328	616.4	1.3328	7.842	615.7	1.3250	7.407	615.0	1.3175			
20	8.542	622.3	1.3452	8.046	621.7	1.3375	7.603	621.0	1.3301	7.203	620.4	1.3231
30	8.753	628.0	1.3570	8.247	627.4	1.3494	7.795	626.9	1.3422	7.387	626.3	1.3353
40	8.960	633.6	1.3684	8.445	633.1	1.3609	7.983	632.6	1.3538	7.568	632.1	1.3470
50	9.166	639.2	1.3793	8.640	638.7	1.3720	8.170	638.3	1.3650	7.746	637.8	1.3583
60	9.369	644.7	1.3900	8.833	644.2	1.3827	8.353	643.8	1.3758	7.922	643.4	1.3692
70	9.570	650.1	1.4004	9.024	649.7	1.3932	8.535	649.3	1.3863	8.096	648.9	1.3797
80	9.770	655.5	1.4105	9.214	655.2	1.4033	8.716	654.8	1.3965	8.268	654.4	1.3900
90	9.969	660.9	1.4204	9.402	660.6	1.4133	8.895	660.2	1.4065	8.439	659.9	1.4000
100	10.17	666.3	1.4301	9.589	666.0	1.4230	9.073	665.6	1.4163	8.609	665.3	1.4098
110	10.36	671.6	1.4396	9.775	671.3	1.4325	9.250	671.0	1.4258	8.777	670.7	1.4194
120	10.56	677.0	1.4489	9.961	676.7	1.4419	9.426	676.4	1.4352	8.945	676.1	1.4288
130	10.75	682.3	1.4581	10.15	682.1	1.4510	9.602	681.8	1.4444	9.112	681.5	1.4381
140	10.95	687.7	1.4671	10.33	687.4	1.4601	9.776	687.2	1.4534	9.278	686.9	1.4471
150	11.14	693.0	1.4759	10.51	692.8	1.4689	9.950	692.6	1.4623	9.444	692.3	1.4561
160	11.33	698.4	1.4846	10.69	698.2	1.4777	10.12	698.0	1.4711	9.609	697.7	1.4648
170	11.53	703.8	1.4932	10.88	703.6	1.4863	10.30	703.3	1.4797	9.774	703.1	1.4735
180	11.72	709.2	1.5017	11.06	709.0	1.4948	10.47	708.7	1.4883	9.938	708.5	1.4820
190	11.91	714.5	1.5101	11.24	714.4	1.5032	10.64	714.2	1.4966	10.10	714.0	1.4904
200	12.10	720.0	1.5183	11.42	719.8	1.5115	10.81	719.6	1.5049	10.27	719.4	1.4987
220	12.48	730.8	1.5346	11.78	730.6	1.5277	11.16	730.5	1.5212	10.59	730.3	1.5150
240	12.86	741.7	1.5504	12.14	741.6	1.5436	11.50	741.4	1.5371	10.92	741.3	1.5309
260	13.24	752.7	1.5659	12.50	752.6	1.5591	11.84	752.4	1.5526	11.24	752.3	1.5465
280	13.62	763.8	1.5811	12.86	763.7	1.5743	12.18	763.5	1.5678	11.56	763.4	1.5617

	42 *13.81°*			44 *15.88°*			46 *17.87°*			48 *19.80°*		
Saturation	*6.731*	*616.0*	*1.3084*	*6.442*	*616.6*	*1.3046*	*6.177*	*617.2*	*1.3009*	*5.934*	*617.7*	*1.2973*
20	6.842	619.8	1.3164	6.513	619.1	1.3099	6.213	618.5	1.3036	5.937	617.8	1.2976
30	7.019	625.8	1.3287	6.683	625.2	1.3224	6.377	624.6	1.3162	6.096	624.0	1.3103
40	7.192	631.6	1.3405	6.850	631.1	1.3343	6.538	630.5	1.3283	6.251	630.0	1.3225
50	7.363	637.3	1.3519	7.014	636.8	1.3457	6.696	636.4	1.3398	6.404	635.9	1.3341
60	7.531	643.0	1.3628	7.176	642.5	1.3567	6.851	642.1	1.3509	6.554	641.6	1.3453
70	7.697	648.5	1.3734	7.336	648.1	1.3674	7.005	647.7	1.3617	6.702	647.3	1.3561
80	7.862	654.1	1.3838	7.494	653.7	1.3778	7.157	653.3	1.3721	6.848	652.9	1.3666
90	8.026	659.5	1.3939	7.650	659.2	1.3880	7.308	658.9	1.3823	6.993	658.5	1.3768
100	8.188	665.0	1.4037	7.806	664.7	1.3978	7.457	664.4	1.3922	7.137	664.0	1.3868
110	8.349	670.4	1.4133	7.960	670.1	1.4075	7.605	669.8	1.4019	7.280	669.5	1.3965
120	8.510	675.9	1.4228	8.114	675.9	1.4170	7.753	675.3	1.4114	7.421	675.0	1.4061
130	8.669	681.3	1.4320	8.267	681.0	1.4263	7.899	680.7	1.4207	7.562	680.5	1.4154
140	8.828	686.7	1.4411	8.419	686.4	1.4354	8.045	686.2	1.4299	7.702	685.9	1.4246
150	8.986	692.1	1.4501	8.570	691.9	1.4444	8.190	691.6	1.4389	7.842	691.4	1.4336
160	9.144	697.5	1.4589	8.721	697.3	1.4532	8.335	697.1	1.4477	7.981	696.8	1.4425
170	9.301	702.9	1.4676	8.871	702.7	1.4619	8.479	702.5	1.4564	8.119	702.3	1.4512
180	9.458	708.3	1.4761	9.021	708.1	1.4704	8.623	707.9	1.4650	8.257	707.7	1.4598
190	9.614	713.8	1.4845	9.171	713.6	1.4789	8.766	713.4	1.4735	8.395	713.2	1.4683
200	9.770	719.2	1.4928	9.320	719.0	1.4872	8.909	718.8	1.4818	8.532	718.7	1.4766
210	9.925	724.7	1.5099	9.474	724.5	1.4954	9.052	724.3	1.4900	8.669	724.2	1.4848
220	10.08	730.1	1.5091	9.617	730.0	1.5035	9.194	729.8	1.4981	8.805	729.6	1.4930
240	10.39	741.1	1.5251	9.913	741.0	1.5195	9.477	740.8	1.5141	9.077	740.6	1.5090
260	10.70	752.2	1.5406	10.21	752.0	1.5350	9.760	751.9	1.5297	9.348	751.7	1.5246
280	11.01	763.3	1.5559	10.50	763.1	1.5503	10.04	763.0	1.5450	9.619	762.9	1.5399

TABLE IV.—PROPERTIES OF SUPERHEATED AMMONIA VAPOR (*Continued*)

Temperature, degrees Fahrenheit	Absolute pressure in pounds per square inch (saturation temperature in italics)										
	50 *21.67°*			55 *26.09°*			60 *30.21°*			65 *34.06°*		
	v	h	s	v	h	s	v	h	s	v	h	s
Saturation	*5.710*	*618.2*	*1.2939*	*5.219*	*619.5*	*1.2860*	*4.805*	*620.5*	*1.2787*	*4.454*	*621.5*	*1.2720*
30	5.838	623.4	1.3046	5.275	621.9	1.2911						
40	5.988	629.5	1.3169	5.415	628.1	1.3037	4.933	626.8	1.2913	4.527	625.4	1.2798
50	6.135	635.4	1.3286	5.551	634.1	1.3156	5.060	632.9	1.3035	4.647	631.7	1.2922
60	6.280	641.2	1.3399	5.685	640.1	1.3271	5.184	639.0	1.3152	4.764	637.8	1.3041
70	6.423	646.9	1.3508	5.816	645.9	1.3381	5.307	644.9	1.3265	4.879	643.8	1.3156
80	6.564	652.6	1.3613	5.947	651.6	1.3489	5.428	650.7	1.3373	4.991	649.7	1.3266
90	6.704	658.2	1.3716	6.075	657.3	1.3593	5.547	656.4	1.3479	5.103	655.5	1.3373
100	6.843	663.7	1.3816	6.202	662.7	1.3694	5.665	662.1	1.3581	5.213	661.3	1.3476
110	6.980	669.2	1.3914	6.329	668.5	1.3793	5.781	667.7	1.3681	5.321	667.0	1.3577
120	7.117	674.7	1.4009	6.454	674.1	1.3889	5.897	673.3	1.3778	5.429	672.6	1.3675
130	7.252	680.2	1.4102	6.528	679.6	1.3984	6.012	678.9	1.3873	5.536	678.2	1.3771
140	7.387	685.7	1.4195	6.702	685.1	1.4076	6.126	684.4	1.3966	5.642	683.8	1.3866
150	7.521	691.1	1.4286	6.825	690.6	1.4167	6.239	689.9	1.4058	5.747	689.4	1.3958
160	7.655	696.6	1.4374	6.947	696.0	1.4257	6.352	695.5	1.4148	5.852	694.9	1.4048
170	7.788	702.1	1.4462	7.069	701.5	1.4345	6.464	701.0	1.4236	5.956	700.4	1.4137
180	7.921	707.5	1.4548	7.190	707.0	1.4431	6.576	706.5	1.4323	6.060	706.0	1.4224
190	8.053	713.0	1.4633	7.311	712.5	1.4517	6.687	712.0	1.4409	6.163	711.5	1.4310
200	8.185	718.5	1.4716	7.432	718.0	1.4600	6.798	717.5	1.4493	6.266	717.1	1.4394
210	8.317	724.0	1.4799	7.552	723.5	1.4683	6.909	723.1	1.4576	6.368	722.6	1.4478
220	8.448	729.4	1.4880	7.671	729.0	1.4765	7.019	728.6	1.4658	6.471	728.2	1.4560
240	8.710	740.5	1.5040	7.910	741.1	1.4925	7.238	739.7	1.4819	6.674	739.3	1.4722
260	8.970	751.6	1.5197	8.148	751.2	1.5082	7.457	750.9	1.4976	6.877	750.5	1.4880
280	9.230	762.7	1.5350	8.385	762.4	1.5235	7.675	762.1	1.5130	7.078	761.8	1.5034
300	9.489	774.0	1.5500	8.621	773.6	1.5386	7.892	773.3	1.5281	7.279	773.1	1.5185

Temperature, degrees Fahrenheit	70 *37.70°*			75 *41.13°*			80 *44.40°*			85 *47.50°*		
	v	h	s	v	h	s	v	h	s	v	h	s
Saturation	*4.151*	*622.4*	*1.2658*	*3.887*	*623.2*	*1.2599*	*3.655*	*624.0*	*1.2545*	*3.449*	*624.7*	*1.2494*
40	4.177	623.9	1.2688									
50	4.290	630.4	1.2816	3.982	629.1	1.2715	3.712	627.7	1.2619	3.473	626.4	1.2527
60	4.401	636.6	1.2937	4.087	635.5	1.2839	3.812	634.3	1.2745	3.569	633.0	1.2656
70	4.509	642.7	1.3054	4.189	641.7	1.2957	3.909	640.6	1.2866	3.662	639.5	1.2779
80	4.615	648.7	1.3166	4.289	647.7	1.3071	4.005	646.7	1.2981	3.753	645.7	1.2896
90	4.719	654.6	1.3274	4.388	653.7	1.3180	4.098	652.8	1.3092	3.842	651.8	1.3008
100	4.822	660.4	1.3378	4.485	659.6	1.3286	4.190	658.7	1.3199	3.930	657.8	1.3117
110	4.924	666.1	1.3480	4.581	665.4	1.3389	4.281	664.6	1.3303	4.016	663.8	1.3221
120	5.025	671.8	1.3579	4.676	671.1	1.3489	4.371	670.4	1.3404	4.101	669.6	1.3323
130	5.125	677.5	1.3676	4.770	676.8	1.3586	4.460	676.1	1.3502	4.186	675.4	1.3422
140	5.224	683.1	1.3770	4.863	682.5	1.3682	4.548	681.8	1.3598	4.269	681.2	1.3519
150	5.323	688.7	1.3863	4.956	688.1	1.3775	4.635	687.5	1.3692	4.352	686.9	1.3614
160	5.420	694.3	1.3954	5.048	693.7	1.3866	4.722	693.2	1.3784	4.434	692.6	1.3706
170	5.518	699.9	1.4043	5.139	699.3	1.3956	4.808	698.8	1.3874	4.515	698.2	1.3797
180	5.615	705.5	1.4131	5.230	704.9	1.4044	4.893	704.4	1.3963	4.596	703.9	1.3886
190	5.711	711.0	1.4217	5.320	710.5	1.4131	4.978	710.0	1.4050	4.677	709.5	1.3974
200	5.807	716.6	1.4302	5.410	716.1	1.4217	5.063	715.6	1.4136	4.757	715.2	1.4060
210	5.902	722.2	1.4386	5.500	721.7	1.4301	5.147	721.3	1.4220	4.836	720.8	1.4145
220	5.998	727.7	1.4469	5.589	727.3	1.4384	5.231	726.9	1.4304	4.916	726.4	1.4228
230	6.093	733.3	1.4550	5.678	732.9	1.4466	5.315	732.5	1.4386	4.995	732.1	1.4311
240	6.187	738.9	1.4631	5.767	738.5	1.4546	5.398	738.1	1.4467	5.074	737.7	1.4392
260	6.376	750.1	1.4789	5.943	749.8	1.4705	5.565	749.4	1.4626	5.230	749.0	1.4551
280	6.563	761.4	1.4943	6.119	761.1	1.4860	5.730	760.7	1.4781	5.386	760.4	1.4707
300	6.750	772.7	1.5095	6.294	772.4	1.5011	5.894	772.1	1.4933	5.541	771.8	1.4859

TABLE IV.—PROPERTIES OF SUPERHEATED AMMONIA VAPOR (*Continued*)

Temperature, degrees Fahrenheit	Absolute pressure in pounds per square inch (saturation temperature in italics)											
	90 *50.47°*			95 *53.32°*			100 *56.05°*			105 *58.67°*		
	v	*h*	*s*	*v*	*h*	*s*	*v*	*h*	*s*	*v*	*h*	*s*
Saturation	*3.266*	*625.3*	*1.2445*	*3.101*	*625.9*	*1.2399*	*2.952*	*626.5*	*1.2356*	*2.817*	*627.0*	*1.2314*
60	3.353	631.8	1.2571	3.160	630.5	1.2489	2.985	629.3	1.2409			
70	3.442	638.3	1.2695	3.245	637.2	1.2616	3.068	636.0	1.2539	2.907	634.9	1.2464
80	3.529	644.7	1.2814	3.329	643.6	1.2736	3.149	642.6	1.2661	2.985	641.5	1.2589
90	3.614	650.9	1.2928	3.411	649.9	1.2852	3.227	649.0	1.2778	3.061	648.0	1.2708
100	3.698	657.0	1.3038	3.491	656.1	1.2963	3.304	655.2	1.2891	3.135	654.3	1.2822
110	3.780	663.0	1.3144	3.570	662.1	1.3070	3.380	661.3	1.2999	3.208	660.5	1.2931
120	3.862	668.9	1.3247	3.647	668.1	1.3174	3.454	667.3	1.3104	3.279	666.6	1.3037
130	3.942	674.7	1.3347	3.724	674.0	1.3275	3.527	673.3	1.3206	3.350	672.6	1.3139
140	4.021	680.5	1.3444	3.799	679.8	1.3373	3.600	679.2	1.3305	3.419	678.5	1.3239
150	4.100	686.3	1.3539	3.874	685.6	1.3469	3.672	685.0	1.3401	3.488	684.4	1.3336
160	4.178	692.0	1.3633	3.949	691.4	1.3562	3.743	690.8	1.3495	3.556	690.2	1.3431
170	4.255	697.7	1.3724	4.022	697.1	1.3654	3.813	696.6	1.3588	3.623	696.0	1.3524
180	4.332	703.4	1.3813	4.096	702.8	1.3744	3.883	702.3	1.3678	3.690	701.8	1.3615
190	4.408	709.0	1.3901	4.168	708.5	1.3833	3.952	708.0	1.3767	3.757	707.5	1.3704
200	4.484	714.7	1.3988	4.241	714.2	1.3919	4.021	713.7	1.3854	3.823	713.3	1.3792
210	4.560	720.4	1.4073	4.313	719.9	1.4005	4.090	719.4	1.3940	3.888	719.0	1.3878
220	4.635	726.0	1.4157	4.384	725.6	1.4089	4.158	725.1	1.4024	3.954	724.7	1.3963
230	4.710	731.7	1.4239	4.455	731.3	1.4172	4.226	730.8	1.4108	4.019	730.4	1.4046
240	4.785	737.3	1.4321	4.526	736.9	1.4254	4.294	736.5	1.4190	4.083	736.1	1.4129
250	4.859	743.0	1.4401	4.597	742.6	1.4334	4.361	742.2	1.4271	4.148	741.9	1.4210
260	4.933	748.7	1.4481	4.668	748.3	1.4414	4.428	747.9	1.4350	4.212	747.6	1.4290
280	5.081	760.0	1.4637	4.808	759.7	1.4570	4.562	759.4	1.4507	4.340	759.0	1.4447
290	5.155	765.8	1.4713	4.878	765.5	1.4647	4.629	765.1	1.4584	4.403	764.8	1.4524
300	5.228	771.5	1.4789	4.947	771.2	1.4723	4.695	770.8	1.4660	4.466	770.5	1.4600

Temperature, degrees Fahrenheit	110 *61.21°*			115 *63.65°*			120 *66.02°*			125 *68.31°*		
	v	*h*	*s*	*v*	*h*	*s*	*v*	*h*	*s*	*v*	*h*	*s*
Saturation	*2.693*	*627.5*	*1.2275*	*2.580*	*628.0*	*1.2337*	*2.476*	*628.4*	*1.2201*	*2.380*	*628.8*	*1.2166*
70	2.761	633.7	1.2392	2.628	632.5	1.2323	2.505	631.3	1.2255	2.392	630.0	1.2189
80	2.837	640.5	1.2519	2.701	639.4	1.2451	2.576	638.3	1.2386	2.461	637.2	1.2322
90	2.910	647.0	1.2640	2.772	646.0	1.2574	2.645	645.0	1.2510	2.528	644.0	1.2448
100	2.981	653.4	1.2755	2.841	652.5	1.2690	2.712	651.6	1.2628	2.593	650.7	1.2568
110	3.051	659.7	1.2866	2.909	658.8	1.2802	2.778	658.0	1.2741	2.657	657.1	1.2682
120	3.120	665.8	1.2972	2.975	665.0	1.2910	2.842	664.2	1.2850	2.719	663.5	1.2792
130	3.188	671.9	1.3076	3.040	671.1	1.3015	2.905	670.4	1.2956	2.780	669.7	1.2899
140	3.255	677.8	1.3176	3.105	677.2	1.3116	2.967	676.5	1.3058	2.840	675.8	1.3002
150	3.321	683.7	1.3274	3.168	683.1	1.3215	3.029	682.5	1.3157	2.900	681.8	1.3102
160	3.386	689.6	1.3370	3.231	689.0	1.3311	3.089	688.4	1.3254	2.958	687.8	1.3199
170	3.451	695.4	1.3463	3.294	694.9	1.3405	3.149	694.3	1.3348	3.016	693.7	1.3294
180	3.515	701.2	1.3555	3.355	700.7	1.3497	3.209	700.2	1.3441	3.074	699.6	1.3387
190	3.579	707.0	1.3644	3.417	706.5	1.3587	3.268	706.0	1.3531	3.131	705.5	1.3478
200	3.642	712.8	1.3732	3.477	712.3	1.3675	3.326	711.8	1.3620	3.187	711.3	1.3567
210	3.705	718.5	1.3819	3.538	718.1	1.3762	3.385	717.6	1.3707	3.243	717.2	1.3654
220	3.768	724.3	1.3904	3.598	723.8	1.3847	3.442	723.4	1.3793	3.299	723.0	1.3740
230	3.830	730.0	1.3988	3.658	729.6	1.3931	3.500	729.2	1.3877	3.354	728.8	1.3825
240	3.892	735.7	1.4070	3.717	735.3	1.4014	3.557	734.9	1.3960	3.409	734.5	1.3908
250	3.954	741.5	1.4151	3.776	741.1	1.4096	3.614	740.7	1.4042	3.464	740.3	1.3990
260	4.015	747.2	1.4232	3.835	746.8	1.4176	3.671	746.5	1.4123	3.519	746.1	1.4071
270	4.076	752.9	1.4311	3.894	752.6	1.4256	3.727	752.2	1.4202	3.573	751.9	1.4151
280	4.137	758.7	1.4389	3.952	758.4	1.4334	3.783	758.0	1.4281	3.627	757.7	1.4230
290	4.198	764.5	1.4466	4.011	764.1	1.4411	3.839	763.8	1.4359	3.681	763.5	1.4308
300	4.259	770.2	1.4543	4.069	769.9	1.4488	3.895	769.6	1.4435	3.735	769.3	1.4385

TABLE IV.—PROPERTIES OF SUPERHEATED AMMONIA VAPOR (*Continued*)

Temperature, degrees Fahrenheit	Absolute pressure in pounds per square inch (saturation temperature in italics)											
	130 *70.53°*			135 *72.69°*			140 *74.79°*			145 *76.83°*		
	v	*h*	*s*	*v*	*h*	*s*	*v*	*h*	*s*	*v*	*h*	*s*
Saturation	2.291	629.2	1.2132	2.209	629.6	1.2100	2.132	629.9	1.2068	2.061	630.2	1.2038
80	2.355	636.0	1.2260	2.257	634.9	1.2199	2.166	633.8	1.2140	2.080	632.6	1.2082
90	2.421	643.0	1.2388	2.321	642.0	1.2329	2.228	640.9	1.2272	2.141	639.9	1.2216
100	2.484	649.7	1.2509	2.382	648.8	1.2452	2.288	647.8	1.2396	2.200	646.9	1.2342
110	2.546	656.3	1.2625	2.442	655.4	1.2569	2.347	654.5	1.2515	2.257	653.6	1.2462
120	2.606	662.7	1.2736	2.501	661.9	1.2681	2.404	661.1	1.2628	2.313	660.2	1.2577
130	2.665	668.9	1.2843	2.559	668.2	1.2790	2.460	667.4	1.2738	2.368	666.7	1.2687
140	2.724	675.1	1.2947	2.615	674.4	1.2894	2.515	673.7	1.2843	2.421	673.0	1.2793
150	2.781	681.2	1.3048	2.671	680.5	1.2996	2.569	679.9	1.2945	2.474	679.2	1.2896
160	2.838	687.2	1.3146	2.726	686.6	1.3094	2.622	686.0	1.3045	2.526	685.4	1.2996
170	2.894	693.2	1.3241	2.780	692.6	1.3191	2.675	692.0	1.3141	2.577	691.4	1.3093
180	2.949	699.1	1.3335	2.834	698.6	1.3284	2.727	698.0	1.3236	2.627	697.5	1.3188
190	3.004	705.0	1.3426	2.887	704.5	1.3376	2.779	704.0	1.3328	2.677	703.4	1.3281
200	3.059	710.9	1.3516	2.940	710.4	1.3466	2.830	709.9	1.3418	2.727	709.4	1.3372
210	3.113	716.7	1.3604	2.992	716.2	1.3554	2.880	715.8	1.3507	2.776	715.3	1.3461
220	3.167	722.5	1.3690	3.044	722.1	1.3641	2.931	721.6	1.3594	2.825	721.2	1.3548
230	3.220	728.3	1.3775	3.096	727.9	1.3726	2.981	727.5	1.3679	2.873	727.1	1.3634
240	3.273	734.1	1.3858	3.147	733.7	1.3810	3.030	733.3	1.3763	2.921	732.9	1.3718
250	3.326	739.9	1.3941	3.198	739.6	1.3893	3.080	739.2	1.3846	2.969	738.8	1.3801
260	3.379	745.7	1.4022	3.249	745.4	1.3974	3.129	745.0	1.3928	3.017	744.6	1.3883
270	3.431	751.5	1.4102	3.300	751.2	1.4054	3.179	750.8	1.4008	3.064	750.5	1.3964
280	3.483	757.3	1.4181	3.350	757.0	1.4133	3.227	756.7	1.4088	3.111	756.3	1.4043
290	3.535	763.1	1.4259	3.400	762.8	1.4212	3.275	762.5	1.4166	3.158	762.2	1.4122
300	3.587	769.0	1.4336	3.450	768.6	1.4289	3.323	768.3	1.4243	3.205	768.0	1.4199
320	3.690	780.6	1.4487	3.550	780.3	1.4441	3.420	780.0	1.4395	3.298	779.7	1.4352

Temperature	150 *78.81°*			160 *82.64°*			170 *86.29°*			180 *89.78°*		
	v	*h*	*s*	*v*	*h*	*s*	*v*	*h*	*s*	*v*	*h*	*s*
Saturation	1.994	630.5	1.2009	1.872	631.1	1.1952	1.764	631.6	1.1900	1.667	632.0	1.1850
90	2.061	638.8	1.2161	1.914	636.6	1.2055	1.784	634.4	1.1952	1.668	632.2	1.1853
100	2.118	645.9	1.2289	1.969	643.9	1.2186	1.837	641.9	1.2087	1.720	639.9	1.1992
110	2.174	652.8	1.2410	2.023	651.0	1.2311	1.889	649.1	1.2215	1.770	647.3	1.2123
120	2.228	659.4	1.2526	2.075	657.8	1.2429	1.939	656.1	1.2336	1.818	654.4	1.2247
130	2.281	665.9	1.2638	2.125	664.4	1.2542	1.988	662.8	1.2452	1.865	661.3	1.2364
140	2.334	672.3	1.2745	2.175	670.9	1.2652	2.035	669.4	1.2563	1.910	668.0	1.2477
150	2.385	678.6	1.2849	2.224	677.2	1.2757	2.081	675.9	1.2669	1.955	674.5	1.2586
160	2.435	684.8	1.2949	2.272	683.5	1.2859	2.127	682.3	1.2773	1.999	681.0	1.2691
170	2.485	690.9	1.3047	2.319	689.7	1.2958	2.172	688.5	1.2873	2.042	687.3	1.2792
180	2.534	696.9	1.3142	2.365	695.8	1.3054	2.216	694.7	1.2971	2.084	693.6	1.2891
190	2.583	702.9	1.3236	2.411	701.9	1.3148	2.260	700.8	1.3066	2.126	699.8	1.2987
200	2.631	708.9	1.3327	2.457	707.9	1.3240	2.303	706.9	1.3159	2.167	705.9	1.3081
210	2.679	714.8	1.3416	2.502	713.9	1.3331	2.346	713.0	1.3249	2.208	712.0	1.3172
220	2.726	720.7	1.3504	2.547	719.9	1.3419	2.389	719.0	1.3338	2.248	718.1	1.3262
230	2.773	726.6	1.3590	2.591	725.8	1.3506	2.431	724.9	1.3426	2.288	724.1	1.3350
240	2.820	732.5	1.3675	2.635	731.7	1.3591	2.473	730.9	1.3512	2.328	730.1	1.3436
250	2.866	738.4	1.3758	2.679	737.6	1.3675	2.514	736.8	1.3596	2.367	736.1	1.3521
260	2.912	744.3	1.3840	2.723	743.5	1.3757	2.555	742.8	1.3679	2.407	742.0	1.3605
270	2.958	750.1	1.3921	2.766	749.4	1.3838	2.596	748.7	1.3761	2.446	748.0	1.3687
280	3.004	756.0	1.4001	2.809	755.3	1.3919	2.637	754.6	1.3841	2.484	753.9	1.3768
290	3.049	761.8	1.4079	2.852	761.2	1.3998	2.678	760.5	1.3921	2.523	759.9	1.3847
300	3.095	767.7	1.4157	2.895	767.1	1.4076	2.718	766.4	1.3999	2.561	765.8	1.3926
320	3.185	779.4	1.4310	2.980	778.9	1.4229	2.798	778.3	1.4153	2.637	777.7	1.4081
340	3.274	791.2	1.4459	3.064	790.7	1.4379	2.878	790.1	1.4303	2.713	789.6	1.4231

TABLE IV.—PROPERTIES OF SUPERHEATED AMMONIA VAPOR (Continued)

| Temperature, degrees Fahrenheit | Absolute pressure in pounds per square inch (saturation temperature in italics) | | | | | | | | | | | |
| | 190 *93.13°* | | | 200 *96.34°* | | | 210 *99.43°* | | | 220 *102.42°* | | |
	v	h	s	v	h	s	v	h	s	v	h	s
Saturation	*1.581*	*632.4*	*1.1802*	*1.502*	*632.7*	*1.1756*	*1.431*	*633.0*	*1.1713*	*1.367*	*633.2*	*1.1671*
100	1.615	637.8	1.1899	1.520	635.6	1.1809						
110	1.663	645.4	1.2034	1.567	643.4	1.1947	1.480	641.5	1.1863	1.400	639.4	1.1781
120	1.710	652.6	1.2160	1.612	650.9	1.2077	1.524	649.1	1.1996	1.443	647.3	1.1917
130	1.755	659.7	1.2281	1.656	658.1	1.2200	1.566	656.4	1.2121	1.485	654.8	1.2045
140	1.799	666.5	1.2396	1.698	665.0	1.2317	1.608	663.5	1.2240	1.525	662.0	1.2167
150	1.842	673.2	1.2506	1.740	671.8	1.2429	1.648	670.4	1.2354	1.564	669.0	1.2281
160	1.884	679.7	1.2612	1.780	678.4	1.2537	1.687	677.1	1.2464	1.601	675.8	1.2394
170	1.925	686.1	1.2715	1.820	684.9	1.2641	1.725	683.7	1.2569	1.638	682.5	1.2501
180	1.966	692.5	1.2815	1.859	691.3	1.2742	1.762	690.2	1.2672	1.675	689.1	1.2604
190	2.005	698.7	1.2912	1.897	697.7	1.2840	1.799	696.6	1.2771	1.710	695.5	1.2704
200	2.045	704.9	1.3007	1.935	703.9	1.2935	1.836	702.9	1.2867	1.745	701.9	1.2801
210	2.084	711.1	1.3099	1.972	710.1	1.3029	1.872	709.2	1.2961	1.780	708.2	1.2896
220	2.123	717.2	1.3189	2.009	716.3	1.3120	1.907	715.3	1.3053	1.814	714.4	1.2989
230	2.161	723.2	1.3278	2.046	722.4	1.3209	1.942	721.5	1.3143	1.848	720.6	1.3079
240	2.199	729.3	1.3365	2.082	728.4	1.3296	1.977	727.6	1.3231	1.881	726.8	1.3168
250	2.236	735.3	1.3450	2.118	734.5	1.3382	2.011	733.7	1.3317	1.914	732.9	1.3255
260	2.274	741.3	1.3534	2.154	740.5	1.3467	2.046	739.8	1.3402	1.947	739.0	1.3340
270	2.311	747.3	1.3617	2.189	746.5	1.3550	2.080	745.8	1.3486	1.980	745.1	1.3424
280	2.348	753.2	1.3698	2.225	752.5	1.3631	2.113	751.8	1.3568	2.012	751.1	1.3507
290	2.384	759.2	1.3778	2.260	758.5	1.3712	2.147	757.9	1.3649	2.044	757.2	1.3588
300	2.421	765.2	1.3857	2.295	764.5	1.3791	2.180	763.9	1.3728	2.076	763.2	1.3668
320	2.493	777.1	1.4012	2.364	776.5	1.3947	2.246	775.9	1.3884	2.140	775.3	1.3825
340	2.565	789.0	1.4163	2.432	788.5	1.4099	2.312	787.9	1.4037	2.203	787.4	1.3978
360	.....	.....	.....	2.500	800.5	1.4247	2.377	800.0	1.4186	2.265	799.5	1.4127
380	.....	.....	.....	2.568	812.5	1.4392	2.442	812.0	1.4331	2.327	811.6	1.4273

| Temperature, degrees Fahrenheit | 230 *105.30°* | | | 240 *108.09°* | | | 250 *110.80°* | | | 260 *113.42°* | | |
	v	h	s	v	h	s	v	h	s	v	h	s
Saturation	*1.307*	*633.4*	*1.1631*	*1.253*	*633.6*	*1.1592*	*1.202*	*633.8*	*1.1555*	*1.155*	*633.9*	*1.1518*
110	1.328	637.4	1.1700	1.261	635.3	1.1621						
120	1.370	645.4	1.1840	1.302	643.5	1.1764	1.240	641.5	1.1690	1.182	639.5	1.1617
130	1.410	653.1	1.1971	1.342	651.3	1.1898	1.278	649.6	1.1827	1.220	647.8	1.1757
140	1.449	660.4	1.2095	1.380	658.8	1.2025	1.316	657.2	1.1956	1.257	655.6	1.1889
150	1.487	667.6	1.2213	1.416	666.1	1.2145	1.352	664.6	1.2078	1.292	663.1	1.2014
160	1.524	674.5	1.2325	1.452	673.1	1.2259	1.386	671.8	1.2195	1.326	670.4	1.2132
170	1.559	681.3	1.2434	1.487	680.0	1.2369	1.420	678.7	1.2306	1.359	677.5	1.2245
180	1.594	687.9	1.2538	1.521	686.7	1.2475	1.453	685.5	1.2414	1.391	684.4	1.2354
190	1.629	694.4	1.2640	1.554	693.3	1.2577	1.486	692.2	1.2517	1.422	691.1	1.2458
200	1.663	700.9	1.2738	1.587	699.8	1.2677	1.518	699.8	1.2617	1.453	697.7	1.2560
210	1.696	707.2	1.2834	1.619	706.2	1.2773	1.549	705.3	1.2715	1.484	704.3	1.2658
220	1.729	713.5	1.2927	1.651	712.6	1.2867	1.580	711.7	1.2810	1.514	710.7	1.2754
230	1.762	719.8	1.3018	1.683	718.9	1.2959	1.610	718.0	1.2902	1.543	717.1	1.2847
240	1.794	726.0	1.3107	1.714	725.1	1.3049	1.640	724.3	1.2993	1.572	723.4	1.2938
250	1.826	732.1	1.3195	1.745	731.3	1.3137	1.670	730.5	1.3081	1.601	729.7	1.3027
260	1.857	738.3	1.3281	1.775	737.5	1.3224	1.699	736.7	1.3168	1.630	736.0	1.3115
270	1.889	744.4	1.3365	1.805	743.6	1.3308	1.729	742.9	1.3253	1.658	742.2	1.3200
280	1.920	750.5	1.3448	1.835	749.8	1.3392	1.758	749.1	1.3337	1.686	748.4	1.3285
290	1.951	756.5	1.3530	1.865	755.9	1.3474	1.786	755.2	1.3420	1.714	754.5	1.3367
300	1.982	762.6	1.3610	1.895	762.0	1.3554	1.815	761.3	1.3501	1.741	760.7	1.3449
320	2.043	774.7	1.3767	1.954	774.1	1.3712	1.872	773.5	1.3659	1.796	772.9	1.3608
340	2.103	786.8	1.3921	2.012	786.3	1.3866	1.928	785.7	1.3814	1.850	785.2	1.3763
360	2.163	798.9	1.4070	2.069	798.4	1.4016	1.983	797.9	1.3964	1.904	797.4	1.3914
380	2.222	811.1	1.4217	2.126	810.6	1.4163	2.038	810.1	1.4111	1.957	809.6	1.4062
400	.....	.....	.....	.....	.....	.....	2.093	822.3	1.4255	2.009	821.9	1.4206

TABLE IV.—PROPERTIES OF SUPERHEATED AMMONIA VAPOR (*Continued*)

Temperature, degrees Fahrenheit	Absolute pressure in pounds per square inch (saturation temperature in italics)										
	270 *115.97°*			280 *118.45°*			290 *120.86°*			300 *123.21°*		
	v	*h*	*s*	*v*	*h*	*s*	*v*	*h*	*s*	*v*	*h*	*s*
Saturation	1.112	633.9	1.1483	1.072	634.0	1.1449	1.034	634.0	1.1415	0.999	634.0	1.1383
120	1.128	637.5	1.1544	1.078	635.4	1.1473						
130	1.166	645.9	1.1689	1.115	644.0	1.1621	1.068	642.1	1.1554	1.023	640.1	1.1487
140	1.202	653.9	1.1823	1.151	652.2	1.1759	1.103	650.5	1.1695	1.058	648.7	1.1632
150	1.236	661.6	1.1950	1.184	660.1	1.1888	1.136	658.5	1.1827	1.091	656.9	1.1767
160	1.269	669.0	1.2071	1.217	667.6	1.2011	1.168	666.1	1.1952	1.123	664.7	1.1894
170	1.302	676.2	1.2185	1.249	674.9	1.2127	1.199	673.5	1.2070	1.153	672.2	1.2014
180	1.333	683.2	1.2296	1.279	681.9	1.2239	1.229	680.7	1.2183	1.183	679.5	1.2129
190	1.364	690.0	1.2401	1.309	688.9	1.2346	1.259	687.7	1.2292	1.211	686.5	1.2239
200	1.394	696.7	1.2504	1.339	695.6	1.2449	1.287	694.6	1.2396	1.239	693.5	1.2344
210	1.423	703.3	1.2603	1.367	702.3	1.2550	1.315	701.3	1.2497	1.267	700.3	1.2447
220	1.452	709.8	1.2700	1.396	708.8	1.2647	1.343	707.9	1.2596	1.294	706.9	1.2546
230	1.481	716.2	1.2794	1.424	715.3	1.2742	1.370	714.4	1.2691	1.320	713.5	1.2642
240	1.509	722.6	1.2885	1.451	721.8	1.2834	1.397	720.9	1.2784	1.346	720.0	1.2736
250	1.537	728.9	1.2975	1.478	728.1	1.2924	1.423	727.3	1.2875	1.372	726.5	1.2827
260	1.565	735.2	1.3063	1.505	734.4	1.3013	1.449	733.7	1.2964	1.397	732.9	1.2917
270	1.592	741.4	1.3149	1.532	740.7	1.3099	1.475	740.0	1.3051	1.422	739.2	1.3004
280	1.620	747.7	1.3234	1.558	747.0	1.3184	1.501	746.3	1.3137	1.447	745.5	1.3090
290	1.646	753.9	1.3317	1.584	753.2	1.3268	1.526	752.5	1.3221	1.472	751.8	1.3175
300	1.673	760.0	1.3399	1.610	759.4	1.3350	1.551	758.7	1.3303	1.496	758.1	1.3257
320	1.726	772.3	1.3559	1.661	771.7	1.3511	1.601	771.1	1.3464	1.544	770.5	1.3419
340	1.778	784.6	1.3714	1.712	784.0	1.3667	1.650	783.5	1.3621	1.592	782.9	1.3576
360	1.830	796.9	1.3866	1.762	796.3	1.3819	1.698	795.8	1.3773	1.639	795.3	1.3729
380	1.881	809.1	1.4014	1.811	808.7	1.3967	1.747	808.2	1.3922	1.686	807.7	1.3878
400	1.932	821.4	1.4158	1.861	821.0	1.4112	1.794	820.5	1.4067	1.732	820.1	1.4024

INDEX

A

Absolute humidity, 163
Absorber, 129, 140–142
  energy equation for, 141
  heat rejected in, 141
  mass flow through, 141
Absorption refrigeration system, 128–158
  ammonia, 137–156
  energy balance in, 154
  three-fluid, 156
Adiabatic changes, 15, 16
  irreversible, 16
  reversible, 15, 16
  for vapors, 24
  work for, 16
Adiabatic mixing, in dual compressor, 116
  under flow, 81
Adiabatic saturation, 161
Adsorbate, 189
Adsorbent, 189
  desirable characteristics of, 192
Adsorption, 189
Adsorption system, 189–193
Air, atmospheric, 162–173
  absolute humidity of, 163
  cooling and dehumidification of, 167–173
  density of, 166
  dew point temperature of, 163
  enthalpy of, 164
  properties of, 162–167
  relative humidity of, 163
  saturated, 163
  specific heat of, 166
  specific humidity of, 164
  specific volume of, 165
Air conditioning, 2
  properties of air for, 160–167
  refrigeration in, 159–174

Air refrigeration system, 34, 42–58
  actual, 50–57
    energy balance for, 56, 57
    energy quantities for, 52–54
    mechanical efficiency of, 53
    net work for, 53
  closed, 35
  dense, 49
  open, 35
  theoretical, 45–50
    net work for, 47, 48
Ammonia, anhydrous, 129
  aqua, 129–135
  liquid, properties of, 207, 208
  Mollier chart for, 218 (Fig. 54)
  saturated, properties of, 199–206
  superheated, properties of, 209–217
Ammonia absorption system, 128–158
Analyzer, 138, 146, 147
Anhydrous ammonia, 129
Aqua ammonia, 129–135
  characteristics and properties of, 129–134
  chart of, 130 (Fig. 39)
  concentration of, 129
    equilibrium, 130
    molal, 129
    weight, 129
  density of, 134
  energy quantities, 134
  specific gravity of, 134
  vapors, 135–137
    partial pressures of, 130 (Fig. 39)
Aqua pump, 129, 142–144
  horsepower of, 143
Atmospheric air, 162–173
  (*See also* Air, atmospheric)

219